Situational Judgement Tests
for Foundation Programme Entry

University
of Glasgow

Situational Judgement Tests for Foundation Programme Entry

Editors

Dr. Susan Shelmerdine, MBBS (Dist), BSc (hons), MRCS Eng
Specialty Registrar in Clinical Radiology, St. George's Hospital, London, UK

Miss Aneesha Verma, MBBS (Dist), BSc (hons), MRCS Eng
Core Surgical Trainee, St. Mary's Hospital, London, UK

Contributing Authors

Mr. Jeremy Lynch, MBChB, MRCS Eng
Core Surgical Trainee, Royal Sussex County Hospital, Brighton, UK

Dr. Ramanan Rajakulasingam, MBBS, BSc (hons)
Foundation Trainee, St. George's Hospital, London, UK

Dr. Arun Thiyagarajan, MBBS (Dist), BSc (hons), AICSM
Academic Foundation Trainee, North West Thames Deanery, London, UK

Dr. Ramyah Rajakulasingam, MBBS (Dist), BSc (hons)
Foundation Trainee, Queen Elizabeth Hospital, Welwyn Garden City, UK

Dr. Semini Sumanasuriya, MBBS (Dist), BSc (hons)
Foundation Trainee, Royal Free Hospital, London, UK

Dr. Matthew James Pywell, MBBS (Dist), BSc (hons)
Foundation House Officer, Bart's and the London Hospitals, London, UK

Situational Judgement Tests for Foundation Programme Entry

Published by:

Anshan Ltd
11a Little Mount Sion
Tunbridge Wells
Kent. TN1 1YS

Tel: +44 (0) 1892 557767
Fax: +44 (0) 1892 530358

e-mail: info@anshan.co.uk
website: www.anshan.co.uk

© 2013 Anshan Ltd

ISBN: 978 1 848290 709

The use of registered names, trademarks, etc, in this publication does not imply, even in the absence of a specific statement that such names are exempt from the relevant laws and regulations and therefore for general use.

While every effort has been made to ensure the accuracy of the information contained within this publication, the publisher can give no guarantee for information about drug dosage and application thereof contained in this book. In every individual case the respective user must check current indications and accuracy by consulting other pharmaceutical literature and following the guidelines laid down by the manufacturers of specific products and the relevant authorities in the country in which they are practicing.

British Library Cataloguing in Publication Data

Copy Editor: Catherine Lain

Cover Design: Susan Shelmerdine

Cover Image: Susan Shelmerdine

Typeset by: Kerrypress Ltd, Luton, Bedfordshire

Printed and bound by:

CONTENTS

ACKNOWLEDGEMENTS

The authors would like to acknowledge their parents, friends and families for their support and encouragement throughout the writing of this book.

ABOUT THE AUTHORS

EDITORS

Dr. SUSAN CHENG SHELMERDINE, MBBS (Dist), BSc (hons), MRCS Eng
Specialty Registrar in Clinical Radiology, St. George's Hospital, London, UK

Susan Shelmerdine graduated with a distinction from St George's Hospital Medical School in 2008 where she also achieved a first class honours in her intercalated BSc degree in Medical Imaging in 2005. She completed her MRCS prior to radiology training and has an active interest in undergraduate education. She has taught on several undergraduate medical courses at the Royal Society of Medicine, Imperial College London and St. George's, University of London. She is currently completing a Postgraduate Certificate in Medical Education and is also an OSCE examiner at St. George's, University of London.

Miss ANEESHA RATAN VERMA, MBBS (Dist), BSc (hons), MRCS Eng
Core Surgical Trainee, St. Mary's Hospital, London, UK

Aneesha Verma graduated with a distinction from Imperial College London in 2008. Her intercalated BSc was in Neuroscience and she attained her MRCS in 2010. She tutors for OSCE medical final examinations and has helped set up and deliver a 20-week revision lecture programme for undergraduate students. Aneesha has taught during conferences at The Royal Society of Medicine and The Royal College of Surgeons of England. She has completed formal teaching courses and was a faculty member for the Training and Assessment in Practice course. Aneesha has enjoyed gaining experience in a broad range of specialties including cardiothoracic, vascular, colorectal, breast, orthopaedic, upper gastrointestinal and plastic surgery.

CONTRIBUTING AUTHORS

Mr. JEREMY OLIVER LYNCH, MBChB, MRCS Eng
Core Surgical Trainee, Royal Sussex County Hospital, Brighton, UK

Jeremy Lynch qualified from Bristol University and has had a keen interest in undergraduate education since his medical school days. He is the creator of the popular medical student revision website www.passmed.co.uk and is an OSCE examiner at the Brighton and Sussex Medical School. He has worked in a broad range of surgical specialties and published research in well-respected journals.

Dr. RAMANAN RAJAKULASINGAM, MBBS, BSc (hons)
Foundation Trainee, St. George's Hospital, London, UK

Ramanan Rajakulasingam graduated from St George's University of London in 2011 and has also completed an intercalated BSc in Infectious Diseases and Immunobiology from King's College London. During his time at medical school he has been actively involved in teaching anatomy and clinical skills for other undergraduate students. He is a qualified clinical skills tutor at St. George's, University of London, and also the director of 'Prep4Osce', an organization that hosts mock clinical skills examinations for medical students. Ramanan is currently a foundation trainee in the South Thames Deanery and has enjoyed gaining experience in rotations which include general surgery, acute medicine and general internal medicine.

Dr. ARUN THIYAGARAJAN, MBBS (Dist), BSc (hons), AICSM
Academic Foundation Trainee, North West Thames Deanery, London, UK

Arun Thiyagarajan graduated with a distinction from Imperial College London in 2011 where he also achieved an intercalated BSc in Gastroenterology and Hepatology. Arun has taken a significant role in the teaching of undergraduates at Imperial College where he regularly teaches final and third year students for upcoming OSCE and PACEs examinations. Arun currently sits on the UKFPO Foundation Doctor Advisory Board. He is an academic foundation trainee and also acts as the 'North West Thames Academic Representative' and the 'London Deanery Academic FY1 Trainee Representative'.

Dr. RAMYAH RAJAKULASINGAM, MBBS (Dist), BSc (hons)
Foundation Trainee, Queen Elizabeth Hospital, Welwyn Garden City, UK

Ramyah Rajakulasingam graduated from Imperial College London in 2011 with a distinction in medical sciences, clinical science and clinical practice. She was awarded the Wallace Prize for the second best performance in Pathology, and obtained an intercalated BSc in Gastroenterology and Hepatology in 2009. Ramyah is currently a foundation trainee doctor in the North Central Thames Deanery and is working towards her postgraduate MRCP examination. She aspires to a career in general medicine.

Dr. SEMINI SUMANASURIYA, MBBS (Dist), BSc (hons)
Foundation Trainee, Royal Free Hospital, London, UK

Semini Sumanasuriya graduated with a distinction from Imperial College in 2011 and achieved a first class honours in her BSc in Reproductive and Developmental Sciences. She tutors medical students for both OSCEs and PACEs exams and has helped to set up a programme through University College London medical school to teach third year medical students over the academic year.

Dr. MATTHEW JAMES PYWELL, MBBS (Dist), BSc (hons)
Foundation House Officer, Bart's and the London Hospitals, London, UK

Matthew Pywell graduated with a distinction from Bart's and the London School of Medicine in 2011 with an intercalated BSc in Neuroscience. He has tutored many seminars and mock OSCEs for medical students and has taught on medical demonstrations for the London Deanery. Matthew is a Foundation Year Representative. At present, Matthew is one of the chief organisers of the Royal Free Year 3 teaching program, a course run by foundation trainee doctors. Matthew has completed clinical jobs in both general medical and surgical firms and has first-hand experience of many of the scenarios in this book.

INTRODUCTION

In August 2011, plans were announced to introduce a new system for the selection of medical students for their first hospital jobs as junior doctors (also known as the Foundation Programme). From August 2013 onwards, all junior doctors will be selected into their first hospital jobs by this method.

Prior to this date medical students were allocated their preferred hospital jobs based on their overall academic ranking (calculated from a variety of assessments during their university training) as well as completion of 'white space' questions. These questions were completed on an online application form requesting applicants to demonstrate many skills including leadership, prioritization and communication skills.

The new method of Foundation Programme allocation will consist of two parts. The first part will be based on university assessments and academic rankings, although the types of assessments for inclusion will be standardized throughout all medical schools. The second part will now remove the need for 'white space' questions and instead an invigilated examination called the Situational Judgement Test will take its place. This test is intended to assess a candidate's reactions towards common and realistic professional dilemmas.

This book contains the scenarios that are commonly encountered by junior doctors and provides answers with explanations on how to deal with these situations, thereby helping medical students to succeed in their Situational Judgement Test.

CHAPTER 1: INTRODUCTION TO SITUATIONAL JUDGEMENT TESTS

The Test

The situational judgement tests are a test of aptitude and clinical judgement in professional dilemmas. They are not a test of clinical knowledge or academic intelligence. Although this method of selection is new to medical students, a few details of what to expect from the test have been released and are available on the 'Improving Selection to Foundation Programme' website (*http://www.isfp.org.uk*).

Below is a summary of what the situational judgement test will be comprised:

Time Limit:	2 hours
Number of Questions:	70 questions
Format:	'Ranking' and 'Multi-Action' style questions (explained further below).
Exam Type:	The examination will be completed on a paper based answer sheet which will then be machine marked. There are plans for future examinations to be wholly computer based however this is currently not the case. There are no free text or essay type questions.
Negative Marking:	No
Invigilated:	Yes
Venue:	You are advised to check this detail with your university ahead of the examination. The examinations will be strictly invigilated and completed under examination circumstances (i.e. you will not be given the examination to take away and complete in your own library or at home).
Pass Mark:	No minimum 'pass' mark. How well you do in this examination only serves to contribute to your overall 'ranking' amongst your peer group and therefore it is in your best interest to do as well as you possibly can.

Question Formats

The questions fall into two main categories:

'Ranking' Style Questions

These questions ask candidates to rank a series of five responses to a professional/clinical scenario from most to least appropriate. You are not allowed to 'tie' any answers in the same position if you can't decide between two options. If you do so, you will not be awarded any marks for either of the options you have chosen as this is deemed as 'not following the instructions' of the question.

'Multi-Action' Style Questions

These questions ask candidates to pick the top three most appropriate actions in response to a professional/clinical scenario. This may not necessarily need to be ranked in any defined chronological order, however, certain options may be deemed completely inappropriate rather than just 'less appropriate' as suggested by the 'ranking' style questions. Candidates do not obtain any marks at all if more than three options are selected as this is deemed as 'not answering the question'.

In Chapter 3 we will elaborate and go through a worked example of both a 'ranking' and 'multi-action' style question with suggestions on how to approach these questions.

The topics for the questions in the situational judgement tests are based on nine various 'domains' which include the following aspects:

- Commitment to Professionalism
- Coping with Pressure
- Effective Communication
- Learning and Professional Development
- Organisation and Planning
- Patient Focus
- Problem Solving
- Teamwork
- Self Awareness

Further details on these domains will be expanded upon in Chapter 2, where common themes are highlighted.

Each situational judgement test will include approximately equal numbers of questions comprising of situations in each of the nine domains. None of these are deemed as being 'more important' or 'more weighted towards'. However, not all types of domains will necessarily be tested in both 'ranking' and 'multiple response' style questions.

The number of types of questions has been documented in the 'ISFP Final Report' to be weighted approximately 60% comprising 'ranking' type questions and approximately 40% being 'multi-action' style questions.

Marking the Test

The marking for the situational judgement test is rather complex. There is no negative marking, and you also do not get awarded any points for not answering questions so it is in your interest to try your best to answer all questions. There are no 'all or nothing' marks for your responses either. That is to say, if you give a slightly different order of actions for the 'ranking' question, or a slightly different combination of the three most appropriate options in the 'multiple response' style questions, you would still be awarded some marks if your answer is partially correct.

There is no minimum pass mark for the situational judgement tests. The score from this test is included with your academic ranking by your medical school to determine your allocation to a Foundation school, after taking your own preferences into account as well. It is therefore in your interest to score as high a mark as possible to ensure you can secure your top choice of hospital jobs.

'Ranking' Style Questions:

For ranking items, the computer marking system allocates an arbitrary 20 marks for each item. For each of the five responses to rank, up to four marks are available, and hence correctly answering all five options will total up to 20 marks. Marks are also given for 'near misses' and the scores allocated are demonstrated in the table below.

'Correct' Ranking Order for the Question

		1	2	3	4	5
Candidate Ranking	1	4	3	2	1	0
	2	0	4	3	2	1
	3	1	0	4	3	2
	4	2	1	0	4	3
	5	3	2	1	0	4

Ranking Style Questions Scoring Marks

The table shows the predetermined correct ranking options to a question along the top row and the candidates answer along the vertical column on the far left. If a candidate ranks in first place the same option that is deemed the 'correct' answer for first place, a total of 4 marks is awarded. However, if a candidate ranks in first place what is deemed to be a second choice answer then only 3 marks are awarded and so on.

'Multi-Action' Style Questions

For multi-action items, 4 marks are available for each option answered correctly, with a total of 12 marks available for each item. The order of the responses for these questions is not important, so long as the correct combination of 3 answers is chosen.

The computed score for each question is then calculated and added together for the whole test paper. This mark is converted into a number that is combined with your medical school academic ranking (otherwise known as the 'Education Performance Measure') to give your final ranking for Foundation Programme entry.

Further information and detail on the marking system can be found on the ISFP Final Report, http.//www.isfp.org.uk.

Suggested Approach

Read the questions carefully and fully. Some question stems may sound correct initially but may end with a false statement that invalidates the response.

Remember that you are being asked for the most appropriate responses not the ones that are definitely correct or wrong, therefore some responses may not seem perfect but you should choose actions where patient safety is maintained. In other words, if you can think of a better response or approach to the solution which is not given in the answers, just pick the one which is most similar to your own idea.

The answers you are asked to provide are the ones detailing actions that you would be expected to take based on GMC guidance, Foundation Programme Person Specification and Foundation Programme curriculum.

If you have time at the end of the examination, re-read your responses. There is a lot of text to comprehend in this test and it is easy to skim read and miss important points in the scenarios. You will be allowed to do this so don't feel you cannot go back and check again.

It is imperative that you take the time to prepare for this situational judgement test by reading the recommended reading in this book. Although there are claims that revision is not required for this test, there are common themes and scenarios that do recur and familiarity with these topics has been shown to translate into successful scores.

Recommended Reading

Improving Selection to the Foundation Programme website

http://www.isfp.org.uk

ISFP Final Report, published August 2011

This document can be found on the following website:

http://www.isfp.org.uk

Foundation Programme Curriculum & Person Specification for the Foundation Programme

Both of these documents can be found on the following website:

http://www.foundationprogramme.nhs.uk/pages/home

Good Medical Practice

A GMC Publication

http://www.gmc-uk.org/guidance/good_medical_practice.asp

Duties of a Doctor Registered with the GMC

A GMC Publication

http://www.gmc-uk.org/guidance/good_medical_practice/duties_of_a_doctor.asp

New Doctor: Guidance on Foundation Training

Published by the GMC, 2009

http://www.gmc-uk.org/New_Doctor09_FINAL.pdf_27493417.pdf_39279971.pdf

Tomorrow's Doctors: *Outcomes and Standards for Undergraduate Medical Education*

Published by the GMC, 2009

http://www.gmc-uk.org/TomorrowsDoctors_2009.pdf_39260971.pdf

Raising and Acting on Concerns about Patient Safety

A GMC Publication, for publication in January 2012

Leadership and Management for All Doctors

A GMC Publication, for publication in January 2012

CHAPTER 2: EXPLANATION OF THE COMMON DOMAINS

Questions posed within the situational judgement tests will fall into one of nine named categories or 'domains' as defined in Chapter 1. The following pages look at the domain topics in more detail giving a clearer definition of what is meant by the various titles, the sorts of professional dilemmas that may be tested and some information that the GMC publications *Good Medical Practice* and *Tomorrow's Doctors* have published on these matters.

Please note that although we have included many of the prime examples of commonly asked situational dilemmas and a 'taster' of what the literature states on recommended actions, these are by no means exhaustive and do not serve as a substitute for reading the recommended texts suggested in Chapter 1.

Commitment to Professionalism

Definition:

The competences and behavior that would be expected from a doctor.

The high standards of skill expected from a professional.

Acting appropriately in a manner that is acceptable towards patients and colleagues.

Maintaining safe medical practice and acting in the best interest of the patient.

Common topics within this domain could include:

- Probity
- Accepting presents
- Behaviour and relations with patients
- Behaviour and relations with colleagues
- Attitudes at work
- Maintaining high standards of work
- Bullying

The GMC's *Good Medical Practice* and *Tomorrow's Doctors* state:

- Never abuse your patient's trust in you or the public's trust in the profession.
- Never discriminate unfairly against patients or colleagues.
- You are personally accountable for your professional practice and must always be.
- Be prepared to justify your decisions and actions.
- Be honest, trustworthy and act with integrity.
- Recognise and work within the limits of your competence.

Coping with Pressure

Definition:

Being able to deal with stressful situations in a constructive manner.

Developing the skills to deal with pressure and stress.

Being calm and professional despite situations that are out of your control.

Keeping abreast of personal stresses whilst maintaining professionalism at work.

Maintaining a work-life balance.

Common topics within this domain could include:

- Coping with postgraduate examinations whilst working
- Rota problems
- Having multiple tasks at the same time to complete
- Dealing with another colleague's mistakes
- Dealing with your own mistakes at work
- Dealing with the angry or abusive patient
- Meeting deadlines (for job applications, research, audit, meetings)
- Avoiding 'burn out' and maintaining good health despite work pressures

The GMC's *Good Medical Practice* and *Tomorrow's Doctors* state:

There is very little in the recommended reading specific to this topic, however, the scenarios are commonly asked in interviews and situational judgement tests.

The main aim of this assessment is to demonstrate that you can maintain professional behaviour and high standards of care.

Effective Communication

Definition:

Actively and clearly engages patients and colleagues in equal and open dialogue.

Communicates verbal and written information concisely and with clarity.

Adapts style of communication according to individual needs and context.

Able to negotiate with colleagues and patients effectively.

Demonstrates active listening.

Common topics within this domain could include:

- Handover information
- Discussions with family and relatives
- Giving instructions to other healthcare professionals
- Requesting scans, pathology results over the telephone

- Taking a patient referral over the phone/referring a patient to another team
- Writing in the notes
- Writing discharge summaries
- Confidentiality

The GMC's *Good Medical Practice* and *Tomorrow's Doctors* state:

- Listen to patients and respond to their concerns and preferences.
- Give patients the information they want or need in a way they can understand.
- Respect patients' rights to reach decisions about their treatment and care.
- Respect patients' rights to confidentiality.

Learning and Professional Development

Definition:

Maintaining and improving your medical knowledge and practice.

Keeping up-to-date with current guidelines.

Improving your technical skills.

Common topics within this domain could include:

- Gaps in knowledge and how you overcome these
- Revising for examinations
- Attendance at courses and conferences
- Audit
- Delivering teaching to medical students and/or other healthcare staff

The GMC's *Good Medical Practice* and *Tomorrow's Doctors* state:

- Keep your professional knowledge and skills up-to-date.
- Recognise and work within the limits of your competence.
- You must work with colleagues and patients to maintain and improve the quality of your work and promote patient safety.
- Reflect regularly on your standards of medical practice.
- Respond constructively to the outcome of audits, appraisals and performance reviews, undertaking further training where necessary.
- You must keep your knowledge and skills up-to-date throughout your working life.
- You should be familiar with relevant guidelines and developments that affect your work. You should regularly take part in educational activities that maintain and further develop your competence and performance.

Organisation and Planning

Definition:

Manages and plans workload effectively.

Displays efficient time management and completes tasks on time.

Able to prioritise effectively and re-prioritise where appropriate.

Is conscientious and maintains accurate records.

Anticipates tasks and issues before they arise and puts in place provisions to deal with them.

Common topics within this domain could include:

- Organising student teaching
- Collecting notes for the multi-disciplinary team meeting
- Writing a presentation for the grand round, morbitiy and mortality meeting
- Planning on-call cover
- Taking annual leave and arranging appropriate cover
- Work-life balance
- Organising multiple tasks to perform during work time

The GMC's *Good Medical Practice* and *Tomorrow's Doctors* state:

There is very little about this domain in the recommended reading. However, it is important to remember that maintaining high standards of patient care should be at the centre of focus. Planning your day and tasks helps to maintain timely and appropriate patient care.

When planning leave, the *Good Medical Practice* states:

"You must be satisfied that, when you are off duty, suitable arrangements have been made for your patients' medical care."

Patient Focus and Safety

Definition:

Works in partnership with patients about their care.

Takes time to build relationships with patients, demonstrating courtesy, empathy and compassion.

Demonstrates understanding and appreciation of the needs of all patients, showing respect at all times.

Common topics within this domain could include:

- Ensuring patients come to no harm
- Understanding the limits of your competence
- Acting in the patients' best interests
- Dealing with colleagues' mistakes
- Dealing with your own mistakes

- Taking into account patient's views and wishes about their treatment
- Supervising junior colleagues

The GMC's *Good Medical Practice* and *Tomorrow's Doctors* state:

- Make patient care first concern.
- Protect and promote the health of patients and the public.
- Work with colleagues in the ways that best serve patients' interests.
- Supervise medical students for whom you are responsible to ensure their learning and patient safety.
- Raise any issues about patient safety.
- Flagging up any aspect of the conduct of colleagues that does not comply with good medical practice.
- If a patient under your care has suffered harm or distress, you must act immediately to put matters right, if that is possible.

Problem Solving and Decision-Making

Definition:

Demonstrates initiative.

Paying attention to detail.

Lateral thinking in problem solving.

Demonstrates an ability to assimilate a range of information and identify key issues.

Engages with the wider issues and thinks creatively to solve problems and reach appropriate decisions.

Common topics within this domain could include:

- Clinical decision-making
- Coping with sensitive patient situations
- Negotiating with colleagues
- Negotiating jobs that need to be done on the ward
- Making decisions in the best interest of the patient

The GMC's *Good Medical Practice* and *Tomorrow's Doctors* state:

- Apply findings from the literature to deal with specific clinical problems.
- Consult and take advice from colleagues, when appropriate.
- Make good use of the resources available to you.
- You are personally accountable for your professional practice and must always be prepared to justify your decisions and actions.
- Doctors must be capable of regularly taking responsibility for difficult decisions in situations of clinical complexity and uncertainty.

Self-Awareness and Insight

Definition:

Demonstrates awareness of the boundaries of their own competence.

Works within the boundaries of one's own confidence.

Recognises that asking for help is not a weakness and you can do so where required.

Exhibits appropriate level of confidence and accepts challenges to own knowledge.

Common topics within this domain could include:
- Asking for help and professional guidance in clinical decisions.
- Understanding the limits of your knowledge and competence and practicing within these limits.
- Coping with personal difficulties.
- Knowing when you have made a mistake and taking steps to correct this.

The GMC's *Good Medical Practice* and *Tomorrow's Doctors* state:
- You must make clear the limits of your knowledge or competence.
- Recognise and work within the limits of your competence.
- Recognise your personal and professional limits.
- Seek help from colleagues and professionals where necessary.

Working Effectively as Part of a Team

Definition:

Understands your role and the roles of others within a team.

Works together within the team to deliver best patient care.

Supports team members in times of need and difficulty.

Common topics within this domain could include:
- Handover between shifts
- Coordinating the admissions and discharges of patients with members of your team
- Compiling the patient ward lists with other members of staff
- Negotiating jobs and annual leave with colleagues
- Asking for help from senior team members when necessary
- Being responsible for the roles within a team you take on

The GMC's *Good Medical Practice* and *Tomorrow's Doctors* state:
- Work with colleagues in the ways that best serve patients' interests.
- Respect the skills and contributions of your colleagues.

- Communicate effectively with colleagues within and outside the team.

- Make sure that your patients and colleagues understand your role and responsibilities in the team, and who is responsible for each aspect of patient care.

- Participate in regular reviews and audits of the standards and performance of the team, taking steps to remedy any deficiencies.

- Support colleagues who have problems with performance, conduct or health.

CHAPTER 3: PRACTICE WORKED EXAMPLES

Before embarking upon the mock examinations in Chapter 4, we have included two detailed worked examples for each of the 'ranking' and 'multi-action' style questions. These questions have been specifically chosen to help demonstrate the principles and skills examined by the situational judgment test and some tips are offered for answering awkward professional dilemmas which may be posed.

'Ranking' Style Questions

Question 1

An elderly female presents to the emergency department with long-standing tiredness, weight loss and intermittent episodes of upper abdominal pain. She mentions that her skin has been looking a little 'yellow' recently but has not had the time to see her GP about this. After assessing the patient, you suspect that she is not acutely unwell but could be suffering with gallstones or worse, a hepatobiliary malignancy. You wish to order some blood tests and an abdominal ultrasound scan for her but she refuses. She tells you she is flying abroad the next day to attend her son's wedding and just wanted to know whether her illness would prevent her from flying or not. She does not have the time to wait around in hospital for the results.

Rank in order the following actions in response to this situation (1= Most appropriate; 5= Least appropriate):

A. Explain the full gravity of the situation with the patient openly and honestly in the hope that she will understand the importance of staying in hospital for the results of the investigations.

B. Allow her to fly abroad but suggest she attends a local hospital immediately if her symptoms worsen and arrange an urgent outpatient clinic appointment for her upon her return.

C. Arrange for the patient to have the abdominal scan and blood tests but allow her to leave the hospital before the results are available. Contact her and/or leave a voicemail on her answerphone if there are any significant findings to report.

D. After discussing the situation with your senior, try to contact the on-call radiologist and pathology laboratory to arrange an urgent scan and blood test.

E. Inform her that she can travel only if she lets her travel insurance company know about her current situation.

Answer Question 1

ADBCE

Option A is the most appropriate action to take as it demonstrates good communication with the patient and allows the patient to understand and take part in the decision-making around their health. There is the possiblity that the patient does not understand the implications of her symptoms and believes the abdominal pain to be secondary to something less serious such as indigestion.

Option D is the next appropriate action. Once discussing the situation in full with the patient and obtaining their understanding, discussion with other healthcare professionals will ensure the patient receives a better standard of care and tests can be prioritised according to clinical need. Any attempt you make to also take the patient's concerns into account will help enrich the doctor-patient relationship.

Options B and C are difficult options to prioritise between. In situations where you feel there may be two options that could be 'tied' in importance, try to decide which one will lead to the least amount of harm to the patient. Here Option B is likely to be the next appropriate step. The patient is educated about possible signs and symptoms of deterioration and the doctor is ensuring the patient will be followed up by a senior member of the team in clinic in the near future.

Option C is less appropriate. Although it would seem to be a good compromise initially for the doctors and the patient, there is the danger that by the time the results are ready, they may be grossly abnormal and the patient will have left the country. The patient may be unreachable and without any pre-arranged appointment or management plan, the patient may be 'lost to follow-up' and not treated. It would be inadvisable and may even breach patient confidentiality to leave an answerphone message with the patient's home telephone. This message may be intercepted by other household members or be left unchecked for several days.

Option E is the least appropriate action. Although a valid suggestion, this advice does not expedite any of the urgent investigations or treatments for this patient. Although travel insurance policies differ between companies, many will only cover emergencies that occur overseas rather than the cost of chronic illnesses or cancer therapy (which this patient could require). There is no guarantee the patient will follow your advice nor any suggestion that they will return to see their local GP or go to hospital again.

Question 2

You are a junior doctor working on the general medical firm. Whilst on ward round, you see another medical team review Mr Brown, an elderly man who was admitted the night before with shortness of breath and elevated inflammatory markers. The registrar asks your colleague, a junior doctor, if he has sent off a 'septic screen' for the patient. Due to a busy day, an ever growing list of jobs and many other sicker patients to attend to, your colleague admits that this has not been done. The registrar begins to berate him in front of the patient.

Rank in order the following actions in response to this situation (1= Most appropriate; 5= Least appropriate):

A.   Suggest to the registrar that this conversation be taken into a side room.

B.   Offer to perform the septic screen for your colleague if he is too busy with other jobs, even though the patient is not actually under the care of your own team.

C.   Step in and tell the registrar he should be ashamed for bullying your colleague and that he should remember what it was like being a junior doctor on a busy medical team.

D.   Advise your colleague that he should be more attentive to the jobs that he is given on ward round and try to be more organised in the future.

E.   Advise your colleague to discuss the event with his consultant if the registrar continues to berate him in public.

Answer Question 2

ABEDC

This scenario highlights a very precarious situation and here you may feel that none of the options available are entirely appropriate. Although patient safety is not directly at risk by this situation, maintaining a good working environment where more junior members feel supported by their seniors is essential for the care of all the patients under the medical team.

Option A is the most appropriate action as it allows the registrar and your colleague to voice their thoughts and concerns in private. Revealing friction within the team especially in front of patients is neither professional nor confidence inspiring.

Option B is the next appropriate action. The Foundation Programme Person Specification states that an applicant for the post of a junior doctor must be able to "demonstrate initiative and understand the importance of effectively working with others". By offering to share some of the jobs with your colleague you can demonstrate both these qualities and ensure better patient care. It is not wrong to help a colleague order an investigation for another patient who is not directly under your care. However, you must explain to your colleague that as the patient is still under the care of their medical team and consultant, they should check the results and act upon these findings after discussion with their seniors.

Option E may be appropriate if your colleague is finding that this registrar is continually berating him and undermining him in front of the patients. In this scenario we are not given sufficient information about how regular this type of occurrence is nor why the registrar felt it was necessary to scold the junior doctor so openly.

Option D is less appropriate than option E. Here we are told the reason behind the investigation not being performed. It appears the junior doctor is feeling quite overwhelmed by the amount of work he needs to perform and has been doing his best to ensure the most urgent investigations for the sickest patients are ordered first. Suggesting that your colleague is not performing 'up to standard' is neither helpful nor necessarily true and can further undermine his morale in the job and confidence in his abilities.

Option C is the least appropriate action and is most likely to cause more friction between not only yourself and the registrar but may also contribute to an awkward relationship between your colleague and his senior. If you feel a strong obligation to step into any disagreement between members of a team that does not involve yourself, it is better if you can offer constructive suggestions rather than to pick sides and contribute to the quarrel.

'Multi-Action' Style Questions

Question 1

You are a junior doctor on a general surgery firm. You are about to see all the post-operative patients on the ward round and your consultant asks you to collect the patient notes from the nurses' office. When you enter the office, you find the nursing team in the middle of their morning handover. You ask politely if you may collect some notes for the ward round but the senior nurse snaps and tells you in a stern and angry voice to leave the room and collect the notes later. You have heard other doctors complaining about this nurse before and that she is prone to regular tantrums.

Choose the THREE most appropriate actions to take in this situation:

A.   Report her to the hospital management and medical staffing.

B.   Ask if you may have a quiet word with her after her handover about her attitude.

C.   Return to the consultant without the notes and pretend you 'can't find them' as you are embarrassed to admit the truth of the situation and don't want the nurse to get in trouble.

D.   Explain the situation to your consultant.

E.   Suggest to your consultant that you see the other patients first and return later to obtain the notes when the nurse handover has ended.

F.   Complete a clinical incident form.

G.   Ask the nurse again politely stating that you insist on taking the notes from the room before leaving.

H.   Arrange with your colleagues to talk to this nurse about the problems all of you have faced because of her attitude in private at a later time.

Answer Question 1

BDG

In this scenario your first duty of care is to your patient. Post-operative patients require careful assessment to ensure no complications from their recent procedure have occurred or are in danger of occurring. To this end, it is important the patient notes are available for documenting the findings and management plans and that these patients are seen sooner rather than later. It is therefore important to try your best to obtain the patient notes by opting for option G and doing so in as polite a manner as possible. It is unwise to pretend you cannot find the notes (option C) or delay patient review (option E).

There is a second issue in this scenario regarding dealing with a difficult colleague. Although you understand that several other colleagues have had issues with the nurse in question, it may not be fair to assume they want to confront the nurse about this or force them to take action if they would prefer not to be involved. It may also cause the nurse to feel threatened if you appear to 'gang up' with colleagues in confronting her about her attitude. It is, however, important that you try to ensure that your working relationship with this nurse is not damaged and having a quiet word in private (option B) would be the best solution to this.

As a junior doctor it is probably premature to report this nurse to medical staffing or the hospital management although her attitude could potentially result in suboptimal patient care (if it hasn't already done so). You should alert your consultant to this fact especially as you know this incident is a common occurrence. Your consultant is the most senior member of your team and would be the more appropriate member of your team to report such serious matters to the hospital management if required.

Question 2

An elderly Caucasian woman presents to the emergency department with rigors, back pain and general weakness in her lower limbs. Her inflammatory markers are found to be elevated. She is mildly tachycardic but haemodynamically stable. There is no significant past medical history of a known malignancy or recent trauma. She denies any recent travel abroad.

Choose the THREE most appropriate actions to take in this situation:

A. Examine the patient to the best of your ability and obtain a full septic screen to determine the source of a potential infectious agent.

B. Discuss the patient with the radiologist and request a CT or MRI scan of the patient's spine.

C. Obtain an abdominal radiograph to rule out abdominal obstruction.

D. Contact the neurosurgeons.

E. Discuss the patient with your consultant and decide on a plan of action for the patient.

F. Get in contact with the clinical infectious diseases registrar.

G. Arrange for an immediate abdominal ultrasound scan to rule out a renal calculus or abdominal aortic aneurysm.

H. Start empirical treatment for suspected tuberculosis.

Answer Question 2

ABE

This scenario is examining your clinical problem-solving ability. The most immediate actions to take in any acutely unwell patient would be to examine and review the patient to the best of your ability (option A), arrange for any appropriate investigations (option B) and discuss the case with your senior (option E) before making the decision to refer to another team.

From the brief patient history provided, the most likely differential diagnoses could include diskitis, a spinal abscess or an occult malignancy. The symptoms are not suggestive of an abdominal aneurysm, renal calculi or bowel obstruction as lower limb weakness would be unusual, although they could all present with either rigors or back pain (options C and G).

Although tuberculosis may be the causative agent for a spinal abscess, in the absence of any exotic travel abroad, infectious contacts or a positive serology, this is unlikely to be the causative agent (option H).

CHAPTER 4: MOCK EXAMINATIONS

Examination 1

PART ONE – Ranking Questions

Question 1

You are seeing a pregnant 20 year old young lady in the emergency department. She can only speak minimal English and her father appears to be speaking on her behalf without consulting her. He explains to you that his daughter would like to have a termination of her pregnancy. When you ask him to directly translate so that you can speak to her, he dismisses you, stating that she will agree with whatever he decides.

Rank in order the following actions in response to this situation (1= Most appropriate; 5= Least appropriate):

A.   Ask for the daughter's view but continue to have the father interpreting for her.

B.   Obtain an official interpreter and discuss the situation with both the daughter and father.

C.   Ask the father if there is anyone else he knows that can translate, such as his wife.

D.   Find an official interpreter to speak to the daughter first in private and then speak to the father.

E.   Try and speak to the daughter despite her basic knowledge of English.

Question 2

Whilst on a ward round you notice some medical students are gathered around one patient trying to take blood. You return to the ward 30 minutes later and find the same patient complaining about the numerous attempts to obtain blood but no blood has been taken yet. You are certain that the patient is easy to bleed and the students have assured you that they have taken blood before. How would you go about improving their venepuncture technique?

Rank in order the following actions in response to this situation (1= Most appropriate; 5= Least appropriate):

A.   Do nothing as the students have probably just been unlucky this time.

B.   Ask your consultant to give some teaching regarding venepuncture technique for the students.

C.   Organise a teaching session yourself for the students on mannequin arms.

D.   Get the students to watch you take blood when you next do it.

E.   Ask a phlebotomist to kindly go through the venepuncture technique with them and go around with them when they take blood.

Question 3

You are one of three junior doctors on a busy surgical firm and there are many high risk, complicated elective surgical admissions planned for today. You are also on-call and hence will be caring for all the new emergency surgical patients who will be admitted. You are slightly worried that a large number of admissions will mean that you will be even more busy than usual. How will you go about prioritising the jobs you have?

Rank in order the following actions in response to this situation (1= Most appropriate; 5= Least appropriate):

A.   Try and do all the jobs for the elective surgical patients as they arise, and ask all three junior doctors to come in early tomorrow to prepare for the post-take ward round.

B.   Try and take on the jobs as and when they come to you.

C.   Allocate a doctor to the on-call duties, one for the elective surgical patients and another for the post-take round jobs.

D.   Always make sure that one person is available to do jobs for the elective surgical patients at all times. The other two doctors can continue with the on-call today and post-take duties tomorrow.

E.   Have all the junior doctors try to do as many jobs as possible today in order ease the workload tomorrow, even if it means staying very late.

Question 4

An elderly female presents to the emergency department with long-standing tiredness and intermittent episodes of mild epigastric and right-sided abdominal pain. She also reports that her skin sometimes turns 'yellow' but has never seen the doctor about this. After a thorough examination you conclude that that although not acutely unwell, she may have gallstones but you also cannot exclude a malignancy. You plan to order some blood tests and an abdominal scan but she is reluctant as she is due to fly abroad the next day to attend her son's wedding. She cannot stay very long in the hospital today to wait for the results.

Rank in order the following actions in response to this situation (1= Most appropriate; 5= Least appropriate):

A.   Admit her immediately and try to arrange the investigations.

B.   Let her leave without trying to do anything, as it is her choice.

C.   Carry out the urgent abdominal scan and blood tests but telephone her with the results once she has left hospital or gone abroad if the results take longer to return.

D.   Discuss with your senior colleagues what the best course of action should be. Contact the on-call radiologist and pathology laboratory to arrange an urgent scan and blood test.

E.   Inform her that she can travel only if she lets her travel insurance company know about her current situation.

Question 5

You are the on-call surgical Foundation doctor and have just clerked in a relatively stable patient in the 'minors' emergency department with abdominal pain. You suddenly realise that you have left your bleep upstairs on the ward so you decide to go back upstairs to get it. As you are about to leave the minors emergency department, the patient you have just clerked becomes hypotensive, tachycardic and states that he "can't breathe".

Rank in order the following actions in response to this situation (1= Most appropriate; 5= Least appropriate):

A.   Ask a nurse to bleep your senior colleague to attend to the patient whilst you go back upstairs to get your bleep.

B.   Contact your senior colleague immediately to attend to the patient. Ask one of the nurses to call switchboard and the main surgical wards to inform them that you can be contacted on your mobile until you retrieve your bleep.

C.   Ask the nurse to prepare a resuscitation bay to transfer your patient into.

D.   Go back upstairs to get your bleep, and then attend to stabilising the patient.

E.   Stabilise the patient according to the ABC (airway, breathing, circulation) algorithm.

Question 6

An elderly gentleman presents to you with what seems to be an acute myocardial infarction. You start him on ACS (acute coronary syndrome) protocol even though his troponin is not significantly raised. On retrieving his GP notes you notice that a recent scan showed that he had an anuerysmal thoracic aorta. The cardiology registrar says she can only review the patient later on as she is busy and the patient is currently stable. What can you do right now to help rule out a possible aortic dissection as a cause of his chest pain?

Rank in order the following actions in response to this situation (1= Most appropriate; 5= Least appropriate):

A.   Request a chest X-ray.

B.   Request a CT aorta angiogram study.

C.   Measure the patient's blood pressure in both arms.

D.   Request for an urgent bedside ECHO.

E.   Repeat a blood test to send for troponin and D-dimer levels.

Question 7

You have been asked to provide ward cover over night as your junior doctor colleague has called in sick. You decline as you have already made plans to attend a party and it is not your turn to cover the night duties. Later in the evening you see your colleague who called in sick at the party you are attending.

Rank in order the following actions in response to this situation (1= Most appropriate; 5= Least appropriate):

A.   Turn a blind eye to the situation.

B.   After considering the event, decide to tell him a few weeks later about your feelings. You feel awkward bringing it up right now and don't want to say anything rash.

C.   Ask your fellow junior doctor colleagues for advice.

D.   Approach your colleague at an appropriate time in the evening. Tell him his behaviour is unethical and you will be forced to report him if it happens again.

E.   Discuss the incident with your own consultant the next day at work.

Question 8

Your registrar has asked you to insert a chest drain even though you have never done one before or observed the procedure. You are aware that such opportunities are hard to come by and this will count as a DOP (directly observed procedure) for your ePortfolio. Your registrar says she will supervise you and step in if necessary. You have just started your first clinical rotation as a new Foundation doctor and feel that this may be out of your depth.

Rank in order the following actions in response to this situation (1= Most appropriate; 5= Least appropriate):

A.   Watch your colleague do the procedure and then try and perform it at the next given opportunity under supervision.

B.   Carry out the procedure unsupervised and try your best to help.

C.   Ask the registrar to carry it out as you do not feel fully competent.

D.   Ask the registrar to do the procedure so that you can learn the technique by observing her, but help out as much as possible within your competency.

E.   Carry out the procedure under supervision.

Question 9

You are a junior doctor working on a busy firm and have been away on annual leave for three days. During your absence the senior house officer on the team has not been ordering the appropriate blood tests and has failed to document these accurately in the blood test results folder. During the afternoon your registrar criticizes you in the office, thinking that you were the culprit for the lack of updated blood test results and says tells you that it is your duty to ensure that these actions are appropriately carried out.

Rank in order the following actions in response to this situation (1= Most appropriate; 5= Least appropriate):

A.   Politely inform the registrar that you have been away though you understand the importance of the situation. Say that you will order any outstanding investigations and that you will take steps to ensure this does not happen again.

B.   Tell the registrar that unfortunately you have been away for a few days and that this was the senior house officer's mistake.

C.   In a private room, speak with your senior house officer to tell her about the mistakes that have been happening and suggest that she liaises with the registrar to prevent future occurrence.

D.   Apologise to the registrar and make every effort to ensure that any outstanding investigations are arranged without delay.

E.   Tell your consultant that your registrar criticised you unfairly.

Question 10

You want to pursue a career in ENT (ear, nose and throat) surgery. Unfortunately you do not have an ENT rotation and are struggling to get much exposure to the specialty as a junior doctor. You have tried discussing the situation with the senior members of your team, but they do not seem to be providing much advice.

Rank in order the following actions in response to this situation (1= Most appropriate; 5= Least appropriate):

A.   Make a visit to the hospital's ENT team concerning a taster week/practical exposure.

B.   Ask to speak to one of the ENT registrars or consultants to see if there are any ENT projects that you could get involved with.

C.   Negotiate time off with your team and when you are not busy, go to the ENT department as and when possible.

D.   Discuss career progression with your educational supervisor and ask his advice regarding gaining exposure to ENT in this hospital.

E.   Look into which exams you must sit to pursue a career in ENT.

Question 11

It is a Wednesday lunchtime and you are about to present at the department's monthly morbidity and mortality meeting, which you have spent a long time preparing for. Suddenly your bleep goes off and it is one of the senior sisters from your ward regarding an urgent matter.

Rank in order the following actions in response to this situation (1= Most appropriate; 5= Least appropriate):

A. Contact one of the doctors on your team and ask them to attend to the matter urgently in your place as you need to present at the meeting.

B. Attend to the matter in hand and inform the department that you have an urgent matter to attend to and you will present your data another time.

C. Tell the senior sister that you will attend to the matter once you have finished your presentation.

D. Attend to the matter urgently without informing anyone. Patient safety takes priority over anything else.

E. Ask one of your colleagues to start the presentation, whilst you call the senior sister back to find out more information about the matter.

Question 12

A patient is admitted with recurrent episodes of diabetic ketoacidosis. It becomes evident to your team that she is not adhering to her insulin regimen due to the restrictions that she feels it places on her daily life. She says her busy work schedule means she does not have time to give herself subcutaneous injections.

Rank in order the following actions in response to this situation (1= Most appropriate; 5= Least appropriate):

A. Explain that if she does not adhere to the regimen then she will eventually have a fatal attack of diabetic ketoacidosis.

B. Explain the pathogenesis of diabetic ketoacidosis and why it is important she complies with her insulin regimen.

C. Empathise with her and explore her ideas, concerns and expectations, then try to work with her to create a regimen which fits in with her lifestyle.

D. Suggest an appointment with the diabetic specialist nurse to talk further about concerns.

E. Explain that it may be possible to develop an insulin regimen that is more compatible with her busy schedule.

Question 13

You are a junior doctor and during a post-take ward round one of your patients goes into cardiac arrest. You and your senior house officer colleague happen to be the only doctors on the ward. Having done your ALS (advanced life support) course last week and been part of several arrest teams you feel confident that you know what to do. However, your colleague who is new to the hospital and has not completed his ALS course shouts orders to you that you know for certain are incorrect.

Rank in order the following actions in response to this situation (1= Most appropriate; 5= Least appropriate):

A. Ensure that you just carry out basic life support until the cardiac arrest team arrive.

B. Do as your senior house officer colleague says even though you know it is wrong.

C. Reassure your colleague that you know what to do in this situation and take over the management of the patient – follow ALS protocols until the crash team arrives.

D. Ask the nurse to call someone more senior, and let your colleague lead the arrest for the meanwhile.

E. Let your colleague take the lead, but correct him when you know that the orders given are wrong.

Question 14

You are a junior doctor working in a GP practice. You see a 70 year old Indian female, Mrs Shah, who is known to have Type II diabetes and hypertension. On examination she appears unwell and is holding her hand clenched over her chest. She speaks no English and is desperately trying to converse with you in Hindi. You cannot understand anything but you think she may have chest pain, which could probably be from a heart attack.

Rank in order the following actions in response to this situation (1= Most appropriate; 5= Least appropriate):

A. Use non-verbal methods to communicate with the patient.

B. Rebook the appointment with an interpreter for the following week.

C. Do an ECG immediately if the equipment is available.

D. Try and communicate to the patient that she needs to go to A & E.

E. Call an ambulance, informing them of the situation.

Question 15

Your team is seeing a patient who has been admitted overnight with pneumonia. During handover the registrar had asked your colleague to send off an 'atypical pneumonia screening test' for a patient. While at the bedside the registrar asks your colleague if he has sent off the screening test yet. It has been a busy morning and, with other more pressing investigations to organise, your colleague admits that this has not been sent. Your registrar becomes very angry and begins to berate your colleague in front of the patient.

Rank in order the following actions in response to this situation (1= Most appropriate; 5= Least appropriate):

A.   Suggest to the registrar that this conversation be taken into a side room.

B.   Step into the conversation and emphasise that there were more urgent jobs that needed attention.

C.   Tell the patient that the registrar is at fault for behaving this way in front of a patient.

D.   Apologise to the patient for the registrar's comments while this is happening.

E.   Report the event to your consultant.

Question 16

You are waiting to speak to a radiologist to discuss a CT request for one of your patients. While waiting outside the room, you hear the radiologist being openly rude and harsh to a colleague, the same level as yourself, who is requesting a CT pulmonary angiogram. He tells her "to get out and stop wasting his time". She walks out of the room almost in tears.

Rank in order the following actions in response to this situation (1= Most appropriate; 5= Least appropriate):

A.   Ensure that your colleague is not feeling too depressed to work when she comes out.

B.   Suggest that she reports the situation to a senior colleague.

C.   Walk into the radiologist's room and state that you believe he was totally inappropriate.

D.   Report what happened to your clinical supervisor.

E.   Mention the scenario at the next Foundation school quality assurance visit.

Question 17

You are a junior doctor on a GP rotation. A 20 year old girl comes in asking you to backdate a sick note. She explains that she has just failed her university medical finals examinations as she was unwell during this time two weeks ago. She is now unable to retake the year unless she has a sick note to certify that she was unwell at the time. When you see her she does have a productive cough and has a fever.

Rank in order the following actions in response to this situation (1= Most appropriate; 5= Least appropriate):

A.   Explain to the patient that you cannot backdate a sick note as she did not contact a doctor at the time she was sitting her exams and therefore you cannot verify that she was unwell at that time.

B.   Backdate the sick note. You know that this is important for the student and she does actually look rather ill and it is possible her infection has been brewing for a while.

C.   Explain to the patient that you cannot backdate a sick note; however, you are able to certify that she is unwell today.

D.   Tell the patient you will not sign a sick note for her at all since you do not believe she is unwell enough to call in sick for her studies.

E.   Backdate the sick note and then write a letter to the university saying you did not actually see the patient while she was unwell.

Question 18

You are called to the emergency department to see a 75 year old female with pneumonia who is going to be admitted under the care of your consultant. She has a large number of co-morbidities and in the last week she has been deteriorating clinically. There has been a discussion among the emergency department staff who feel that cardiopulmonary resuscitation (CPR) would be futile in the event that she arrested. Her family, however, have previously expressed on several occasions that they wish everything to be done for her.

Rank in order the following actions in response to this situation (1= Most appropriate; 5= Least appropriate):

A.   Discuss this matter with your consultant.

B.   In view of the family's wishes, document that the patient is for cardiopulmonary resuscitation in the event of a cardiac arrest.

C.   Discuss the matter with the patient alone, explaining they are not for resuscitation, and document the conversation in the medical records.

D.   Discuss this matter with your registrar.

E.   Discuss this with the patient but do not record any information in the notes.

Question 19

An elderly gentleman on the ward complains of chest pain after a coronary angiogram. You understand from the angiogram report that a coronary stent was not inserted and that the cardiology consultant believes the patient would benefit more from a coronary artery bypass surgery. You ask for an ECG and see no acute changes. The patient's clinical observations are stable but his pain remains despite having two puffs of his GTN spray.

Rank in order the following actions in response to this situation (1= Most appropriate; 5= Least appropriate):

A.   Contact your senior registrar for advice.

B.   Prescribe morphine 2.5 mg as required until the pain is resolved.

C.   Prescribe an intravenous GTN infusion.

D.   Reassure the patient that there is nothing to be concerned over.

E.   At handover, tell the on-call cardiologist about the patient.

Question 20

You are having lunch with a junior doctor colleague, who briefly mentions that he is not feeling very well. He excuses himself to go to the bathroom and returns to tell you that he has been experiencing nausea and vomiting since the morning and now thinks he may have some diarrhoea. You happen to also know that he is the on-call doctor for the day.

Rank in order the following actions in response to this situation (1= Most appropriate; 5= Least appropriate):

A.   Suggest that he need not worry about his symptoms and carry on through the day.

B.   Suggest that he immediately report that he is unwell to a senior member of his team.

C.   Inform the rota coordinator that it is likely they will need to find a substitute for his on-call shift this evening.

D.   Fill in a clinical incident form.

E.   Comfort your colleague and explain that he should not be at work as it is detrimental to him and his patients' health.

Question 21

You are one of the two surgical junior doctors who are on-call until 8pm. So far you haven't had many ward jobs to do. At 7pm, the vascular registrar bleeps you informing you that there are five elective surgical patients to clerk who require the insertion of a cannula and blood tests sending off. All of them are due to have surgery the next day. You are aware that you are not supposed to clerk elective patients during on-call shifts but realise that there is nobody else to do this as the vascular registrar himself is attending to a trauma call.

Rank in order the following actions in response to this situation (1= Most appropriate; 5= Least appropriate):

A.   Do not clerk any of the patients as you feel it is not your duty to do so.

B.   Only clerk one or two patients when you feel you can fit them in-between your ward jobs.

C.   Attend to any emergencies on the ward first.

D.   Inform the vascular registrar that you will see all the patients and ask him for a brief background about them.

E.   Inform the registrar that you are on-call and this is not really your duty but you will ask your fellow junior doctors to carry your bleep while you clerk the elective patients.

Question 22

You are a junior doctor working in general surgery. Your team was asked to review one of the general medical patients on another ward with abdominal pain last week and suggested a management plan in the patient's notes. You have just been told by one of the nursing staff that the medical consultant in charge of this patient would like a word with you to clarify the plan that was written in the notes. You were not personally present when your team reviewed this patient and the members of your team who were present are on annual leave today.

Rank in order the following actions in response to this situation (1= Most appropriate; 5= Least appropriate):

A.   Read the patient's notes to get an understanding of the patient's history and how your team treated him.

B.   Ask the nurse if she knows what the outcome of the surgical ward review was.

C.   Try and contact your junior doctor colleague at home to find out the outcome of the surgical ward review.

D.   Tell the medical consultant that you cannot tell him anything and he just has to wait until your consultant and the other junior doctor colleague are back.

E.   Ask your registrar for advice and more information on how to proceed.

Question 23

After a ward round, you start to experience abdominal cramps and have a few episodes of diarrhoea in the acute medical ward toilet. You think that this may be related to some fast food that you ate after your on-call shift the night before.

Rank in order the following actions in response to this situation (1= Most appropriate; 5= Least appropriate):

A.   Ignore it and if it recurs then raise the issue with your rota coordinator.

B.   Immediately alert the rest of your team that you are not well and need to go home.

C.   Alert your rota coordinator that you are unwell and need to go home.

D.   Carry on throughout the day and do not tell anyone that you are unwell as you do not want to burden them with extra work by going off sick.

E.   Leave the hospital and do not return to work until the diarrhoea has completely resolved.

Question 24

Your team is under-staffed due to illness and annual leave. It has become evident that you shall be doing the ward round alone without another junior doctor colleague. Although you have a registrar present, he is required to go to clinic for the morning. There are 15 patients on the ward, most of who are medically stable and do not require any complex medical input.

Rank in order the following actions in response to this situation (1= Most appropriate; 5= Least appropriate):

A.   Sit down with a senior colleague before the ward round to seek out advice about any particularly complicated patients.

B.   Contact/seek senior advice when you come across something which you feel unsure about during the ward round.

C.   Relay any issues about the patients to your registrar when the round is over.

D.   Ensure clear and accurate documentation in the notes during the ward round.

E.   State that you do not feel comfortable doing a ward round by yourself and insist the registrar joins you.

Question 25

You are on your way to your night shift and whilst driving on the motorway, you notice a road traffic accident. The police and ambulance are present already. There are two casualties who appear rather badly hurt.

Rank in order the following actions in response to this situation (1= Most appropriate; 5= Least appropriate):

A.   Travel in the ambulance and provide medical attention to victims of the accident, leaving your car on the motorway side road.

B.   If your help is required, inform work that you will be late and then assess the patients.

C.   If your help is required, start to assess the injured patients first without informing the hospital of your delay.

D.   Ask the police/ambulance staff if they require any help.

E.   Inform work that you cannot attend your shift at all today as you have to attend an emergency on the motorway.

Question 26

You are the surgical junior doctor on-call, and have been called to the emergency department by your registrar to help him arrange urgent blood tests as one of the patients being admitted under your consultant needs immediate surgery. When your consultant arrives in the emergency department, your registrar leaves to go and prepare the operating theatre. You notice that your consultant is slurring his words and smells of alcohol.

Rank in order the following actions in response to this situation (1= Most appropriate; 5= Least appropriate):

A. Do not say anything as you feel awkward raising this with your consultant and do not want him to get into trouble.

B. Call theatres directly and tell the anaesthetist what you have noticed.

C. Speak to your consultant in private and explain your concerns regarding him slurring his words and smelling of alcohol.

D. Inform the nurse in charge in the emergency department about what you have noticed, without speaking to your consultant.

E. Call your registrar and inform him what you have noticed, without speaking to your consultant.

Question 27

You are a junior doctor working on a breast surgical firm. Your registrar is held up in theatre with a case and has asked you to go and consent the next patient booked for theatre to save time in-between cases. The patient is booked for a 'Hadfield procedure'. You have no idea what this is and have never seen one performed before.

Rank in order the following actions in response to this situation (1= Most appropriate; 5= Least appropriate):

A. Ask the senior house officer to consent the patient instead as he is more senior than you and will probably know a bit more about what this procedure involves.

B. Look up all the relevant information about the procedure on the internet and try to explain the potential complications as best as possible to the patient on the ward.

C. Tell the registrar that you do not think you will be able to do this as you have never seen the procedure before. Suggest that you can help with other tasks but he should consent the patient himself.

D. Discuss the procedure with your registrar whilst he is scrubbed in theatre and ask him if he will go with you to carry out the consent as you don't feel confident you can address all the patient concerns.

E. Print a leaflet off the internet for the patient and ask them to read it and sign the consent form if they are happy with what they have read. Guess the answers to any of their questions.

Question 28

You are a junior doctor working in orthopaedic surgery. You review a young patient with mechanical back pain in the emergency department. You have ruled out any fractures with a spinal X-ray and the patient's blood results are normal. When you tell the patient that you think they can go home with simple analgesia they become very angry and demand to be reviewed privately by an orthopaedic consultant straightaway or alternatively, if the consultant is too busy, to be kept in the hospital overnight and seen in the morning.

Rank in order the following actions in response to this situation (1= Most appropriate; 5= Least appropriate):

A.   Negotiate with the patient and tell them that the consultant is not available but if they want a second opinion then you can ask the most senior member of your team present to re-examine them.

B.   Contact your consultant immediately at home and ask him to drive into hospital to the emergency department to review the patient.

C.   Discuss the situation with your registrar and seek his advice on the situation.

D.   Tell the patient that if he wants to be seen privately he can ask his GP to refer him formally but his condition does not require an urgent referral.

E.   Contact the hospital security and ask for the patient to be taken off the premises as they are refusing to leave.

Question 29

You are a junior doctor working in general practice. A young patient attends clinic with a history of depression. She tells you that the antidepressants she has recently been prescribed are not effective and she is thinking of stopping taking them. A friend of hers has recommended she buy some natural herbal pills from the internet. She tells you they are made in India and the contents are an ancient 'secret' remedy that has worked for millions of people over the decades.

Rank in order the following actions in response to this situation (1= Most appropriate; 5= Least appropriate):

A.   Prescribe the patient stronger antidepressants such as tricyclic antidepressants so that she will not be tempted to use the herbal remedies.

B.   Agree with the patient that the herbal pills sound very good and encourage them to 'give it a go' even though you do not know much about the medication she is talking about.

C.   Discuss the risks and benefits of various treatment options for depression, including alternative therapies, and suggest that the final decision is up to the patient.

D.   Listen to what the patient is telling you but strongly encourage them to stick with the original antidepressants they have been prescribed as they can take up to two weeks for them to work.

E.   Tell the patient that you think the herbal remedy sounds rubbish and may be detrimental to their health.

Question 30

You are a junior doctor working in obstetrics and gynaecology. A patient of yours was recently admitted with an ectopic pregnancy and is currently recovering on the ward after surgery. She is only 14 years old and has told you that she does not want you to tell her parents that she is sexually active or any details regarding why she was admitted. You are confronted by her father later in the day who demands that you tell him all the details of the admission as she is not talking to him and he is very worried.

Rank in order the following actions in response to this situation (1= Most appropriate; 5= Least appropriate):

A. Tell the father to mind his own business and that if he wants to know the details then he should have worked harder at building a stronger relationship with his daughter.

B. Tell the father all the details regarding his daughter's admission as she is underage and you believe he has a right to know.

C. Apologise to the father that you are unable to disclose any personal information despite the patient's young age and suggest that he speak to his daughter about her medical condition again.

D. Pretend that you do not know anything about the patient. As a result you can get away without saying anything that causes a confrontation.

E. Tell the father that you are sorry you cannot give him any details but say you can ask your consultant in charge to speak to him if he wishes to speak to a more senior doctor.

Question 31

You are a junior doctor working in general medicine. All the hospital beds are occupied and the bed manager is putting a lot of pressure on the doctors to discharge patients who are not acutely unwell. You are asked by the manager to send home all the patients you possibly can.

Rank in order the following actions in response to this situation (1= Most appropriate; 5= Least appropriate):

A. Go and review all your patients on the ward and discharge patients that the consultant has already told you in the morning ward round are fit for home. Make sure all the discharge prescriptions for these patients are completed.

B. Tell the bed manager that you can't help as you are not senior enough to make discharge decisions.

C. Discharge all the patients that are able to walk and are not strictly bedbound to help the hospital out, regardless of what the plan from the morning ward rounds were.

D. Contact your registrar and/or consultant to explain the situation. Ask if they can go through the patient list with you again and tell you who they think can be discharged.

E. Ask all the patients on your list if they would like to go home and discharge all the patients who say 'yes'.

Question 32

You are asked to review a sick patient on the ward during a weekend on-call for general medicine. They have spiked a temperature but are actually already midway through a course of co-amoxiclav for a chest infection, even though the patient's notes say they are allergic to penicillin.

Rank in order the following actions in response to this situation (1= Most appropriate; 5= Least appropriate):

A.   Assume that as the patient has already had co-amoxiclav for a few days they cannot be allergic to it and allow the patient to continue to finish the whole course.

B.   Cross off the co-amoxiclav from the patient's drug chart and re-prescribe an alternative antibiotic in line with the hospital antimicrobial policy.

C.   Write a clinical incident form about what you have seen.

D.   Alert the nurses that you have changed the drug chart and make them aware of the patient's allergies. Tell them that even if co-amoxiclav is prescribed, they should double-check the prescription with the doctor in charge as the medicine contains penicillin.

E.   Ask the hospital pharmacist if they would be willing to deliver some teaching sessions for the junior doctors in the hospital regarding safe prescribing.

Question 33

You are a junior doctor working on a busy general medical ward. You are asked to review one of your patients who has collapsed and subsequently found to have an extremely low blood sugar. Later on in the day you accidentally overhear one of the nurses speaking to her husband on the phone, admitting that she had accidentally given the patient in question an overdose of insulin and that she hoped no one would find out about it.

Rank in order the following actions in response to this situation (1= Most appropriate; 5= Least appropriate):

A.   Call the police immediately and ask that the nurse in question be arrested for causing harm to a patient.

B.   Report the incident to the matron in charge and your consultant and ask for their advice on what the next step should be.

C.   Confront the nurse in question about what she has done and encourage her to disclose this information to her seniors.

D.   Ignore the information you have overheard as there is no way you can prove to anyone what has happened.

E.   Try to spy on your colleague during working hours and wait for them to make the mistake again so that you can 'catch them in the act'.

Question 34

You are a junior doctor on a busy medical firm. One afternoon a patient of yours asks if they can speak to you in private and tells you that he has had his wallet stolen from his bedside and is visibly upset. He tells you that he doesn't have any other money on him now and the wallet contained his credit cards as well.

Rank in order the following actions in response to this situation (1= Most appropriate; 5= Least appropriate):

A. Ignore the patient's concerns and ask him to double-check all his coat pockets and cupboards again. After all, he is old and his eyesight is poor so he could have easily mislaid it.

B. Get a detailed description of the wallet, how much money it contained and when he last saw it. Make a general enquiry amongst the nursing staff about whether anyone has seen the item.

C. After getting a detailed description about the alleged theft, ask the senior nurse on the ward to report the theft to the police and help the patient cancel his credit cards.

D. Fill out a clinical incident form.

E. Ask the patients on the ward to clear out their cupboards and look around their beds in case they have accidentally picked up the wallet unintentionally.

Question 35

You are a junior doctor working in the emergency department. You attend to a patient with multiple bruising and injuries to her face. She discloses to you in private that her boyfriend beat her up this evening because she didn't manage to do all of his laundry on time. She begs you not to tell anyone else about this and doesn't want to leave the boyfriend as she is currently pregnant with his child and doesn't want to end up as a single parent.

Rank in order the following actions in response to this situation (1= Most appropriate; 5= Least appropriate):

A. Encourage the patient to contact the police about her situation, otherwise say you will contact them and report the matter yourself.

B. Report the incident to the police even though the patient has asked you not to tell anyone about her situation.

C. Encourage the patient to leave her abusive partner. Warn her that her life could potentially be in danger.

D. Do nothing about the situation as the patient is not keen to have anything done.

E. Offer the patient written information and advice on avenues for help if she changes her mind and wants to discuss her situation.

Question 36

You are nearing the end of your attachment on a general surgical firm. A patient of yours stops you and tells you how much they appreciate your help and compliments you on your kindness and intelligence. They ask if you would like to join them for dinner after work next week when they will be discharged, or alternatively whether they can buy you a coffee sometime.

Rank in order the following actions in response to this situation (1= Most appropriate; 5= Least appropriate):

A. Thank the patient for their kind words but decline meeting them outside of the hospital as you do not feel this is professional behaviour.

B. Agree to go out to dinner with the patient and thank them for their kindness as you think it would be rude to refuse and do not want to hurt their feelings.

C. Agree to go for a coffee or dinner but insist that another colleague joins you.

D. Discuss the matter with your registrar and consultant to see what advice they can give you because you don't want to hurt the patient but also do not want to do anything that would be professionally frowned upon.

E. Accept the invitation to dinner and if it goes well, continue to meet them regularly in the future for dinners and coffees.

Question 37

You are a junior doctor working on a paediatric medical rotation. Whilst on-call you review a sick patient and try to get in contact with your registrar for his advice. After he answers the phone, he tells you that he is going to take at least 20 minutes to get to you as he has popped out of the hospital to have dinner with his friends in town. You know that the registrar is supposed to be on-site during his on calls. What do you do?

Rank in order the following actions in response to this situation (1= Most appropriate; 5= Least appropriate):

A. Apologise to the parent and patient about the long wait but reassure them that they will be reviewed by a senior and you will begin by sending off all relevant investigations first.

B. Contact the consultant on-call and report the registrar's actions.

C. When you see the registrar, make it clear that he is not supposed to leave the hospital in case of an urgent referral/emergency. Tell him you will make a complaint if he does this again.

D. When you see the registrar pretend there is no issue with him leaving the hospital to have dinner. You do not want to create a negative work atmosphere.

E. Ask the senior house officer on-call to help you deal with the sick patient in the interim whilst you wait for the registrar to arrive as you are unsure what sort of management should be instigated.

Question 38

During your rotation as a junior doctor working in general medicine you are asked to help give a weekly teaching session to a group of medical students. You notice that one of the students is struggling to understand some basic clinical principles and is starting to hold back the other students because he keeps asking lots of irrelevant questions. The other students look visibly annoyed but no one seems to say anything about it.

Rank in order the following actions in response to this situation (1= Most appropriate; 5= Least appropriate):

A. Ask to have a private word with the student who is struggling and ask if there are any aspects of your teaching he does not understand and would like you to explain in more detail.

B. Recommend some textbooks that the student who is struggling can read to help him better understand some of the basic concepts.

C. Speak to the struggling student in private and tell him that he is holding the rest of the class back and it would be better for the rest of the class if he no longer attended your teaching sessions.

D. Ignore the struggling student's irrelevant questions during teaching and try to increase the pace of your teaching so that the rest of the students will find it interesting, even if one of your students is not keeping up.

E. Tell the consultant and registrar on your firm that there is one student who is really struggling and ask them for their advice and help in dealing with this matter, such as flagging up the issue with the medical school.

Question 39

You are a junior doctor working in general practice. A medical student who you know relatively well attends the clinic and starts crying about how much stress she feels she is under at university. She asks you to write her a sick note so that she won't need to attend her classes and examinations next week. She feels she has left all her work to the last minute and there is no hope of her passing the examinations anymore.

Rank in order the following actions in response to this situation (1= Most appropriate; 5= Least appropriate):

A. Tell them that it is their fault for not preparing for the examination sooner and refuse to write them a sick note.

B. Sympathise with the student and write them a sick note even though they are not actually unwell with any medical or mental illness.

C. Ask the student whether there is anything you can do to help them for the exam such as lending them your old textbooks or giving them some extra teaching after work.

D. Apologise to the student and explain that you cannot write a sick note as this would be unethical as they are not actually unwell with any illness.

E. Encourage the student to speak to their university tutor and discuss their levels of stress and difficulty in keeping up with their studies.

Question 40

You are a junior doctor working in general surgery. You notice a junior colleague of yours is looking rather low and not paying much attention to her jobs at work. When confronted about it she tells you that her father passed away last week and she misses him very much. She begs you not to tell the consultant because she doesn't want to appear weak or as if she is not coping. She feels that the ward is already short-staffed and does not want to cause more problems by asking for compassionate leave.

Rank in order the following actions in response to this situation (1= Most appropriate; 5= Least appropriate):

A. Persuade your junior doctor colleague to discuss the matter with her educational supervisor if she is afraid to speak to her consultant.

B. Listen to your colleague's problems and offer emotional support.

C. Contact the medical staffing unit to check whether there is some way of getting a part-time locum doctor to cover your colleague's shifts if she decides to take time off work.

D. Sympathise with your colleague but explain to her that she should decide whether she might benefit from some compassionate leave as she has gone through a tough time and making careless mistakes at work may jeopardise patient safety.

E. Do nothing about the situation as you do not want to pry into other people's business and your colleague has begged you not to tell anyone.

Question 41

You are a junior doctor working in clinical medicine and are helping to write up a case report on an interesting patient. When you are ready to submit the work, you find that the journal requires the patient to sign a consent form so that the case can be published. Your registrar tells you that as the patient details are anonymised no one will know the case is specifically your patient and you should just forge the signature on the consent form as it will save time.

Rank in order the following actions in response to this situation (1= Most appropriate; 5= Least appropriate):

A. Forge the patient signature on the consent form. After all, you were told to do this by a senior registrar and no one will ever find out.

B. Ask another registrar or your consultant whether it would be fine for you to forget the patient's signature. If they say yes, then go ahead and forge the signature.

C. Telephone the patient and ask if he would mind helping to sign a consent form so other healthcare professionals can learn about the treatment of his rare medical condition. Explain what details are included in the case report and assure the patient his name will be anonymised.

D. Email the patient the consent form as an attachment and ask him to sign the form and post it to you. Say it is important but don't go into too much detail about what it is for.

E. Report your registrar to the GMC (General Medical Council).

Question 42

You are a junior doctor working in the emergency department. You are asked to review a depressed patient who attempted to commit suicide earlier in the evening. She is accompanied by her 13 year old daughter who is very angry and distraught. As you enter the cubicle you see the daughter slap her mother hard across the face and shout, "Why are you so selfish?!"

Rank in order the following actions in response to this situation (1= Most appropriate; 5= Least appropriate):

A.   Ignore what has happened and just get on with your job. It is not for you to get involved in the patient-daughter relationship issues.

B.   Ask one of the nurses to take the daughter into a separate room and get her a cup of tea to calm her down. She is clearly upset and needs some space to reflect on what has happened.

C.   Report the daughter to the hospital security and ask for her to be supervised by one of the security guards on the premises.

D.   Shout at the daughter and tell her to behave herself. Explain that this sort of behaviour is utterly inappropriate and she should be ashamed of herself for slapping her mother.

E.   Assess the patient for signs of cardiorespiratory compromise and perform a toxicology test. Administer an antidote for the overdose, if appropriate.

Question 43

You are a junior doctor working in general surgery. A patient of yours is due for a right hemicolectomy with a defunctioning ileostomy the next day to treat a caecal tumour. Although he has already been consented by your consultant and had the surgery fully explained, he changes his mind only hours before the procedure is scheduled for and wants to self-discharge. He tells you he is very upset about having to have a stoma and the more he thinks about it the more upset he becomes.

Rank in order the following actions in response to this situation (1= Most appropriate; 5= Least appropriate):

A.   Ask the stoma nurses if they can come to the ward to discuss the issue of having a stoma with the patient and reassure him that many patients are able to continue daily tasks as normal.

B.   Allow the patient to self-discharge as he has been given all the relevant information already and has come to a considered decision.

C.   Discuss the matter in-depth with the patient and explain that if he does not get treatment, he will eventually need an operation anyway for bowel obstruction and will still need a stoma but his chances of a cure will be markedly reduced.

D.   Contact your consultant and registrar about the matter. Ask them to come and speak to the patient personally and decide if it is appropriate to cancel or postpone the operation so the patient can have more time to think this over.

E.   Explain that the stoma is a temporary solution until his bowel 'heals' and can be reversed at a later date. Reassure the patient that he is in the best possible hands for the surgery.

Question 44

You are a junior doctor working in orthopaedic surgery. A young patient of yours was recently involved in a road traffic accident and unfortunately was injured so badly that one of his limbs was amputated below the knee. He is extremely depressed about this and during a ward round you hear him mumble very quietly under his breath that "he wishes he was dead".

Rank in order the following actions in response to this situation (1= Most appropriate; 5= Least appropriate):

A. Pretend that the patient didn't say anything. He is just upset and this feeling will pass as he gets used to the situation.

B. Tell the patient that if he was more careful crossing the road then this would not have happened to him.

C. Find time after the ward round to talk to the patient in more depth about the situation and ask whether he would find it helpful to speak to a professional about his depression.

D. Arrange a physiotherapy review for the patient. Perhaps getting out of bed and learning to walk again will cheer him up and show him how he can continue in his future life rather than thinking about his disability in bed all day.

E. Sympathise with the patient, but quickly determine how serious he is about the statement he has made and whether has any suicidal intent.

Question 45

You are a junior doctor working in the intensive care unit. One of your patients is suffering with multi-organ failure and your team has made the decision on the ward round to stop life support. The patient's wife is distraught about the decision and begs your team to reconsider. She tells you she will pay any price to the hospital to keep her husband alive.

Rank in order the following actions in response to this situation (1= Most appropriate; 5= Least appropriate):

A. Ask the wife how much she can afford and contact the finance department in the hospital regarding the matter.

B. Refuse to entertain the patient's wishes and bluntly tell her she will just have to cope.

C. Arrange for the wife to have a meeting with your consultant and registrar in private so that they can discuss the matter in greater depth.

D. Ask if the wife would like to invite other family members to the hospital for support during this hard time and what their views about the situation are.

E. Tell the wife that if she gives you some money, then you can help her try to persuade your team to change their mind or to keep the life support machine going for a bit longer.

Question 46

You are a junior doctor working in general medicine. One of your patients tells you how much they appreciate your help and kindness during their stay and wants to keep in touch after they are discharged. They ask you if they can add you as a 'friend' on Facebook (a social networking site).

Rank in order the following actions in response to this situation (1= Most appropriate; 5= Least appropriate):

A. Apologise but tell the patient that you do not feel adding him as a 'friend' on Facebook would be appropriate and refuse to give him your email address.

B. Agree to be 'friends' with the patient on Facebook and give him your personal email address and details.

C. Ask the patient to give you his email address and tell him that you will consider being 'friends' but you need to check first. Do not give him your email details.

D. Tell the patient you will need to speak to your seniors about this and get back to him later. Do not give him any of your personal details for now.

E. Apologise and refuse to add the patient as a friend on Facebook but give him your hospital email address. Let him know that you only want to stay in touch regarding professional matters.

PART TWO – Multi-Action Questions

Question 47

You are a junior doctor working on a busy colorectal surgical firm. Unfortunately the MDT coordinator has been sick with the flu and your consultant has asked that you take notes during the MDT meeting regarding the discussion outcomes for each patient. As one patient is being discussed in the meeting, you find yourself lost and do not understand some of the information being said. You know the patient well and also realise something important is being missed out. As the most junior member of the team you feel hesitant to interrupt everyone.

Choose the THREE most appropriate actions to take in this situation:

A. Write down all the information that is being discussed, even if you don't understand it or it doesn't make sense as you would prefer not to interfere.

B. Politely admit that you are a little lost in the discussion and ask whether your consultant can sum up the main points for you to write in the notes.

C. Wait until the meeting has ended and ask the senior house officer if they can give you an overall conclusion for what has been decided for the patient.

D. Only write down the information you understand and ask the consultant after the meeting if there was anything else that you might have missed out.

E. Before moving onto the next patient for discussion, raise any issues you feel may be outstanding that you don't think a management agreement has been decided upon.

F. Raise any outstanding issues or important information about the consultant at the end of the meeting as you would prefer not to interrupt the MDT discussion. The consultant can then bring it up the following week.

G. Ask the person sitting next to you if they have any clue what is going on.

H. Don't write anything down. You would prefer to leave the notes blank than to document misleading information.

Question 48

You have been asked to discuss a complicated surgical patient with the haematology registrar regarding anticoagulation post-surgery. The patient is an elderly immobile man with a past medical history of ischaemic heart disease, prosthetic heart valves and has recently undergone a hip replacement for osteoarthritis. Your team are uncertain what should be done regarding restarting his aspirin and the doses of his low molecular weight heparin injections and warfarin.

The haematologist tells you he is very busy and can't speak for long but quickly blurts out a long list of recommendations over the phone and tells you that all this information should be easily found on the internet. He tells you to ensure you pass his suggestions on to your team but you realise that you haven't really understood or heard most of what he has just told you.

Choose the THREE most appropriate actions to take in this situation:

A.   Try and remember to the best of your ability everything he said and relay this to a member of your team.

B.   Check the internet for suitable changes to your patient's medicines. The registrar sounds very busy and you don't want to annoy him by asking him to repeat what he has said.

C.   Repeat the facts that you have understood back to the haematologist and ask him to correct you on any facts you may have misheard.

D.   Politely ask the haematologist if he minds repeating what he has just said slowly so you can write all the information down.

E.   Document in the notes all the information you have been given in a legible manner and instigate any immediate changes based on the recommendations.

F.   Ask the haematologist to contact your consultant personally instead.

G.   Only write the bare minimum in the patient notes as you are not sure how accurately you have remembered the information and don't want to write any false facts down.

H.   Ask the haematologist to review the patient.

Question 49

You are a junior doctor on a surgical firm. After a busy ward round you are bleeped by one of the nurses who tells you that she is concerned that you have written incorrect information in one of the patient notes. You have written in the notes for Mrs Jones that she had a recent abdominal ultrasound scan revealing cholecystitis when in fact this was the scan result for a different patient, Mr Smith! As a result Mrs Jones has been started on a course of antibiotics and Mr Smith has not been prescribed any new medications because this scan result was not brought up on the ward round when the team reviewed him.

Choose the THREE most appropriate actions to take in this situation:

A.   Find the notes for Mrs Jones and tear out the page where you have written in the wrong entry.

B.   Find the notes for Mrs Jones and put a neat cross through the incorrect scan results and sign it. Rewrite a new entry below the mistake and acknowledge that the scan results that have been crossed out are wrong and to be ignored.

C.   Cross out the antibiotics that were prescribed on Mrs Jones' drug chart during ward round and apologise for the mistake to the patient.

D.   Leave the incorrect entry in Mrs Jones' notes but stick a Post-it note beside the entry saying it was wrong and sign your signature beside the message.

E.   Write up the correct ultrasound scan results in Mr Smith's notes and document that he will be started on a course of antibiotics for his cholecystitis.

F.   Discuss the findings of the recent ultrasound scan results with Mr Smith and warn him that he may require an urgent operation to remove his gallbladder.

G.   Discuss your mistake with the consultant and/or surgical registrar. Review a new management plan for Mr Smith and Mrs Jones.

H.   Write up the antibiotics for Mr Smith that was originally wrongly prescribed for Mrs Jones.

Question 50

A middle-aged man presents to the emergency department with a rather strange history. Whilst on a flight from New Zealand the previous day he suddenly developed what he called 'psychotic symptoms', shortness of breath and chest pain. When questioned further about the 'psychotic symptoms' he explains that he was anxious, confused and hallucinating. He has no previous psychiatric history and the 'psychosis' seemed to disappear once the plane landed. His oxygen saturations are rather low at present and he still has symptoms of breathlessness and chest pain which are not getting better.

Choose the THREE most appropriate actions to take in this situation:

A. Section the patient under the Mental Health Act so that if his psychosis returns he will not try to abscond from the hospital.

B. Admit the patient under psychiatry care and try to treat the psychosis.

C. Arrange an urgent computed tomographic pulmonary angiogram (CTPA) after discussion with a senior team member.

D. Treat the patient with antibiotics for a suspected chest infection.

E. Administer the patient with high flow oxygen to encourage his saturations to pick up.

F. Ask for advice from the liaison psychiatry team.

G. Admit the patient under the general medical team.

H. Consider administering the patient with a prophylactic dose of low molecular weight heparin.

Question 51

You are the junior doctor on the Medical Assessment Unit (MAU). You receive a call from the haematology laboratory half an hour before your shift will finish concerning one of your patients. His potassium has been found to be very high and this is a rather unexpected finding as the patient has been admitted for a chest infection and is not on any medications which you would expect to raise the potassium levels.

Choose the THREE most appropriate actions to take in this situation:

A. Ask the haematology laboratory clinician to contact the on-call junior doctor as your shift has already finished.

B. Treat the hyperkalaemia with calcium resonium.

C. Attend to the patient on the ward, examine them fully and ask the nurse to recheck the patient's observations including performing an electrocardiogram (ECG).

D. Ask the nurse to perform an ECG on the patient and then to contact the junior doctor on-call to review this when they come on the ward.

E. Contact your registrar at home (who has also finished their shift) to alert them to this blood result.

F. Contact the on-call junior doctor yourself and explain the situation that has occurred and to check the repeat blood sample.

G. Wait until you are at work the following day to sort out the potassium levels.

H. Take a repeat sample of the patient's blood potassium levels to ensure the blood result that was sent to the laboratory was not a spurious result.

Question 52

A senior nurse on the ward has challenged your decisions regarding patient care on a number of occasions, despite the fact that you are a safe doctor and regularly confirm the management plans you have made with your registrar. She continuously undermines you in front of your consultant on daily ward rounds and you are now finding this behaviour increasingly frustrating. You are starting to feel undermined and doubt yourself on many occasions even though you know you are in the right.

Choose the THREE most appropriate actions to take in this situation:

A. Confront the nurse directly on the ward in front of your team and patients so that they can back you up if she challenges you again.

B. Speak to other nurses on the ward about the nurse in question's behaviour. You hope that some of them may feed this back to her without you having to have an awkward discussion about the matter.

C. Consult with other junior doctor colleagues to see if they have similar problems with the same nurse and encourage them to join you in confronting her.

D. Discuss with your registrars and consultant how to handle the situation.

E. Fill in a clinical incident form as you believe her attitude is preventing you from doing your job, thereby endangering prompt patient treatment.

F. Arrange a meeting with the nurse to discuss your work relationship in private.

G. Be more insistent and confident when giving instructions to the nurse in question and clearly document all medical plans in the patient notes to ensure they are followed.

H. Avoid working or dealing with the nurse in question in the future.

Question 53

A colleague who is also a junior doctor has come to you for some advice. She is extremely upset as she feels her consultant has been making inappropriate racist jokes and sexist comments. She feels increasingly uncomfortable but is unsure of how to react to the situation. She has seen how the consultant acts with other junior doctors and notices that he is much more polite and helpful towards them.

Choose the THREE most appropriate actions to take in this situation:

A. Talk to other members of her team to determine how they feel regarding the consultant in question.

B. Encourage your colleague to speak to her clinical supervisor.

C. Discuss the situation with your clinical supervisor and see whether he/she can confront your colleague's consultant.

D. Suggest that your colleague discusses this issue with other members of her team, such as her registrar, to determine whether they also feel the consultant is acting unfairly towards her.

E. Talk to your colleague about the situation in-depth and offer emotional support.

F. Advise your colleague that the best course of action would be to ignore the remarks and 'get over it'. After all, she will be confronted with other similar people in the future and should learn to not be so sensitive.

G. Advise your colleague to speak to someone else about this matter as you do not want to get involved in this drama.

H. Advise her to take a few days of annual leave to get some relief from the situation without telling anyone the reason.

Question 54

You have just undertaken a mini-clinical examination (mini-CEX) assessment with your consultant on a ward round. You feel quite upset that he was rude and undermined your knowledge in front of the team and patient during the assessment. Among many things, he stated that you 'would never become a good doctor'. You realise that perhaps you should have known more about the patient's case but this was no reason for the consultant to act in the way he did. Even the patient and rest of the team seemed slightly taken aback by the consultant's behaviour! You are visibly upset and want to confront the consultant about his attitude.

Choose the THREE most appropriate actions to take in this situation:

A.   Speak to your consultant in private at an appropriate time about how you feel. Ask if there is anything you might be able to do to improve your clinical work and become a 'good doctor'.

B.   Apologise to the patient for the consultant's behaviour and reassure them that he is not normally like this.

C.   Ignore the consultant's comments and avoid performing further assessments so that you will not have to go through the same degrading situation with this consultant or anyone else.

D.   Write to the GMC (General Medical Council) and make a formal complaint about the consultant being a 'bully' towards you and his attitude towards his patients.

E.   Don't say anything. Ignore the consultant's comments as he was clearly in a bad mood and his comments do not reflect your general performance as a doctor so far.

F.   Reflect on whether any criticism was justified and make an action plan of how you could improve.

G.   Do not say anything as your consultant may get angry with you and you don't want to hear any more abuse after you have already had to deal with some.

H.   Accept that it is unacceptable for you to have known as little as you did and that you will never become a 'good doctor'.

Question 55

You are a junior doctor working on a general medical firm. The on-call surgical team is seeing one of your patients who is known to have oesophageal and stomach cancer and now presents with severe persistent vomiting and dysphagia. They suggest a palliative care referral but are keen to also delineate the extent of the tumour as they may consider the insertion of an oesophageal stent to relieve his symptoms. They wonder if you would be able to organise any necessary imaging for this and leave without writing in the notes.

Choose the THREE most appropriate actions to take in this situation:

A. Document the discussion you have had with the surgical team in the notes, including their recommendations for obtaining some sort of imaging of the oesophagus.

B. Ask a member of the surgical team to write the outcome of their review in the patient notes with a clear management plan detailing specifically which imaging requests they believe the patient requires.

C. Discuss the situation with your junior colleagues and ask them what sort of imaging should be requested for the patient.

D. Order a chest X-ray.

E. Request a MRI scan of the neck and mediastinum to look for added soft tissue around the oesophagus and any metastatic mediastinal spread.

F. Discuss the situation with a consultant radiologist and ask them what imaging would be most appropriate for the patient.

G. Arrange a diagnostic OGD with a biopsy.

H. Contact the palliative care team and ask for a review as per the instructions of the surgical team. You do not want to delay any referral if a review will help improve the comfort of the patient whilst they wait for any pending imaging.

Question 56

A patient under your care has been fit and well for discharge for the last three days but has been unable to leave hospital due to several community follow-up issues and a delay in obtaining an occupational therapist review of his home. You have been told by the senior nurse that his GP will sort this out and you should just wait for them to confirm this is in place. Nevertheless, the patient has no acute medical problems and you feel that it is unnecessary for him to stay in hospital for more days than necessary. Your team members are reluctant to get involved.

Choose the THREE most appropriate actions to take in this situation:

A.   Try to arrange the community follow-up yourself by speaking to district nurses and occupational health staff personally.

B.   Send the patient home without any follow-up in place as the hospital is short on beds.

C.   Liaise with the community discharge team on the ward to help speed up the process.

D.   Arrange the same follow-up as the patient's previous admissions even though his needs are now slightly different. It is much faster putting in place something that was there before than creating new plans.

E.   Contact the GP concerning community follow-up and check that he/she is aware of the patient's current situation.

F.   Try and look into any issues in the follow-up that may prevent discharge and raise this with your consultant.

G.   Try to ask other team members to help in expediting the discharge process even though they have shown no interest in helping with this matter in the past.

H.   Leave the current arrangements as they are. You have already been told not to interfere.

Question 57

Both you and your senior house officer colleague are aspiring general surgeons. Whilst you are both working on a busy surgical firm, the opportunity presents to assist in an open appendicectomy. The wards are relatively quiet compared with usual and only one junior doctor is required to cover the outstanding ward jobs. You feel that you deserve to go to theatre as you have been staying late at work every evening this week completing outstanding tasks when your senior house officer has gone home early and unlike yourself, the senior house officer has already attended several operations during the week.

Choose the THREE most appropriate actions to take in this situation:

A. Be courteous and suggest that your colleague goes into theatre to assist even though you feel you deserve to go to theatre more.

B. Politely suggest to your colleague that you would like to go into theatre and explain your feelings in a calm and collected manner.

C. Demand that your senior house officer carry your bleep whilst you are in the operating theatre as it is their turn to do some ward work.

D. As there are still outstanding jobs on the ward, suggest that the fairest solution is that neither of you go into theatre.

E. Explain your feelings to the senior house officer. Suggest that he attends this operation but if there is another emergency surgical procedure, you would like to scrub for this. Ensure that your registrar is aware and knows how to get hold of you to call you to theatre.

F. Ask one of the other surgical junior doctors to carry your bleep so you and your senior house officer could both go to the operating theatre. Accept that although one of you might not scrub in, the observation of the operation will still be useful to your learning.

G. Suggest that you scrub in for the first half of the operation and your senior house officer scrub in for the second half of the operation.

H. Suggest that if your senior house officer goes into theatre instead of yourself, then at the very least you should get to go home on time for a change whilst they stay late to finish any outstanding jobs.

Question 58

You are a junior doctor working in general surgery and have just finished your morning consultant ward round. You have a long list of jobs to complete but they all appear to be equally important to you. Unfortunately your junior doctor colleague is currently on night shifts and is not present during the day to help you with the jobs that you would normally share out.

Choose the THREE most appropriate immediate actions to take in this situation:

A.   Review a patient with low blood pressure who has just collapsed on the ward.

B.   Complete a discharge summary for a patient who is celebrating their birthday today and wants to go home as soon as possible.

C.   Order a chest X-ray for a patient to check for improvement of pneumonia after a course of antibiotics.

D.   Order a group and save from the blood bank for a patient undergoing an elective procedure on the morning operating list.

E.   Check blood results for all your patients on your patient list.

F.   Complete an audit with your registrar which you hope to submit for a publication.

G.   Write up pain relief for a patient who is post-operative and due to come off their PCA (patient controlled analgesia).

H.   Assess a patient in the pre-operative day surgery clinic who is due for an elective procedure next week. They have already been waiting for you for the last 10 minutes.

Question 59

You are the junior doctor on-call dealing with the acute surgical admissions. You admit an elderly patient with a distended, peritonitic abdomen who undergoes an emergency laparotomy for perforated bowel. Unfortunately the patient deteriorates rapidly post-operatively and dies 12 hours after the operation. You are asked to pronounce the patient dead and fill in the death certificate.

Choose the THREE most appropriate actions to take in this situation:

A.   Refuse to pronounce the patient dead as you have not seen him in the last 24 hours.

B.   Speak to the patient's family and explain what has happened. Arrange a meeting with the family and consultant if they have further questions you can't answer.

C.   Ask your senior colleague to complete the paperwork because you are not allowed to sign death certificates as a junior doctor.

D.   Listen for heart sounds for at least 4 minutes to confirm the death.

E.   Consult your registrar for advice as you are uncertain what should be done in this situation.

F.   Report the case to the coroner as the death happened within 30 days of an operation.

G.   Ask your registrar to complete the paperwork as he was the last person to examine the patient and it is therefore his responsibility.

H.   Perform cold caloric testing to confirm brainstem death.

Question 60

It is reaching the end of your 12 hour shift on-call. You are exhausted and have several jobs to handover to the night team. You decide to make a plan to write all the jobs down in order of priority to ensure the night team perform the most important tasks first and no tasks are missed off the handover list.

Choose the THREE most appropriate actions to take in this situation:

A.   Write up intravenous fluids for a patient whose oral intake is inadequate and who is also suffering from aspiration pneumonia.

B.   Examine a patient who is complaining of a tickly cough and is bringing up small quantities of mucous.

C.   Take some blood cultures from a patient and send them to the laboratory for a septic patient. They are already on an empirical treatment of antibiotics.

D.   Rewrite a drug chart for a geriatrics patient who is on several cardiac medications. He only has a space left on the chart for one more dose of all his drugs for this evening.

E.   Assess a neutropenic patient who is febrile on the haematology ward.

F.   Take a blood sample to check the clotting of a patient on a heparin infusion. This should have been done one hour ago, but there was no time. He is allergic to warfarin and cannot be given this instead.

G.   Speak to the family member of one of the patients who has been put on the Liverpool Care Pathway earlier in the day.

H.   Discuss your list of jobs for handover with the other junior doctors on the day shift to ensure all important jobs are handed over properly.

Question 61

You are looking after Mr Joe Bloggs who is under care of the respiratory team. A diagnostic lung biopsy of a large pulmonary mass has been performed and the results are still pending. Mr Blogg's family are with him and ask to have a private word with you. They ask you to promise them that if the test confirms the diagnosis of cancer, not to mention it to him as he is under a lot of stress and worry and he will not be able to bear hearing such awful news.

Choose the THREE most appropriate actions to take in this situation:

A.   Tell the patient the results of the biopsy when they are available but for now just promise the family that you won't tell him so they won't cause a fuss.

B.   Agree with the family not to inform Mr Joe Bloggs and stick to your word when the results are available.

C.   Talk to Mr Bloggs about his current frame of mind and enquire whether he would like to know the results of the biopsy when they are made available.

D.   Tell his family that it is entirely Mr Bloggs' decision as to whether or not he wants to know the results and you can't promise them anything.

E.   Try to avoid giving the family a definite answer and tell them that you will wait and see what the results are first, then discuss this with them again another time.

F.   Ask another junior doctor on the ward what you should do.

G.   Discuss with Mr Bloggs whether he wishes for you to inform the family of the result of the biopsy when it is made available or whether he would like to tell them himself.

H.   Tell the family that you are not in a position to promise anything to them but can offer Mr Bloggs some counselling and a psychiatric review to help him cope with any stress he is feeling.

Question 62

You review a patient in fracture clinic who sustained a fractured radius one week ago after falling on an outstretched hand. He is complaining about intense pain in his right arm under his cast. This pain gets worse with any movement of his wrist. He feels this has been worsening over the last couple of hours and is now unbearable.

Choose the THREE most appropriate actions to take in this situation:

A.   Order urgent repeat X-ray images of the right arm.

B.   Await a review by your consultant at the end of clinic when he will be free to see your patient.

C.   Remove the cast urgently and see if this relieves the patient's symptoms.

D.   Ensure adequate analgesia and assess the patient's arm for any sensation, motor function and a pulse.

E.   Discuss the case urgently with the orthopaedic registrar on-call.

F.   Reassure the patient that this is a normal reaction to a tight-fitting cast and prescribe him some strong analgesia to take home in the meantime.

G.   Review the images of his fracture from last week and compare them to current images.

H.   Admit the patient to the ward for observation and intravenous morphine infusion to relieve the severe pain. You believe the fracture may have become displaced again and will require an operation.

Question 63

You are clerking Mrs Jenkins in the emergency department who is accompanied by her husband. She was out gardening earlier in the day and tripped over her cat, consequently hitting her head and 'blacking out' for 3 minutes. You are very pressed for time and find it very hard to take a history as the patient will not stop talking about her pet cat.

Choose the THREE most appropriate actions to take in this situation:

A.   Apologise for interrupting the patient but explain that you really need to get as much information about her presenting complaint as possible so that you can give her urgent medical treatment.

B.   Allow the patient to talk about her cat but examine her as she talks about it. Hopefully by the time you finish examining her she will have run out of things to say and you can go back and re-take a focused history.

C.   Let the patient talk for as long as she likes in case she inadvertently gives you some useful information about her clinical history.

D.   Ask the patient's husband if he has noticed anything unusual about the patient and try to gain a collateral history.

E.   Subtly check your watch to indicate you are in a hurry. Hope that the patient picks up on this body language and will stop talking about irrelevant facts.

F.   Tell the patient that you have some quite specific questions you would like her to answer in short sentences. Hope that this will make the history more focused.

G.   Ask one of your junior doctor colleagues to clerk in the patient instead. Tell them that the patient is really getting on your nerves and you don't feel able to deal with her.

H.   Cut the consultation short and order multiple investigations from the haematology and radiology departments. Hopefully this will bring up an abnormality you can act upon as the patient is not very good at giving you a relevant history.

Question 64

One of your patients has been left severely disabled following a large cerebrovascular accident. The patient is a 57 year old gentleman who was previously working and led an active lifestyle. The stroke has left the patient bed-bound, incontinent and unable to communicate effectively. He is now dependent on carers for all activities of daily living. One day while you are taking blood from him he mumbles to you that he wants to die, and asks for your help.

Choose the THREE most appropriate actions to take in this situation:

A. Ask whether the patient's family has been aware of any change in the patient's mood and if so, how long he has been feeling this way or whether they know of specific reasons for this.

B. Discuss the situation with your seniors with a view to arranging an urgent psychiatric assessment for the patient.

C. Recommended the patient be transferred to a different rehabilitation centre with better facilities to deal with mental health issues.

D. Increase the patient's analgesia and sedation to make the patient more comfortable so he will not think too much about his state of affairs.

E. Get a formal psychiatric review and advice without discussing the matter with your team first as you think the patient needs an urgent review.

F. Commence the patient on regular first-line anti-depressant medications.

G. Involve all members of the nursing, rehabilitation and medical staff regarding your concern for the patient's mental welfare at the next multidisciplinary meeting.

H. Ask the nurses to monitor the patient more closely and make them aware of the patient's state of mind.

Question 65

You are a junior doctor working on the medical assessment unit. One of your patients is a 92 year old lady with advanced dementia who usually resides in a nursing home. Staff at the nursing home are increasingly concerned as she has stopped eating and drinking over the last few weeks. She is refusing all forms of oral intake.

Choose the THREE most appropriate actions to take in this situation:

A. Insert a wide bore nasogastric tube.

B. Request a full speech and language assessment (SaLT).

C. Commence parenteral feeding in the form of TPN (total parenteral nutrition) via a central venous catheter.

D. Try to force-feed the patient so that she will put on more weight and gain energy.

E. Request a full review from the dietician.

F. Prescribe maintenance intravenous fluids to keep the patient hydrated.

G. Examine the patient for an organic cause for her being off her food such as an occult malignancy or infection.

H. Wait to see if the situation resolves itself.

Question 66

You are a junior doctor working in general surgery. Your team has just admitted an elderly gentleman from a nursing home with dementia with abdominal pain. A CT of his abdomen confirms that he has perforated his bowel and will require an emergency laparotomy. You have tried to explain this to the patient but he lacks any form of capacity and cannot retain the information you give him. The patient's son is present during the consultation and is very unhappy about his father having to undergo surgery. He asks you if you can please leave his father alone and just give him strong painkillers rather than cause him more pain with surgery.

Choose the THREE most appropriate actions to take in this situation:

A. Explain that the operation will still be performed as it is in the patient's best interests regardless of what the son's concerns are.

B. Treat the patient conservatively with analgesics and commence the Liverpool Care Pathway.

C. Speak to the staff at the nursing home and ask them more questions about the patient's general state of health and any previously expressed wishes or if advanced directives exist.

D. Explore the son's concerns and enquire as to why he does not want his father to have the operation, reassuring him as much as possible.

E. Pressurise the son to consent to the operation as it cannot go ahead without his consent. Try to explain that this will give his father the best chance of survival in the long-term.

F. Inform the son of the risks and benefits of having the operation and explain that he will still be put on strong painkillers during and after the operation to minimise as much discomfort as possible.

G. Apply to the court to obtain consent to do the operation.

H. Fill out a consent form 4.

Question 67

You are a junior doctor working on a general medical firm. One of your patients is complaining of chest pain and palpitations. The nurse contacts you and requests that you come to see the patient. Over the phone you ask her to perform an ECG and a full set of observations so that they will be ready for you to analyse when you arrive. When you reach the ward, you realise that neither the observations nor the ECG have been performed and you find that out from another nurse that the person you just spoke to has now gone on their tea break.

Choose the THREE most appropriate actions to take in this situation:

A. Perform the ECG and repeat observations yourself.

B. Wait for the nurse in question to return from her tea break to perform the relevant investigations.

C. Ask for help from another nurse to get the ECG and repeat observations whilst you examine the patient.

D. Assess the patient's airway, breathing and circulation. Obtain a brief and focused history from the patient.

E. Retrieve the patient notes and try to see if there is anything in the history that might give you a clue as to why the patient is suffering with chest pain.

F. Administer oxygen to the patient and encourage them to take slow deep breaths, reassuring them accordingly.

G. Go to the tea room to find the nurse you spoke to. Tell her off for leaving a patient who is acutely unwell.

H. Prescribe paracetamol for the pain in the immediate instance.

Question 68

You are a junior doctor working on a general surgical firm. During the consultant ward rounds, you regularly witness your consultant flirting and making inappropriate risqué remarks to one of the nurses. The nurse appears visibly uncomfortable each time this happens and tries to ignore them. You feel this is completely unprofessional behaviour.

Choose the THREE most appropriate actions to take in this situation:

A.   Confront your consultant publicly the next time you witness a similar incident.

B.   Inform the hospital clinical director about your consultant's inappropriate remarks.

C.   Ask another consultant for their advice about how to approach the situation.

D.   Inform the GMC of your consultant's behaviour and accuse him of sexual harassment.

E.   Confront your consultant directly and inform him that you believe his actions are inappropriate and may be causing some distress to the nurse in question.

F.   Inform the nurse that you have observed what has happened, and that she should speak to her senior about this matter if it is making her uncomfortable.

G.   Ask the other registrars, nurses and junior doctors in the department whether they have experienced any similar incidents with this consultant.

H.   Encourage the nurse to address this matter privately with the consultant as it will continue to happen unless something is mentioned.

Question 69

You go out to get some lunch with one of your junior doctor colleagues from a restaurant near to the hospital. Whilst at the cashier your colleague drops his wallet on the floor accidentally and out falls a small clear bag which looks like it contains cannabis. He immediately picks it up and puts it back into his pocket. He appears flustered and tries to change the conversation.

Choose the THREE most appropriate actions to take in this situation:

A.   Ask your colleague not to return to work as you do not believe him fit to see patients.

B.   Directly ask your colleague what was in the bag and whether he is taking recreational drugs.

C.   Immediately report your colleague to your consultant. Doctors should clearly not be taking illicit drugs and you should act upon this issue straightaway.

D.   Approach a senior colleague in your team that you trust and ask them what should be done about the situation.

E.   Do nothing about the situation as your colleague has never, to your knowledge, been 'high' at work or put patient safety at risk.

F.   Ask other Foundation year doctors if they have noticed any odd behaviour relating to your colleague.

G.   Sit down with your colleague and state what you saw, admitting that you may not be correct about presuming the bag contains illicit drugs, but if you are then you are willing to help him.

H.   Act as if nothing has happened as you are not completely sure that the bag does contain marijuana and don't want to stir up any trouble.

Question 70

On your first ever on-call as a junior doctor you review a surgical patient who is in recovery following a hernia repair. He is suffering from nausea and vomiting and complains of generally feeling very 'groggy'. You write up a moderate strength anti-emetic in the drug chart but the nurse refuses to give this drug stating that 'you do not know what you are doing' and she wants your senior house officer to review the patient instead. Taken aback by her response you begin to question yourself but still feel confident that you are acting accordingly.

Choose the THREE most appropriate actions to take in this situation:

A. Do nothing. The nausea is probably just a side effect from the anaesthetic and although not pleasant for the patient, you know the symptoms will eventually subside anyway.

B. Call the surgeon responsible to come and see the patient even though you know he is scrubbed in theatre with another hernia case at present.

C. Insist to the nurse that she gives the medication you prescribed. Threaten to inform her senior and the consultant in charge if she does not comply.

D. Discuss with the nurse why she believes your management plan is wrong.

E. Call someone senior to discuss the best course of action and confirm your management plan. Ask if they would be happy to re-review the patient again with you.

F. Re-evaluate the scenario again after reading the patient's notes and checking his drug allergies. Perhaps there is some information you were not aware of initially.

G. Dispense the anti-emetic yourself anyway and wait to see if his symptoms resolve. You are pretty confident you have properly analysed the situation.

H. Write in the medical notes that the stated nurse refuses to give the medication. Ask another nurse in recovery to help you instead.

Answers to Examination 1

PART ONE – Answers to the Ranking Questions

Answer Question 1

DBACE

The main issue here is to try and get the young lady to express her wishes without her father influencing her. Despite only being a junior doctor, you can take the initiative in getting the views of the daughter and father, and then consult a senior colleague to decide the best course of action. Clearly the father is imposing his views and asking an official interpreter is the best way forward. You might need to examine the woman, which may be hard with her father present and hence seeing her separately is best. The next best choice is to have both her and the father present, although her wishes might be influenced by him. In the absence of an interpreter, the father or another family member will have to continue translating, although this is not ideal. Clearly, speaking to the daughter (who has minimal command of English) about a complicated topic such as pregnancy is not appropriate.

Answer Question 2

CEDBA

Venepuncture is a crucial skill for all medical students and junior doctors. In this situation it is clear that their technique might be flawed, and a simple teaching session could rectify this. Organising teaching yourself is probably best as you can ensure that the teaching is delivered in a timely manner and you can also assess the students' progress. Using mannequin arms to practise will allow them to perfect their technique before performing this skill on real patients. Phlebotomists are experts in taking blood and asking them to teach the students is another option. Getting the students to observe you in practice is less ideal as they will lack the tactile experience of performing this skill. There is no need for a consultant to give teaching on a procedure that is more regularly performed by other skilled doctors.

Answer Question 3

ADCBE

In such a scenario priority will have to be given to the most immediate issues and people allocated accordingly. Clearly, the elective surgical patients fall under this category. Thus the best way to deal with this is to try and do all the jobs for these patients immediately as a collective team. If this overruns so be it as you can always come in early to organise other duties. Keeping in mind that the elective surgical patients are the priority option D is the next best option as all the jobs are being done and if something crops up at least someone can sort that out with no interruption to the other jobs. One person doing all the jobs is not feasibly possible and will lead to poor management if a problem arises. Thus, allocating one person for each role is better even though it may take longer to do the jobs.

Answer Question 4

DCAEB

Her symptoms may be well due to gallstones but a more sinister cause such as cancer which may need urgent treatment needs to be excluded. By contacting radiology, the scan will be done and reported quickly before she leaves. If it is gallstones she can be reassured and if it is malignancy then it has been picked up. It would be sensible to get the results before leaving because she could be in a position where she is given abnormal results but nothing can be done as she is no longer in hospital. She does not need emergency admission as she is not acutely unwell. Regarding insurance, it would be prudent to let the travel insurance know. Problems could arise if the patient became ill whilst abroad and subsequently filed a claim. If this were to happen then the insurance company would request a copy of the medical reports.

Answer Question 5

EBCAD

In this case it is most appropriate to stabilise the patient first and then to seek senior support. As this patient is deteriorating, he should be moved out of minors to a place where he can receive more support if required. It is sensible to inform switchboard and the main surgical wards that you can be reached on your mobile in case there is an emergency on the ward. However, it is impractical to go back to the ward to get your bleep when there is an ill patient who needs to be seen immediately.

Answer Question 6

CDEBA

Despite appearing stable, the patient in this scenario could still have an aortic dissection and this condition needs to be ruled out. Considering that the cardiology registrar will only see the patient later on, the most immediate action you should take is to check the patient's blood pressure in both arms. If significantly different, this indicates a life-threatening emergency which needs to be acted upon. Following the blood pressure measurement, other tests should be performed which include a bedside ECHO which could be used to give a good estimate of the size of the patient's aortic root. Having the results of the patient's scan from two years previously means that the size of the aorta can be checked. An alternative differential diagnosis for the patient could be a myocardial infarction, in which case a repeat troponin would be useful. A CT angiogram is diagnostic of the condition and should be organized if clinical suspicion is high. A chest X-ray would only be useful if the aorta was grossly enlarged to demonstrate a widened superior mediastinum on plain film.

Answer Question 7

DCEBA

The most appropriate option is D. You are making your colleague aware that his actions are wrong and allowing him a chance to explain himself/make amends. Speaking to others in option C gives you the opportunity to see if someone else has a useful suggestion as to how to approach this problem. As the issue affects everyone on the rota, it would make sense to discuss the situation with everyone involved together. If, however, you feel unable to tackle the situation yourself, informing your consultant means you can have senior input in addressing the situation. Option B does not address the situation in a timely manner and option A is unethical as you are indirectly condoning your colleague's behaviour.

Answer Question 8

DACEB

It is dangerous to carry out procedures without having ever seen the procedure being done. In general you should always watch the procedure first to understand the technique, before attempting to carry it out yourself under direct supervision from a senior colleague (who should be competent of performing the procedure themselves). Initially it would be best to assist in the procedure while watching your registrar carry the procedure out. You will learn the procedure and be helping your colleague by assisting them.

Answer Question 9

ADCBE

Although it is clear that you were not at fault in this scenario, you must remember that it is patient care that has been affected. For this reason, even though you were not the guilty party, you must take every effort to ensure that this does not happen again. Both the senior house officer and the registrar should discuss the events and the necessary actions to be taken to prevent recurrence. There is no need to include the consultant given that the situation can be handled appropriately without their involvement.

Answer Question 10

ABCDE

Most departments are happy to provide advice and opportunities to people who take a special interest in their field. It would be advisable to find a mentor, someone who can guide you through the applications and your career progression. If you can negotiate time off with your team then you can gain experience within your chosen specialty. It would also be wise to discuss your aims with your educational supervisor who may be able to assist you in fulfilling your aspirations. Sitting exams is important, but gaining exposure to the specialty first is more important.

Answer Question 11

AEBDC

This case highlights the importance of protecting patient safety and prioritising different important tasks. You must first address the urgent matter on the ward. This, however, does not mean that you need personally attend to the task concerned, so long as you ensure someone else does. In this case, it is more sensible to bleep one of the doctors on your team to attend to the job urgently which will cause minimal inconvenience to the doctors in the audit meeting. Nevertheless, if this is not possible, then it may be appropriate to ask one of your colleagues to start the presentation whilst you call the senior sister back to enquire further about the matter. This again ensures that there is minimal inconvenience to the doctors in the audit meeting.

Answer Question 12

CEDBA

This patient needs adequate emotional counselling and support from a multidisciplinary team. A twice daily regimen would suit this patient better than one with more frequent injections. Diabetes specialist nurses are excellent at providing supervision and education about insulin injecting and daily regimens. The pathogenesis of diabetic ketoacidosis needs to be explained but in simple digestible terms that the patient will be able to remember and understand.

Answer Question 13

CAEDB

As you are the most experienced in life support, taking the lead yourself with your senior house officer colleague assisting you would be the safest approach. Option A is also safe and would be done if nobody had ALS (Advanced Life Support) training. In option E, you highlight the wrong orders even though you still allow your senior house officer to lead the life support. Nevertheless this is a safer option than option D where you do not correct your colleague at all. Option B is wholly inappropriate – all doctors have a duty of care and must speak up if they know something is wrong, even if this means going against someone more senior.

Answer Question 14

CEDAB

There is an evident patient safety issue that will need to be dealt with immediately as the patient could be having a cardiac event. However, the scenario is complicated by the fact that you are unable to take a history due to the language barrier. It is most appropriate to perform an ECG so that if there are any changes suggestive of a cardiac event you have more information to refer the patient to the hospital. It may be cautious to call an ambulance given that this patient does have risk factors for cardiac disease, but you should still do the ECG. It would be futile to keep trying to communicate with the patient as she is unlikely to understand you, and in cases of a potential emergency, you do not have much time to spare. Simply rebooking an appointment with an interpreter is inappropriate and dangerous as the patient may be experiencing a medical emergency.

Answer Question 15

AEDBC

This is a very precarious situation and most of the options provided are not entirely appropriate at the current time. It is clear that this conversation should not be occurring in front of a patient and the consultant should be made aware of such issues (especially if they are recurrent). Although it is correct for an apology to be made to the patient, this should probably not be done while the event is unfolding. You can tell the registrar that more urgent jobs needed to be done, but again this should not be done in front of the patient. It is not suitable to tell the patient that the registrar is behaving inappropriately, as this is also unprofessional behaviour and the patient should not be involved in the situation.

Answer Question 16

ABDEC

Good medical practice includes being aware of another colleagues' well-being. Your junior doctor colleague may be upset after what happened with the radiologist and therefore may need emotional support. You should encourage her to raise the issue with her clinical or educational supervisor so that she can give her account of events and receive support and steps can be taken to stop this event happening again. It would be unwise to aggravate the situation further by giving your opinion to the radiologist, but the issue can be raised as a matter of concern at the next quality assurance visit.

Answer Question 17

CADEB

The GMC's *Good Medical Practice* publication clearly states that "you must do your best to make sure that any documents you write or sign are not false or misleading". Hence you are obliged to be honest and explain to the patient why you cannot backdate a sick note. You can offer to help her by certifying that she is unwell today in case that may support her arguments in being able to retake the year.

Answer Question 18

ADCEB

You must discuss the matter with a senior colleague – your consultant is the most appropriate person to make any such decisions – and speak to the family. The next best option would be to speak with your registrar. If you speak to the patient about this matter you must document your conversation in the notes. It is not appropriate to base big decisions on the family's wishes alone, even though it is important to involve the family and reassure them that all decisions are made with the patient's interest in mind.

Answer Question 19

BDACE

In this scenario the most urgent action would be to prescribe morphine. The patient is unlikely to relax and accept your reassurance until his pain has gone or is alleviated. If morphine does not work, a GTN infusion may be necessary but you should contact their registrar before making this decision. You could also inform the on-call cardiology team for their advice.

Answer Question 20

EBCDA

Your most immediate action should be to reassure your colleague and to explain to him that it is in his and others' best interests that he takes time off to recuperate. He should be advised to inform his senior colleagues so that adequate cover can be arranged and the rota coordinator should be made aware that it is likely that he/she will need to find a replacement for the on-call shift. An incident form does not need to be filled. However, he should in no circumstance be encouraged to persevere throughout the day as this puts other patients and staff at risk.

Answer Question 21

CDEBA

There will be times that a junior doctor will have to work under pressure and adapt to new circumstances. Despite the fact that clerking these patients is not part of your on-call duties, not doing anything or just the minimum may actually lead to patients' surgeries being cancelled. As these extra jobs are not urgent, you should tend to ward emergencies first. You should then tell the registrar you will do what you can and notify him of your progress. This also gives you the chance to prioritise the clerking accordingly. Following a sufficient handover, you should inform your team of the situation and see whether they can help you manage the situation by holding your on-call bleep while you clerk the patients. You should ideally clerk all the patients rather than the minimum. If your junior doctor colleagues are free at some point they could also help you clerk the patients.

Answer Question 22

AECBD

Liaising with other team members concerning patient care is a common task carried out by junior doctors. As a consultant wants to speak with you directly it is best to prepare yourself by reading the notes and understanding what has happened. You can speak to other members of the team who were present to ask them what the medical decision regarding the patient was. If this is not possible you could also try and contact your junior doctor colleague to find out the relevant details. Asking the nurses what the outcome was is better than simply telling the consultant that he has to wait until your colleagues return for more information.

Answer Question 23

BCEAD

Diarrhoea is extremely dangerous to patients in hospital, especially those who are acutely unwell or already immunocompromised. With respect to safeguarding patients, it is imperative that you go home and do not return to work until you feel completely well again. You should let your team know immediately and also inform the rota coordinator. It is unwise to stay at work as you would be endangering colleagues and patients.

Answer Question 24

ABDCE

Your registrar should advise you about specific points before the ward round starts so that you will be aware of any difficulties before they arise. Any new issues raised during the ward round should be relayed to your registrar and you should be able to contact him/her at all times. Clear and accurate documentation will help you and your team when you re-visit each patient later on in the day should they require reviewing. Seeing patients by yourself is not an ideal situation, but it is better to see the patients and seek help than refusing to do the ward round at all.

Answer Question 25

DBCAE

The GMC's *Good Medical Practice* guidelines state that in an emergency you must offer medical attention "taking into account of the availability of other options for care". In this case, both the police and the ambulance are already present and so it is unlikely that your services will be needed, and by stopping to help you may be leaving your patients unattended at the hospital. It is most appropriate here to check whether your assistance is required, and if not return to work.

Answer Question 26

CEDBA

Patient safety is the first priority, and the consultant should not be operating if he is under the influence of alcohol. You should speak to him directly about what you have noticed. However, if you do not want to approach him, then the next best thing would be to speak to another member of your team (e.g. registrar) or another senior member of staff who is already involved in the patient's care (e.g. the nurse in charge). Informing the anaesthetist is better than doing nothing.

Answer Question 27

DCABE

The healthcare professional carrying out the medical/surgical procedure is ultimately responsible for ensuring the patient is genuinely informed about the procedure that will take place. Consent can be delegated to another healthcare professional even if they are unable to perform the procedure so long as they have had adequate training in seeking consent for that procedure. In this scenario you have not had such training, nor are you able to perform the procedure and therefore you should not carry out the consent yourself. The registrar or consultant should consent the patient and ensure they are fully informed about the surgery. Although a patient leaflet on the procedure is a useful adjunct to delivering information verbally during the consenting process, giving the patient a leaflet alone without offering the chance to answer any of their concerns is not appropriate.

Answer Question 28

ACDBE

This scenario demands you to be calm and make use of your communication skills to negotiate with an angry patient. Clearly it is inappropriate to contact your consultant from home about a non-urgent case, but asking the hospital security to take an angry patient off the premises may actually cause the patient to be more angry! It is best to try to resolve situations verbally in a professional manner. Trying to discover why the patient is so concerned about being re-reviewed may be useful. It may be that they want a second opinion or that they have had a previous bad experience. If you ever feel out of your depth, it is important to contact a senior member of your team for support.

Answer Question 29

DCAEB

It is important to make patient safety your primary concern and to ensure they are fully informed and aware of the benefits and risks of their current treatment. It is important that the patient gives their current treatment the full benefit of working before trying to change medications. If after this time they are still unhappy with the treatment, a deeper discussion of alternative therapies would be appropriate and changing to a different drug can be arranged. The ultimate decision about their own treatment lies with the patient. However, if you are not aware of the actual risks of the herbal remedy the patient is talking about, you should refrain from giving advice on this drug. Asking the patient to try an unknown herbal remedy without knowledge of its risks is on the whole more dangerous than trying to deter them from this medication.

Answer Question 30

CEDAB

Patient confidentiality must be maintained in this scenario even though the patient has been involved in underage sexual intercourse. If you feel that a relative or patient is placing undue pressure on yourself and you do not feel able to deal with the situation, you can always refer them to a senior colleague for further advice. Although it is wrong to lie to relatives and pretend you do not know your patients, this is the more appropriate of the options listed than being rude to the patient's father or breaking patient confidentiality. Breaking confidentiality in this scenario will only serve to diminish the trust within the patient-doctor relationship.

Answer Question 31

ADBCE

As a junior doctor, you should not be making the decision to discharge patients on your own without senior advice. You should ensure that all patients who are supposed to have been discharged from your ward have been sent home and had their paperwork sorted. Next you must alert your seniors regarding the situation so that they may advise you further. You should try to be helpful to the bed manager given the hospital crisis but this should not be at the risk of patient safety. Options C and E are clearly inappropriate.

Answer Question 32

BDCEA

Your first concern should be patient safety and to ensure that appropriate therapy is being instigated. Although the patient notes say they are allergic to the antibiotic and though they have not yet mounted an allergic reaction, it is important that this is not ignored or continued. The patient should still be changed to an alternative drug and the nurses attending the patient should be alerted to this. An incident form should be completed for a patient being prescribed a drug they are 'allergic' to. Asking the pharmacist to deliver some teaching to junior doctors is a good idea but in this situation, will have the least amount of immediate effect.

Answer Question 33

BCAED

This is a very serious incident and unfortunately without any hard evidence, mentioning this fact to the police will only result in a 'he said, she said' affair. You must not ignore the situation, and directly speak to a senior matron or consultant for their advice. Asking the healthcare professional to admit to their mistake will be the best way to resolve the situation short of actually catching them 'in the act'. Asking the police to arrest your colleague without hard evidence, although difficult to back up, is more appropriate than ignoring the situation or waiting for the nurse to harm another patient.

Answer Question 34

BECDA

It is important to listen to the patient and assist them in their problems. In the first instance a clear history followed by a search of the ward and through the patient's belongings for their wallet would be appropriate. If the patient is adamant that their wallet was stolen, then the ward nurses can help the patient contact the police and file a report. It is distressing for the patient and inappropriate to ignore their concerns.

Answer Question 35

CEADB

You must place patient safety first and the best method is to try to make the patient aware of their situation and seek help on their own accord rather than force them out of a difficult situation. Offering them advice on how to seek help and from whom will ensure that even in desperate circumstances they are aware of avenues for help. If you feel that the patient is in severe danger, it may be worth asking them to report the situation to the police. However, ignoring the situation is inappropriate. Reporting the situation yourself and breaking confidentiality will damage the patient-doctor trust and there is also the danger that the patient will not admit the situation and deny anything they have told you when the police arrive.

Answer Question 36

ADCBE

According to the GMC's *Good Medical Practice* guidelines you must not "use your professional position to establish or pursue a sexual or improper emotional relationship with a patient". In this situation, you should not encourage meeting up with the patient alone in an intimate location or a put yourself in a position where your relationship may be brought into question. Discuss the matter with your seniors for advice if you feel uncertain, or if you want to meet the patient, ensure you are not going alone where your actions may be misinterpreted.

Answer Question 37

EACBD

Clearly the registrar is acting 'out of line' and should not be socialising with friends 'out on the town' when their duty is first towards their patients. Initially, if your patient requires immediate review, you should contact another senior member of your team who is on site and able to help. Keep the patient's family informed of the situation and offer reassurance so that they are aware of what is happening. If your registrar is unaware that their on-call is meant to be 'on-site' and not 'off-site' you should reiterate this fact to them and ensure that you are able to contact them at all times should the same situation recur. However, if this circumstance repeats itself you should report the actions of your senior to the consultant in charge. You should not pretend that there is no issue and continue as normal.

Answer Question 38

ABEDC

According to the GMC's *Good Medical Practice* "you must be honest and objective when appraising or assessing the performance of colleagues" as "patients will be put at risk if you describe as competent someone who has not reached or maintained a satisfactory standard of practice". Bearing this in mind, you should try to rectify any areas your student is having problems with. This can easily be achieved by directing them to recommended texts, organising further teaching or offering useful suggestions on how you think they can revise some more complex concepts (e.g. by drawing mind maps, diagrams or perhaps suggesting the use of online enhanced podcasts).

Answer Question 39

DECAB

Being honest and trustworthy is at the heart of medical professionalism and if you know that the student in question is not genuinely ill then you must not write them a sick note suggesting this to be the truth. If they are feeling out of their depth regarding upcoming examinations you may wish to encourage them to talk to their tutors, or if you feel so inclined you could offer to do some clinical teaching. (You should not be rude or blame your patients for their problems.)

Answer Question 40

DBACE

The GMC's *Good Medical Practice* guidelines state that you should "support colleagues who have problems with performance, conduct or health" but also that you should "protect your patients from risk of harm posed by another colleague's conduct, performance or health". In this situation, there is no evidence that harm has come to any of your patients. However, you do understand that your colleague has recently suffered a life event and may not be completely emotionally stable. You should try to support your colleague and ask them to reassess whether or not they would benefit from compassionate leave. If they agree, they should discuss the matter with their consultant or educational supervisor. If you find that you are subsequently being short-staffed on the ward, discussing the matter with medical staffing will alert them to the issue so they can act upon it.

Answer Question 41

CDEBA

Forging a patient's signature on a consent form is fraud and illegal. This should not be done, even if your senior tries to convince you that this is OK. You should try to contact the patient in question and ask them to sign the form explaining the circumstance and obtain their informed consent. Although meeting them is the best option, you could try to email them as well but make sure you contact them through an NHS email account rather than a personal email account.

Answer Question 42

EBCDA

Your first concern should be towards your patient. You should attempt to resuscitate the patient in the first instance by checking their airway, breathing and circulation for signs of compromise. If you find the daughter to be interfering in your assessment, try to calm her down and allowing her some space to reflect on the events of the evening would be the best initial approach. It has clearly been a traumatic event for the daughter and she may also require some counselling. If, however, she is not able to refrain from being abusive towards her mother, then it is unsafe for her to be near the patient and hospital security may be required to intervene. It is inappropriate to shout at relatives and to be rude and even less appropriate to completely avoid the situation you have witnessed.

Answer Question 43

CEADB

Signing a consent form is not legally binding and patients are allowed to change their mind up until the very last second before the procedure is due to occur. It is important that the patient's views and their reasons behind self-discharge are explored. A full understanding of the risks of avoiding surgery and possible consequences should be outlined in a simple manner so that the patient understands fully what they will be potentially suffering from in the future. Involving other healthcare professionals such as stoma nurses and your seniors, after a frank discussion with your patient, may be beneficial.

Answer Question 44

ECDAB

Euthanasia is illegal in the United Kingdom and you must not assist the patient or lead them to believe that you can help them achieve any such wish, no matter what your personal beliefs on this topic are. The patient has delivered a rather alarming statement and it is hard to determine how serious they are about this. In the first instance you should speak to the patient and decide whether there is any suicidal intent and whether they may benefit from a professional psychiatric review. The least appropriate responses would include ignoring the situation completely or blaming the patient for their condition, which might exacerbate their feelings of depression.

Answer Question 45

CDBAE

The decision to stop life support is a medical one and it should not be determined by the patient's relatives or friends. In this scenario you should refrain from accepting any money from the wife and refer the wife to speak to one of your seniors if she would like to discuss the matter further. You should offer emotional support and try to assist the patient in other ways. Being curt with the patient is obviously not ideal. However, it is more appropriate than accepting any money from the relative.

Answer Question 46

ADECB

It is important to maintain a good professional relationship with your patients, but adding your patients as your friends on a social networking site does put you at risk of developing 'an improper emotional relationship with a patient' which the GMC's *Good Medical Practice* warns against. Ideally the patient should contact your consultant or the hospital if they require further advice on their medical matters once discharged, rather than contact yourself. If the patient presses you, then you should ask for advice from a senior colleague. If, however, the patient is insistent, then offering them your hospital email account to keep in touch with on medical matters is the next appropriate action.

PART TWO – Answers to the Multi-Action Questions

Answer Question 47

BDE

During a MDT (multidisciplinary team) meeting, it can be confusing knowing what the overall patient management decision is when there are so many different healthcare professionals making various decisions about patient's care. Nevertheless, your responsibility in documenting the meeting outcomes in the patient's notes is a vital one and it is paramount that you are clear about the group decision plan. It is also an important time during these meetings to raise any key issues about the patient and that everyone is encouraged to participate, no matter how junior.

The MDT discussions are usually consultant-led and, although intimidating, it would be appropriate to ask your consultant to sum up any key discussion points if you are uncertain of the final outcome decisions (option B). Asking the consultant at the time of discussion about the patient and raising any issues of your own (rather than waiting until the end of the meeting) ensures that none of the information is forgotten and other healthcare professionals who would like to add to your comments have the option of doing so at this point (option E).

If you still feel you do not understand the outcomes or that you would like to ensure that what you have documented is accurate then the next appropriate action would be to write only what you know is accurate and double-check with your consultant at the end of the meeting (option D).

Asking the person next to you or your senior house officer what is going on may not be effective if they are also lost in the discussion (options C and G).

Answer Question 48

CDE

Your first priority should always be towards patient care. You have been given the responsibility of contacting another specialist for advice on a patient under your care and must ensure that the information you receive is accurate and comprehensive. You should correctly document all the recommendations that have been suggested by the haematology registrar (including the time, date and name of the registrar who has given you this advice) in the patient notes (option E).

Although the registrar is very busy and stressed, you should not be afraid to ask them to repeat this information (options C and D) and ensure that what you have understood from the discussion is correct. It is unnecessary to ask the haematology registrar to review the patient or speak to your consultant at this point unless there is anything that you or your team feel is dubious about the information given (options F and H) or unless the patient is in a critical state and requires urgent attention.

Answer Question 49

BCG

Rarely, incidents such as incorrectly documenting information do occur and these need to be addressed immediately. There is a danger of leaving the incorrect entry as it is may cause people to think that the ultrasound result was valid despite a later entry stating that this was not the case. A Post-it note may get lost or fall out of the notes so this is not a good option (option D). The best option would be to put one clean line across the part about the ultrasound scan and write next to it and then sign and date it (option B). Tearing up a legal medical document must not be done (option A).

Although it would be tempting to quietly write up the same antibiotics that were prescribed for Mrs Jones in Mr Smith's drug chart (option H), this is best left for after discussion with the more senior members of your team (option G). The scenario here does not offer you enough clinical information about Mr Smith to allow you to determine whether surgery or a course of antibiotics would be appropriate in his case (options E and F), nor is there any information regarding his past medical history.

Answer Question 50

CEG

It is important to make patient safety your first concern. In this scenario, given the patient's risk factors and recent history of long distance travel, a pulmonary embolism should be considered. The clinical scenario depicts a man with clinical symptoms out of keeping with his normal state, with clinical signs of hypoxia which could have been partially responsible for his transient confusion during his flight. Oxygen (option E), a CTPA (option C) and admission of the patient (option G) should be considered. Although it may be appropriate to refer the patient eventually to psychiatry if his symptoms of psychosis do not resolve (option F), this should only occur after all organic causes are excluded. Treatment for a pulmonary embolism should include warfarin and heparin in the initial stages, if there are no contraindications, before the correct INR level is reached, rather than just heparin (option H).

Answer Question 51

CFH

As a junior doctor there are certain emergency situations that you should be aware of how to treat, one of which includes dealing with hyperkalaemia as this can lead to ventricular and cardiac arrest if not dealt with promptly. Therefore, this cannot wait until the next day (option G) and you should not leave the patient to be assessed by another doctor who may not be able to review your patient promptly (option D).

The initial assessment of the patient should include reviewing the patient, the patient's observation chart, ECG (option C) for arrhythmias and drug chart for any medication that may contribute to the electrolyte imbalance. If the patient is well and there is no obvious cause for the imbalance or clinical signs of distress, you should repeat the patient's blood test (option H) again to ensure that the initial sample was not erroneous or haemolysed.

As it is nearing the end of your shift it is important to relay this important information to the on-call doctor (option F) yourself to make sure they will check the repeated blood results and act upon an erroneous result by administering insulin and calcium gluconate. Calcium resonium (option B) is given to treat hyperkalaemia, but takes time to work and would not lower the potassium with immediate effect.

Answer Question 52

DFG

As part of the 'Foundation Programme Person Specification', a junior doctor should be able to work and communicate effectively with colleagues. If your working relationship with a nurse in question is affecting both your performance at work and also patient care, it is important you get advice on how to handle the situation from senior colleagues (option D) or, if you are confident regarding your instructions, it is important they are clearly delivered and documented to prevent any confusion or errors (option G). It could also be that the nurse has perfectly legitimate reasons for challenging your decisions, and so it would be beneficial to arrange a meeting with her (option F) to discuss this in a civilised manner.

There is no need for aggressive confrontation on the ward (option A) or involving other colleagues (options B and C) in what could easily be a misunderstanding. Filling in a clinical incident form (option E) may be necessary if there have been occasions where this behaviour has resulted in specific adverse clinical events. If the situation is irresolvable then speaking to the nurse's manager may be appropriate, but only after the initial steps have been taken.

Answer Question 53

BDE

According to the GMC's *Good Medical Practice* "doctors should not discriminate unfairly against colleagues or patients" and it appears that the consultant in this case is guilty of doing so. In the first instance, you should offer your colleague emotional support (option E). It would be worth suggesting to your colleague that they determine whether other people have noticed this consultant's behaviour (option D). If their attitude is seriously affecting the doctor's ability to work well in the team, then a private word with the consultant in question or encouraging discussion with your colleague's educational supervisor would be recommended (option B).

Ignoring the remarks (option F) and not getting involved (option G) would not be suitable options and may make your colleague even more distressed. Asking the colleague to take annual leave (option H) would also be ignoring the situation and would not help it be resolved.

It is best to not involve your own educational supervisor (option C) as they may not have as much power in resolving the situation as your colleague's supervisor.

Answer Question 54

ABF

Performing assessments are essential during the Foundation Programme and also later in specialty training. According to the *New Doctor* publication, "Foundation doctors must have regular feedback on their performance" with "feedback about performance helping to identify strengths and weaknesses…allowing changes to be made". It is therefore inappropriate to never perform any future assessments (as stated in option C) and better to reflect on all feedback, good or bad, that is received (option F).

Although it is unprofessional for the consultant in question to have humiliated their junior doctor in this scenario, he may not have been aware of his behaviour and discussing this in a private setting would be the most appropriate first step (option A), as well as receiving further specific points for improvement. If your consultant is not empathic to the situation or forthcoming with reasons for their feedback, the *New Doctor* publication does state that "Foundation doctors must have opportunities to discuss issues or problems, including commenting on the quality of the training and supervision provided". The best person to discuss these issues with would be your educational supervisor.

Finally, you should ensure your patients have not been placed in an awkward situation by what has happened and are put at ease with gentle reassurance (option B).

Answer Question 55

BFH

When working with different healthcare teams, the *New Doctor* publication states Foundation year 1 doctors should "demonstrate that they can communicate in different ways" and also "work effectively as a member of a team...including during handover and taking over the care of a patient safely and effectively from other health professionals".

It is important to clearly ask the reviewing team exactly which investigations, imaging and medications should be started (option B), including asking the team to write their opinions in the patient notes. However, if the reviewing surgical team does not have a clear opinion about what imaging to request, then a specialist (i.e. radiologist) can be consulted (option F). Other instructions recommended by the surgical team, such as referral to a palliative care team (option H) should be followed, if appropriate.

Arranging a diagnostic OGD with biopsy (option G) is not appropriate in this case as the patient's diagnosis is already known and this procedure will not add any new information. A chest X-ray will not delineate the extent of the tumour exactly (option D), although it may demonstrate a mediastinal mass. A MRI scan could help delineate the tumour (option E), although in order to place an oesophageal stent, a contrast study such as a gastrografin swallow, may be more appropriate.

Answer Question 56

CEF

Although there is no urgency for the patient to be discharged, he is clearly not ill enough to require prolonging his stay in hospital. By remaining in hospital for longer than required, he would be at risk of developing hospital-acquired infections.

This scenario requires you to show your initiative in patient care, whilst ensuring patient safety is maintained. Although there is no urgency for the patient to be discharged, he clearly does not require a hospital bed and by staying in, may be at increased risk of developing hospital-acquired infections. The best option is to liaise with the discharge team to check on progress (option C) and find out whether there are any aspects of the process you might be able to help with or discuss with your consultant (option F). Alternatively, speaking to the patient's GP is also a good option as much of the community follow-up will be arranged by him/her (option E).

It is dangerous to try and arrange discharge by yourself (option A) when you may not have the appropriate contacts for all the community teams, or to just arrange the same follow-up as before if a patient's medical needs may be different (option D). Although you could involve your other junior colleagues to help you (option G), you have been told that they have shown no interest in helping and this may therefore not be an effective method in this case.

Answer Question 57

BEF

According to the *New Doctor* publication, "Foundation programmes should ensure that Foundation doctors have appropriate learning opportunities to meet the learning outcomes for their period of training". Although being able to perform an appendicectomy is too advanced an outcome for a Foundation doctor to achieve and is more appropriate for a trainee in surgical training, having the opportunity to 'scrub in' and observe procedures are important.

It is important when communicating with colleagues that if you feel you are missing out on training opportunities, you should explain this in a calm and composed manner (option B). You should be open to negotiation and if you are unable to attend the appendicectomy, then perhaps you can scrub for a subsequent case (option E) or go to theatre with your senior house officer but accept you might not scrub in (option F).

Scrubbing in for different parts of the same operation is not appropriate for the smooth running of the case (option G). Preventing both you and your junior doctor from attending theatre will stop either person taking advantage of the teaching opportunity (option D).

Answer Question 58

ADG

According to the Foundation Programme curriculum (2011), one of the competences of a Foundation year 1 doctor includes prioritizing and re-prioritising their workload appropriately as well as delegating or calling for help when knowing that they are falling behind.

In this scenario the THREE most pressing jobs include assessing a sick patient who has just collapsed (option A), ensuring that a patient who is due to go for surgery in the same morning is able to still have their operation safely (option D) and lastly ensuring a post-operative patient is not in pain (option G).

All the other options depict patients who are stable and do not require immediate attention, although you should eventually see to them all during the course of the day.

Answer Question 59

BEF

The *New Doctor* publication states that Foundation year 1 doctors should "be able to complete or arrange for the completion of legal documents correctly such as those certifying sickness and death and liaise with the coroner…where appropriate".

Any qualified doctor can help to confirm the death of a patient on the ward (unlike the response suggested in option A), however, only doctors who have provided care during the patient's last illness and who have seen the deceased within the last 14 days of death should complete the death certificate. Junior doctors are allowed to complete part of the death certificate (unlike that suggested in option C). Exceptions to any doctor signing a death certification occurs in cases where referral to the coroner is required (such as within 24 hours of admission to hospital or deaths related to surgery or anaesthetic). Therefore in this scenario, referral to the coroner would be required (option F).

In order to certify the patient's death, the following criteria should be sought:

- Absence of all major pulses.

- Absence of breath sounds and heart sounds for at least 4 minutes (not just heart sounds as suggested in option D).

- Fixed, dilated pupils with absent corneal reflexes.

- Patient should be confirmed to be not suffering from hypoxia (as this can mimic death if not excluded).

Cold caloric testing (option H) is usually not performed on the ward in the clinical confirmation of death. Although it is difficult to be the junior doctor who has to face the family with the bad news of the patient's death (option B), it is important to ensure that they are aware of the current events and to arrange a meeting with a senior colleague if they have further questions that require clarification.

Answer Question 60

EHF

This question requires you to prioritise urgent tasks and be able to handover effectively to members of your team on a different shift. According to the Foundation Programme curriculum relating to continuation of patient care, the role of the Foundation year 1 doctor is to:

- "be punctual for start of shifts, meetings, handovers and other duties

- keep a list of tasks

- prioritise and re-prioritise workloads appropriately

- ensure satisfactory completion of tasks at the end of the shift with appropriate handover".

Ideally you should complete your job list before handover and be able to give clear instructions to the night team who may not know all the patients. You should ensure all the jobs on your handover list are accurate and comprehensive by liaising with your other colleagues during the day shift (option H).

The most important jobs of the options given above after ensuring your list is comprehensive include dealing with the neutropenic febrile patient (option E) and ensuring the patient on the heparin infusion does not have deranged clotting with their optimal APTT in range whilst on the medication (option F).

Although other options are important to deal with (and the next important patient would be the patient with aspiration pneumonia, option A), they are not as pressing and can probably be done within the next two hours of the shift rather than needing to be seen to immediately.

Answer Question 61

DCG

According to the Foundation Programme curriculum, Foundation doctors are required to treat the patient as the centre of care and "respect the patient's right to autonomy and confidentiality".

In this situation, it is important to be mindful of the patient's relatives' concerns. However, you should be polite and reiterate that you cannot withhold information from your patient unless they specifically have told you that they are not interested in knowing the outcomes (option D). You could offer to ask your patient what they think about their condition and whether they feel their family's concerns are appropriate (option C). You should try to resolve this issue prior to the results of the biopsy being released (such as in option E). Asking what the patient would prefer regarding doctors disclosing medical information to the family before the results are available (option G) would be best.

You should not lie to the patient's family by promising one thing but doing the opposite action (as in option A) and neither should you promise something that you are uncomfortable about or not confident that you are allowed to do (option B). If you are uncertain what the best action would be, you should ask a senior member of your team rather than another junior doctor (option F). There is no evidence in this scenario that the patient has any mental health issues and offering full counselling and a mental health review may not be appropriate (option H).

Answer Question 62

CDE

In this scenario it is vital to rule out compartment syndrome, which is a surgical emergency. If this is not identified and treated quickly it can result in rhabdomyolysis and amputation. As a junior doctor you should be familiar with such life and limb-threatening events and understand the urgency of such matters. Simple initial management steps include removing the restrictive cast (option C), conducting a full neuromuscular investigation of the limb in question (option D) and also adequate analgesia. You should involve your seniors immediately and request an urgent registrar review (option E) as the patient may require an emergency fasciotomy.

It would be unsafe to discharge the patient (option F) or to wait for your consultant to review if this is not possible immediately (option B). Repeat images will not help and will waste precious time (options A and G). Although the patient will undoubtedly be admitted to hospital, this should be for more than just pure observation (option H).

Answer Question 63

AFD

Good clinical care includes taking a thorough history and examination. You may have to be blunt with the patient in this scenario to ensure you can achieve this. However, be mindful to remain polite and to never insult the patient or make them feel uncomfortable (unlike in option E). Reassuring the patient that the reason for gaining a quick history is in their best interest (option A) in case urgent therapy is required, getting a collateral history from the patient's partner (option D) or asking the patient specific questions you want them to answer (option F) can be good ways of overcoming this problem.

It is also important to manage your time and jobs well as a junior doctor and letting the patient talk for as long as possible (option B or C) can mean that you waste time where you could be treating the patient or obtaining important investigations. It is not appropriate or professional to refer patients that you do not feel you can be bothered to treat to another colleague (option G) and all investigations that are sent off in a hospital should be justified based on your differential diagnoses from the patient history (unlike in option H).

Answer Question 64

BAG

Depression is common amongst stroke patients, and managing this should not be overlooked as part of their rehabilitation. The fact that the patient appears to have suicidal thoughts is deeply concerning and efforts should be made to determine whether these feelings are serious. All members of the MDT should be involved (option G) including members of your own team.

Although a formal psychiatric opinion should be sought (option B), this should be after careful discussion with members of your team (i.e. not like in option E). Anti-depressants may be commenced (option F) but would be more appropriate after a formal review. Increasing other medication, such as analgesia (option D), is only necessary if the patient is complaining of pain, but it will not benefit his mental status.

Discussing the patient's mood with his family may be necessary and yield important information when making the psychiatric referral but should be done sensitively (option A) and patient confidentiality must still be maintained. A rehabilitation unit (option C) may be appropriate in certain circumstances, but should only be performed if it is the joint view from discussion at a MDT meeting.

Answer Question 65

EFG

This scenario is testing your ability to work with different healthcare professionals in a multidisciplinary manner and properly assess a patient in the first instance.

Prior to asking for a review from another healthcare professional, you should ensure that your patient is well hydrated with maintenance intravenous fluids (option F) and that you have excluded other causes for the patient being 'off their food' such as depression, infection, malignancy or peptic ulcers where the patient may feel pain on eating (option G). It is inappropriate to wait for the condition to resolve as there is the suggestion that this sign has been ongoing for quite some time now (option H).

If, however, after all reasonable assessment no organic cause can be found, it is prudent to seek help from a dietician who can prescribe and recommend an appropriate diet regime for the patient. This may include feeding the patient via a thin bore NG tube (not wide bore which is used for decompression as in option A), or via a central venous catheter for total parenteral nutrition (TPN) (as in option C). This decision should depend on multiple factors and it would be better to await the outcome of the dietician review and discussion with senior colleagues than to start this management yourself.

Answer Question 66

CDF

In certain circumstances where a patient is deemed to lack capacity to consent, no other person or relative is able to consent on their behalf. Treatment in such circumstances is carried out in the patient's best interest as deemed by the patient's medical team.

In this scenario, it is difficult to decide what is in the patient's best interest as there is little information on the patient's quality of life prior to the event. It is important to seek more information on this from the patient's son and nursing home (option C) and to also investigate reasons for the patient's son's concerns (option D). It may be that he is not completely sure what is going on or what the proposed operation will involve and is only worried about his father's welfare. Giving a full account of the risks and benefits of treatment versus non-treatment may be useful in helping the relative understand the medical decision that the surgical team are trying to make (option F).

A consent form 4 (option H) is a type of consent form that will be filled out by a member of the surgical team where a patient is deemed to lack capacity, stating that the surgical team feel treatment is in the patient's best interest. The patient is not required to sign the form.

Answer Question 67

CDF

This scenario is testing your ability to put patient safety at the forefront of your care despite feeling annoyed or angry with a colleague, and ensuring you maintain professional behaviour at all times.

It is therefore not professional to shout at the nurse in question (option G) or delay patient treatment (option B). You should ask for assistance from another nurse to help you perform the ECG (option C) so that you can examine the patient at the same time rather than waste time looking for the ECG machine yourself and assess the patient in an 'ABC' approach (options D and F).

Answer Question 68

EFH

According to the GMC's *Good Medical Practice* guidelines all doctors should "respect the skills and contributions from colleagues". In this scenario the consultant in question appears to be undermining the nurse's position by making inappropriate sexist and risqué remarks. This is clearly unprofessional and your role in this scenario should be in supporting your nursing colleague.

It is important that you discuss the issue with the nurse in question and enquire about her feelings and thoughts on the matter. If she feels that this is interfering with her ability to care for her patients or is making her feel uncomfortable at work then she should be encouraged to raise the issue with her seniors or with the consultant in question (options F and H). You may wish to gently bring the subject up with your consultant if you feel that the remarks are creating an unfriendly working atmosphere for the team and the patients as well (option E). If discussing the matter with your consultant does not appear to help the situation, it may then be appropriate to ask another consultant for their advice on the issue (option C).

In the first instance it may not be appropriate to report the consultant to the GMC before trying to resolve the issue internally (unlike in option D) and confronting the issue in public on the ward may only make matters worse and create an uneasy atmosphere (option A). Spreading rumours and discussing a delicate matter such as this in front of multiple medical staff (option G) may not be appropriate and could embarrass the nurse in question further.

Answer Question 69

DBG

This is a difficult scenario as your loyalties may be split between protecting your colleague and your patient's interests. The case above, does not give you any reason to believe that patient care is being jeopardised, nor does it mention the fact that your colleague is actually taking the drugs during working hours. Given these ambiguities, it may not be wise to jump to conclusions and exclude your colleague from his patients (option A) or report them to your consultant (option C). Neither should you however ignore what you have witnessed (option H or E).

You should offer your colleague appropriate emotional support and discuss it with him face-to-face to clarify the matter (options G and B). If you are uncertain what should be done about the scenario, you could liaise with a senior colleague for advice without unnecessarily implicating your colleague until you are clearer about your facts (option D).

Answer Question 70

DFE

As with every scenario, it is important to put patient safety at the forefront of your actions. If you have a colleague who believes that you may not be acting in the patient's best interest, it is their prerogative to ensure their opinions are heard. You should enquire further into reasons behind the nurse's opinions (option D) rather than ignoring them (option C or G) or branding the nurse as a 'trouble maker' by stating their refusal to dispense medication in the medical notes (option H).

If after reassessing the situation (option F) the nurse gives you reason to doubt your initial plan or you do not feel you are able to reason with the nurse, you should contact a senior colleague (option E). Contacting the surgeon who you know to be too busy to attend would be inappropriate (option B). However, if there are no other available senior colleagues to ask for help, going yourself into the theatre and asking for advice might be the only option available.

Examination 2

PART ONE – Ranking Questions

Question 1

You are a junior doctor on a busy post-take ward round seeing a patient. The patient's family is present and your consultant discusses the patient's care with them. The conversation is quite extensive and you are not sure if everything mentioned needs documenting.

Rank in order the following actions in response to this situation (1= Most appropriate; 5= Least appropriate):

A. Write down as much as possible as everything said may be important.

B. Write down the main points discussed and the views of the relatives as well as the overall course of action.

C. Do not write anything as you are not sure and discuss this afterwards with someone more senior before wasting your energy in writing it down.

D. Write what you can and clarify anything unclear with the consultant during the discussion.

E. Only write down what the action plan discussed is as this is the only important thing that the team needs to know about with regards to management.

Question 2

You are very keen on pursuing surgery as a career and you are currently working in one of the top surgical departments in the country. However, the job itself mainly consists of ward work. Out of the three junior doctors on the firm, you are the only one interested in surgery and you all seem to manage the workload easily. You think it is a reasonable request for more surgical experience on the job.

Rank in order the following actions in response to this situation (1= Most appropriate; 5= Least appropriate):

A. Take charge of any future surgical opportunities at the expense of your other two colleagues.

B. Tell your consultant that you are keen to get more exposure to surgery and that the ward jobs are all easily covered already.

C. Arrange a taster week within the department to focus on practical surgical skills.

D. Ask your senior colleagues to kindly give you some practical surgical opportunities which you may find interesting if they have time and are happy to do so.

E. Change your future job rotations to those that give more surgical exposure.

Question 3

You have just finished a long working schedule of nights and on-calls and have been given an updated rota for next month. You are keen to take a week's holiday but have realised that your senior house officer colleagues will be on annual leave during the time you want to take annual leave as well. All of you seem desperate to keep your allocated holidays but it is imperative that at least one person is present in the hospital at all times to continue to do the ward duties.

Rank in order the following actions in response to this situation (1= Most appropriate; 5= Least appropriate):

A.   All doctors should cancel their holidays as this is the fairest solution.

B.   Ask the consultant/registrar how many people need to be around and what level of doctor is needed, then decide who should be present and cancel their holiday.

C.   Decide amongst yourselves who can easily rearrange their holiday. It may be that you have to stay behind even if you have already worked a long stint.

D.   Try to get one or more of your colleagues to swap their leave to another time so that an excessive number of doctors on the team are not away all at the same time.

E.   Try and speak to your general services manager concerning arranging locum doctors.

Question 4

You are a junior doctor and have noticed that your fellow junior doctor colleagues on the firm always seem to get told off by the consultant for no apparent reason. They appear to have low morale and some have started thinking about quitting medicine.

Rank in order the following actions in response to this situation (1= Most appropriate; 5= Least appropriate):

A.   Speak to a consultant on a different firm about the situation to see if they can discuss the matter with your own consultant.

B.   Tell your parents about the situation and ask them to write your consultant an angry letter.

C.   Speak to your colleagues and ask them how they feel. If they are upset then advise them to tell the consultant how they are feeling.

D.   Speak to your registrar and see what advice they can offer about the situation or offer a reason for the consultant's actions. Perhaps he is unhappy with the management these junior doctors are giving to his patients but has not mentioned it to them.

E.   Tell the Foundation Programme director about what you have noticed and request he/she speaks to your consultant about the matter urgently.

Question 5

You are on a respiratory firm and your colleague is a budding respiratory physician. She explains to you that she is very keen to gain more experience in this field and would like to spend some time with the consultant shadowing him in the tuberculosis clinic. This will mean that she will not be able to help you on the ward in the afternoon. However, you do not have many outstanding ward jobs or sick patients.

Rank in order the following actions in response to this situation (1= Most appropriate; 5= Least appropriate):

A.   Go through the ward list with your team so you are up-to-date with the patients that your colleague has been handling in case you need to deal with them.

B.   Suggest that you will cover the wards while your colleague goes to the tuberculosis clinic.

C.   Ensure you have a method of contacting your colleague should you need help.

D.   Inform your registrars of the plan and ensure that this is satisfactory with them.

E.   Refuse to allow your colleague to go to the clinic as you would prefer to have support on the ward.

Question 6

A breast cancer patient was initially considered for a bilateral mastectomy. However, it was discovered that she is an overseas patient and ineligible for free NHS treatment unless she elects to pay for her surgery. You have been told by the finance department that if the patient refuses to pay for the treatment, then her operation should be cancelled and you should not provide her with any medication.

Rank in order the following actions in response to this situation (1= Most appropriate; 5= Least appropriate):

A.   Do not do perform the surgery as she cannot pay and is therefore not entitled to treatment from the NHS.

B.   Find out the exact cost of the operation and relay this to the patient.

C.   Discuss alternatives to treatment that do not require surgical therapies (including the risks of these and not having the surgery), which could be more affordable.

D.   Ask the consultant to do the surgery anyway as she will die eventually without it.

E.   Ask her if it is possible to have the surgery in her home country as it is not an emergency and she has time to arrange this for the near future.

Question 7

Your best friend has asked you to prescribe some antibiotics for an ear infection which he seems to suffer from on a regular basis. He tells you that he would normally have asked his GP but has moved home and is not registered with one nearby. He insists that this is a one-off situation and will 'owe you a favour' back if you help him.

Rank in order the following actions in response to this situation (1= Most appropriate; 5= Least appropriate):

A.   Refuse to prescribe the medication yourself but ask another Foundation doctor colleague to prescribe it.

B.   Take the relevant antibiotic from the ward store cupboard and give it to your friend, making sure that another senior doctor and nurse are aware of this.

C.   Inform him that he must register with his local GP and ask them instead.

D.   Write a private prescription for the medication and arrange for his local GP to see him as soon as possible.

E.   Take the relevant antibiotic from the ward store cupboard and give it to your friend but do not mention it to your colleagues as you do not want them to be involved in this situation.

Question 8

You have just clerked an 89 year old patient from the emergency department who presented with severe weight loss, abdominal and bone pain. You request a CT scan which shows several metastatic deposits with an unknown primary origin. The nurse hands you the patient's drug chart and asks you to write up a long list of the patient's usual medication. You are aware that this patient is having compliance issues with the medication due to the symptoms of the cancer and feel that he should be started on the Liverpool Care Pathway. The patient has vomited several times today and is experiencing moderate amounts of pain.

Rank in order the following actions in response to this situation (1= Most appropriate; 5= Least appropriate):

A.   Write up all the drugs as the patient still needs to have their comorbidities treated.

B.   Ask the palliative care registrar for advice before writing up any medication.

C.   Write up some simple analgesia, fluids and anti-emetics for now and then consult the palliative care team.

D.   Only write up the drugs given to someone started on the Liverpool Care Pathway.

E.   Do not give any treatment before a diagnostic biopsy has been carried out.

Question 9

You are a junior doctor on a hepatology placement. Mrs Green has chronic cirrhosis of the liver and is due to undergo a liver transplant later in the week. You are called to see her as she is refusing a cannula. When you get to her she explains that she no longer wants the procedure and just wants to die.

Rank in order the following actions in response to this situation (1= Most appropriate; 5= Least appropriate):

A. Take the patient to a private area with a nurse chaperone to fully discuss her concerns.

B. Explain to Mrs Green that she has to have the procedure since the donor liver has been found and the consent form has been signed.

C. Contact a senior colleague to talk to Mrs Green.

D. Assess Mrs Green's competence to see if she is fully aware of the consequences of her decision.

E. Ask Mrs Green to reconsider her decision by contacting a family member or friend who might be able to persuade her otherwise.

Question 10

You are looking after Mrs Goodman who has just been diagnosed with breast cancer. On the morning ward round she is very upset and seems distracted. The nurse reports that she hasn't been sleeping well and has been refusing her food. The general surgical consultant is preoccupied with obtaining consent from the patient and doesn't seem to notice.

Rank in order the following actions in response to this situation (1= Most appropriate; 5= Least appropriate):

A. Talk to the consultant in private after he has finished talking to the patient and explain your concerns about her being depressed. Offer to arrange a psychological referral if he thinks it would be appropriate.

B. Ignore it. If it's important the consultant will pick up on it.

C. After the ward round, talk to Mrs Goodman about her concerns and assess her mood. If necessary, ask your registrar whether you should arrange for a psychologist to see her.

D. The consultant must have missed it. Point out to them on the ward round that Mrs Goodman is obviously depressed and needs to see a psychologist.

E. Ask Mrs Goodman if she is feeling OK and hope the consultant will pick up on her change in mood.

Question 11

You are looking after Mr Burns who as recently had a CT scan, which showed a lesion in his pancreas highly suggestive of an invasive carcinoma. You get a phone call on the ward from his sister in Australia asking for the results.

Rank in order the following actions in response to this situation (1= Most appropriate; 5= Least appropriate):

A.   Ask the sister to hold the line while you obtain consent from Mr Burns, allowing you to talk to her. Then explain to the sister that it is suggestive of cancer but you do not have all the results yet. Document the conversation in the patient's notes.

B.   Ask the sister to talk to Mr Burns personally via his own mobile so that he can pass on any information to her if he wishes.

C.   To avoid any awkward conversation reassure the sister that Mr Burns will be fine.

D.   Contact your registrar for advice and to talk to the sister if he feels this is appropriate.

E.   Tell the sister that you are busy at present ask her to call back later so you can fully discuss her worries.

Question 12

You are out for a drink with your team when your registrar starts talking loudly about patients on the ward using their full names. Sitting in the corner, you recognise one of the patient's families.

Rank in order the following actions in response to this situation (1= Most appropriate; 5= Least appropriate):

A.   Quickly and discretely inform the registrar that the family are there and suggest he change the topic of conversation.

B.   Interrupt the registrar and tell them not to use patient's names.

C.   Allow the registrar to continue but quietly tell them later that there are relatives present.

D.   Don't say anything but tell the consultant the next day.

E.   Ask your senior house officer to have a word with him as soon as possible as he is better friends with your registrar than you are.

Question 13

An 11 year old girl, Emma, is brought into the emergency department following a road traffic accident. A scan has revealed that there is free intra-abdominal blood and that she will require emergency surgery to increase her chances of survival. Her parents are not present, and you are unable to get through to them at this present moment. Emma is haemodynamically unstable.

Rank in order the following actions in response to this situation (1= Most appropriate; 5= Least appropriate):

A. Delay surgery until you can get consent from Emma's parents.

B. Delay surgery until you can obtain consent from one of Emma's relatives if you are unable to get through to her parents.

C. Speak to the legal department of the hospital to clarify that you can proceed with surgery.

D. Act in Emma's best interests and book her in for emergency surgery.

E. Treat Emma with conservative management as you are unable to obtain consent for surgery.

Question 14

As a junior doctor you are entitled to protected teaching once a week. Your consultant has not been letting you attend these sessions on time and you always miss the register. You are worried that you will fail the year, as you have not met the required 70% attendance.

Rank in order the following actions in response to this situation (1= Most appropriate; 5= Least appropriate):

A. Ask your junior doctor colleagues to sign you in each week instead and aim to get there as early as possible.

B. Talk to your consultant and explain the importance attending teaching on time, otherwise you will end up failing the year.

C. Discuss the problem with your educational supervisor.

D. Try to make up your attendance on your other rotations. If your attendance is insufficient at the end of the year then explain why.

E. Talk to your junior doctor year representative and ask them what to do in these situations.

Question 15

A patient is admitted with Brown-Séquard syndrome. Your consultant asks you to take some students to examine the patient and then teach about Brown-Séquard syndrome. However, aside from remembering it as one of hundreds eponymous syndromes you learnt about during finals, your knowledge about it is quite hazy.

Rank in order the following actions in response to this situation (1= Most appropriate; 5= Least appropriate):

A.   Have a quick read of the medical notes before you see the patient.

B.   Tell your consultant you do not feel confident teaching on it.

C.   Use resources available at the hospital library/internet to brush up on it before teaching.

D.   Ask your consultant or registrar to quickly recap the aetiology with you.

E.   Apologise to the students that you need to cancel teaching today.

Question 16

You are exhausted after finishing a week of nights on-call. You have handed over to a colleague and are about to head home for some much needed sleep when your consultant asks you to assist him in theatre as the registrar is away. You will be paid locum rates and you will gain valuable theatre experience.

Rank in order the following actions in response to this situation (1= Most appropriate; 5= Least appropriate):

A.   Agree, despite feeling very tired as you are desperate to log theatre hours and need the money. You don't feel at your best but think you could manage staying awake for another couple of hours.

B.   Refuse and leave, apologizing to the consultant, as you feel unsafe to work any longer.

C.   Refuse, and explain you are tired and that you will try and find alternative cover.

D.   Refuse, and explain you are tired and want to go to sleep.

E.   Agree, as you are uncomfortable saying no to your consultant, even though you are exhausted and feel it is unsafe for you to be at work.

Question 17

You have just finished the ward round and only have a few jobs to do. You realise that this is the perfect time to finish your audit on the ward. However, you are aware that the post-night and post-take teams have lots of jobs to do. What would you do next?

Rank in order the following actions in response to this situation (1= Most appropriate; 5= Least appropriate):

A.   Spend the rest of the day doing the audit and avoiding the post-take teams.

B.   Review your patients again with a senior to make sure there are no outstanding jobs.

C.   After completing your jobs, try and help out the other teams if needed.

D.   Spend the rest of the day helping out with other jobs and do the audit as well.

E.   Do not help with the other jobs as they are not your responsibility and go home early.

Question 18

It is a busy weekend on the Medical Assessment Unit (MAU) and you are the junior doctor responsible for covering all the patients on two large wards. Your bleep has been going off constantly, and you find your jobs list growing overwhelmingly longer and longer. Just when you think you cannot cope with the workload, you get asked to see a patient who is hypotensive (their blood pressure measures 74/43).

Rank in order the following actions in response to this situation (1= Most appropriate; 5= Least appropriate):

A.   Attend to the hypotensive patient immediately and after managing them, prioritise the other jobs accordingly, working through them systematically in order of importance.

B.   Ask the nurse to give the hypotensive patient an initial fluid bolus while you quickly do a few other jobs, before assessing him in about 15 minutes to see if he has responded.

C.   Bleep the medical registrar on-call and ask for assistance in managing the acutely unwell patient and some other jobs as you feel overwhelmed.

D.   Call your friend, another junior doctor, who is covering the surgical wards to see if they are free to assist you.

E.   Assess the acutely unwell patient immediately and consider calling for senior help. Continue with your jobs list when this situation has been adequately managed.

Question 19

You are working on an audit with a junior doctor colleague. It is demanding a lot of time and effort, and requires you to put in several extra hours after work and on the weekends. You find that your colleague is not contributing as much, and is constantly making excuses instead of working on the audit. You have tried to broach the subject with him but he appears unconcerned by your comments.

Rank in order the following actions in response to this situation (1= Most appropriate; 5= Least appropriate):

A.   Withdraw from the audit and refuse to do any more work on it as you have had enough!

B.   Discuss the matter with your clinical supervisor to see if they can come up with a solution.

C.   Continue to put in extra time on the audit as it is important for your CV regardless of your colleague's contribution.

D.   Replace your colleague with another junior doctor who will be more likely to pull their weight.

E.   Attempt to speak to your colleague more firmly with a clear action plan.

Question 20

You are leaving the ward to go to lunch when you notice one of the patients struggling to walk out of the ward. He is using a walking stick but appears unstable and looks like he is about to fall over.

Rank in order the following actions in response to this situation (1= Most appropriate; 5= Least appropriate):

A.   Discuss with the ward manager why and how this patient was allowed out of the ward without supervision or support.

B.   Support and walk the patient back to his bed with extra help if needed.

C.   Discuss with the physiotherapists the need for further input with this patient regarding ongoing mobility plans.

D.   Document in the notes the events and your discussions.

E.   Advise the patient that he should not be doing things that he does not feel that he can cope with.

Question 21

You are the on-call junior doctor and have been handed over by the day team a review of an elderly female who is day 5 post-total hip replacement. When you see her she is short of breath and the nursing staff tell you that she coughed up a small amount of blood earlier in the morning.

Rank in order the following actions in response to this situation (1= Most appropriate; 5= Least appropriate):

A.   Start her on oxygen therapy via a Hudson mask.

B.   Request an urgent portable chest X-ray on the ward.

C.   Ask the nurses to re-check the patient's clinical observations and start to examine the patient in an ABC (airway, breathing, circulation) manner.

D.   Send an arterial blood gas to assess for any metabolic or respiratory disturbance.

E.   Call your senior colleague for further input and management advice.

Question 22

You are a junior doctor in the emergency department. You have just seen a 10 year old girl who presents with vaginal discharge and is accompanied by her grandma. On taking a more extensive history, she tells you that she has been having a sexual relationship with a 17 year old boy and that they do not use any condoms.

Rank in order the following actions in response to this situation (1= Most appropriate; 5= Least appropriate):

A.   Call social services and the police.

B.   Inform the girl's parents and let them deal with the situation.

C.   Discuss the case with the child protection lead of the hospital.

D.   Inform the boy's parents about the situation.

E.   Assess whether the girl is competent to make a decision to enter into a sexual relationship.

Question 23

You are a junior doctor assisting during a hernia operation in theatre. You realise that you have just administered local anaesthetic to the patient that is out-of-date. The patient is currently under a general anaesthetic.

Rank in order the following actions in response to this situation (1= Most appropriate; 5= Least appropriate):

A.   Check the expiry dates of all the local anaesthetic vials in stock after the operation.

B.   Inform the consultant in the operation about what happened and ensure the patient's wounds and clinical status is assessed properly on the ward.

C.   Once the patient wakes up from the general anaesthetic, inform the patient what has happened and apologise.

D.   Fill out a critical incident form.

E.   Do not say anything to the patient.

Question 24

You are about to get on the train to go home when you realise that you have forgotten to prescribe a bag of intravenous normal saline fluids for a patient with dehydration. Your registrar asked you write up some fluids before he went home and it completely slipped your mind at the time.

Rank in order the following actions in response to this situation (1= Most appropriate; 5= Least appropriate):

A.   Ring the on-call junior doctor through the hospital switchboard and ask them to prescribe the fluids.

B.   Ring the on-call senior house officer through the switchboard and ask them to prescribe the fluids.

C.   Do not do anything as it is likely that somebody else would have prescribed the fluids.

D.   Do not go back to the hospital but ensure that the night team are aware of the patient.

E.   Go back to see the patient and prescribe the fluids.

Question 25

An elderly patient presents with overt type two respiratory failure. She has an extensive past medical history including previous colonic malignancy, COPD (chronic obstructive pulmonary disease), type two diabetes and chronic heart failure with an ejection fraction of 15%. On the ward round, after discussion with the patient, the consultant signs a 'do not resuscitate' form. Later that day, during visiting hours, the husband and rest of the family dispute the do not resuscitate form and start arguing with the nursing staff.

Rank in order the following actions in response to this situation (1= Most appropriate; 5= Least appropriate):

A.   Go to the ward and suggest that you talk to the family in a quiet side room.

B.   Explain to them how and why the decision to sign the do not resuscitate form was made.

C.   Document the discussion in the notes that you have had with the family.

D.   Relay your discussion to the rest of your team so that they are abreast of the situation.

E.   Tell the family that you do not have time to discuss the situation with them and that the decision is a medical one and it is final.

Question 26

You are on a night shift as a junior doctor. One of your patient's cannula has stopped working, and they are on intravenous antibiotics for a chest infection. You have been bleeped to insert another cannula. You have three attempts but fail to get one in. You contact your senior house officer to ask them to help you; however, they are busy assisting in an emergency case in theatre.

Rank in order the following actions in response to this situation (1= most appropriate; 5= Least appropriate):

A. Document in the notes that you have attempted, what the cannula is for and that you have contacted your senior colleague.

B. Apologise to the patient for failing to get a cannula sited.

C. Ask the patient if they will let you try again in a while or whether they are in too much pain.

D. Leave the patient without a line and hand the job over to the day team.

E. Try and contact another doctor to attempt the cannula.

Question 27

You are an on-call medical junior doctor. You are currently on the ward attending to a patient who has had two episodes of haematemesis and is haemodynamically unstable. You then get bleeped by one of the senior sisters on a different ward asking for an urgent review of a patient with chest pain.

Rank in order the following immediate actions in response to this situation (1= Most appropriate; 5= Least appropriate):

A. Immediately review the patient with chest pain as he could be having a myocardial infarction.

B. Continue to stabilise the patient you are attending to and bleep the medical senior house officer on-call to see if he is able to urgently review the patient with chest pain. If he is busy, attend to the patient with chest pain once the patient you are seeing is stable. Ask the senior sister to perform an ECG in the meantime, as well as a repeat of the patient's observations.

C. Stabilise the patient you are currently attending to and then attend to the patient with chest pain. Ask the nurse to perform an ECG in the meantime, as well as a repeat of the patient's observations.

D. Ask the senior sister about the history of the patient's chest pain.

E. Ask the senior sister to bleep the on-call cardiology registrar.

Question 28

You are a surgical junior doctor on your first, extremely busy, general surgery night shift. During the night the ENT (ear, nose and throat) ward nurses consistently bleep you despite your rota co-coordinator being very clear that it is not part of your cover. Later on the ENT registrar bleeps you explaining he is in theatre and needs you to clerk in a patient.

Rank in order the following actions in response to this situation (1= Most appropriate; 5= Least appropriate):

A. Establish from the nurses and registrar whether the patient needs urgent medical care. If not, explain that you cannot help at present.

B. Apologise but explain firmly that you are very busy and unable to help.

C. Clerk in the patient quickly and only write up the drugs for that night.

D. Ignore bleeps from that number for the rest of the night.

E. Prioritise the job with your own jobs and explain you will try to do it if you get time later on.

Question 29

You are a junior doctor in the emergency department on a busy Friday night. A known alcoholic is in the waiting room to be seen and is becoming increasingly confused and restless by the long wait. When a nurse tries to take his blood pressure he lashes out and strikes her.

Rank in order the following actions in response to this situation (1= Most appropriate; 5= Least appropriate):

A. Ask the nurse to fill in an incident form.

B. Talk to the patient to try to calm him down. Reassure him he will be seen soon.

C. Ask hospital security to restrain the patient until he calms down.

D. Tend to the nurse to assess and treat her injuries.

E. Sedate the patient until you have time to see him.

Question 30

You are a cardiology junior doctor and one of your patients, Mr Thomas, is ready for discharge from the ward. One of his daughters has come to pick him up and asks to see you. When you arrive on the ward Miss Thomas tells you she has been feeling really sick over the last few days and this morning she had an episode of vomiting. She asks you to give her an anti-emetic.

Rank in order the following actions in response to this situation (1= Most appropriate; 5= Least appropriate):

A. Prescribe her an anti-emetic and send her on her way.

B. Reassure her that it is probably nothing but if it does continue she should see her GP.

C. Tell Miss Thomas to go to the emergency department.

D. Inform your registrar of the situation.

E. Give the patient an anti-emetic but tell her she should see her GP if it persists.

Question 31

You are the hepatology junior doctor and you are called to see Mr Jones who is threatening to self-discharge. He has full mental capacity but is being aggressive towards the nursing staff on the ward and is refusing to stay at his bed space.

Rank in order the following actions in response to this situation (1= Most appropriate; 5= Least appropriate):

A.   Allow Mr Jones to leave but try to arrange for him to return to clinic in the near future.

B.   Politely invite Mr Jones into a side room with a male chaperone and explore his concerns, ensuring you are sitting nearer the door.

C.   Talk to the patient in a private area. If he continues with his aggressive behaviour then persuade him to wait so you can get a senior colleague to talk to him.

D.   Sedate Mr Jones and contact your registrar so he may come to help.

E.   Call security to restrain Mr Jones.

Question 32

You are the cardiology junior doctor and on a consultant ward round you see that Mr Dzeckvic has not been receiving his important anti-hypertensive medications. The nurse has written that they are not available on the ward. However, you are aware there are many other patients on the same medications on the ward who have been receiving it appropriately.

Rank in order the following actions in response to this situation (1= Most appropriate; 5= Least appropriate):

A.   Tell the consultant about the omission and say that you will talk to the nurse and the pharmacist to ensure he receives all of his appropriate therapy.

B.   Write this on the drug chart: "Please find and give this medication!!!"

C.   Ask the nurse looking after the patient whether there is any problem with the medication or patient you should know about. If you have concerns that the patient will continue to not receive the medications then talk to the charge nurse.

D.   Complain to the charge nurse about the lapse of care and ask her to put a different nurse in charge of your patients.

E.   Investigate the matter and write up an incident form.

Question 33

You are a junior doctor on vascular surgery and are asked to clerk in Mr Goffman. On doing so, you establish that the patient is a heavy smoker but is very interested in quitting.

Rank in order the following actions in response to this situation (1= Most appropriate; 5= Least appropriate):

A.   Offer him some smoking cessation advice and nicotine replacement therapy.

B.   Wish him luck and suggest he looks on the NHS website.

C.   Acknowledge his intentions but being realistic, accept it probably won't happen.

D.   Offer to refer him to the smoking cessation clinic and find a leaflet for him to read in the meantime.

E.   It is far too late to help him now and he is probably only saying these things because he wants to please you as the doctor.

Question 34

You are one of two vascular surgery house officers on the day shift. Your colleague asks if you will hold both of the bleeps so he may go into theatre and says he is not sure how long he will be absent for. The wards are currently quiet and there are no pressing outstanding jobs to complete.

Rank in order the following actions in response to this situation (1= Most appropriate; 5= Least appropriate):

A. Take the bleep and agree that next time an opportunity arises you can go to theatre whilst they cover the ward.

B. Explain that you really want to go to theatre and ask if they will cover your bleep instead.

C. Ensure you take an appropriate handover and have a way to get hold of them in theatre if you need to.

D. Go down to theatre with your colleague and observe un-scrubbed whilst covering the bleeps.

E. Tell them that it could get very busy and you should both just wait on the ward in case someone becomes acutely unwell.

Question 35

You are clerking in a patient with whom you have developed a great rapport. At the end of the clerking the patient offers you a £10 tip. He will not take no for an answer and says he will leave it on his bed if you refuse it.

Rank in order the following actions in response to this situation (1= Most appropriate; 5= Least appropriate):

A. Take the money and consider setting up a tip jar. Doctors, after all, do a lot more work than waiters.

B. Take the money and use it to buy the ward a box of chocolates.

C. Leave the money on the bed for the cleaners.

D. Suggest he instead sends a nice thank you card to the ward staff instead with a box of chocolates.

E. Declare the money to the charge nurse and ask if you can put it in a kitty for the ward Christmas party.

Question 36

You are coming to end of your shift after a busy day on cardiology. You are due to handover to the night junior doctor but they are busy in the emergency department and will be another hour at least. You have a train to catch in 10 minutes to get home for a social engagement with your partner – but you know you will miss your train.

Rank in order the following actions in response to this situation (1= Most appropriate; 5= Least appropriate):

A.   Join your colleague and handover whilst they examine a patient in the emergency department.

B.   Write a list detailing all of the patients you need to handover including any outstanding jobs and leave it in the doctor's office.

C.   Write a list of your patients and investigations and take it to the emergency department. Give it to your colleague and then go home.

D.   Go to the emergency department and when your colleague has a spare moment, handover face-to-face away from other patients.

E.   Phone your partner to inform them you will have to get the later train.

Question 37

You are a junior doctor on a busy medical ward round and you realise you have misplaced your patient list. On retracing your steps you find Mr Jacobs, one of your patients, sitting in bed reading the list full of confidential information.

Rank in order the following actions in response to this situation (1= Most appropriate; 5= Least appropriate):

A.   Take the list off Mr Jacobs and scold him for reading it.

B.   Politely ask Mr Jacobs for the list back and then ask him if there are any concerns he has about anything he read on the sheet.

C.   Retrieve the list and explain to Mr Jacobs that it is very sensitive information and to please keep it confidential.

D.   Explain the situation to your registrar to determine if any further action is needed.

E.   Ensure the patient hasn't read anything about himself to cause concern and explain the confidential nature of the material.

Question 38

You see a 29 year old lady in the GP practice who wishes to be referred to a gynaecologist for sterilisation. She already has two children aged 3 and 5 and wants a definitive method of birth control. She has requested that you do not mention anything to her husband who has an appointment with you later that day. He still wishes to have at least two more children and she does not want to tell him until after she has been sterilised.

Rank in order the following actions in response to this situation (1= Most appropriate; 5= Least appropriate):

A.   Refer her to the gynaecologist straightaway.

B.   Tell her husband when you see him later that afternoon.

C.   Discuss alternative methods of contraception with her.

D.   Encourage her to talk to her husband herself.

E.   Suggest that she considers asking her husband to get a vasectomy.

Question 39

During a surgical ward round you realise that your consultant has intentionally missed out seeing a patient. She is known to be a troublesome patient to deal with due to her constant moaning about abdominal pain and background of multiple psychiatric problems. The patient has had a surgical cause for her abdominal symptoms ruled out and the general medical team are not convinced there is a medical issue here that they need to treat either. Given these factors, the consultant wants her to be discharged.

Rank in order the following actions in response to this situation (1= Most appropriate; 5= Least appropriate):

A.   Discharge the patient even though she still has symptoms which are unaccounted for.

B.   Tell your consultant that the patient needs to stay in hospital until the medical team can be convinced to properly review the patient.

C.   Try and talk to the medical team again, emphasising that a surgical problem has been ruled out and that her symptoms are unaccounted for.

D.   Try and get another team, such as a psychiatric team, to take over the patient's care as soon as possible so that they are not wasting space on the surgical ward.

E.   Review the patient's notes and investigations again and look for any other possible cause of her symptoms.

Question 40

You are a junior doctor working on a late shift. On more than one time, you notice your fellow junior doctor stealing printer paper, pens and a stapler from the ward office and putting it in her bag. The same day after one occasion an email is sent out pleading for any members of staff who have information about printing supplies going missing from the office.

Rank in order the following actions in response to this situation (1= Most appropriate; 5= Least appropriate):

A. Wait until your colleague steals something of considerable value before you report her.

B. Speak to your colleague directly about the matter and convince her to hand back the stolen equipment.

C. Report the incident to your registrar and ask them to deal with the matter.

D. Ask other colleagues on the ward if they have noticed anything unusual.

E. Do not do anything as it you may be interpreting her actions wrongly and do not want to cause friction or be thought of as a 'snitch'.

Question 41

Your registrar wants you to speak to a consultant radiologist to arrange a scan for a complicated ward patient who has had several operations and is currently an inpatient with multiple complex medical issues. You do not really understand what the scan is for or what the team is worried about with regards to this patient.

Rank in order the following actions in response to this situation (1= Most appropriate; 5= Least appropriate):

A. Request the scan from the radiologist, but guess at the answers when they ask you questions about why the scan is needed.

B. Ask your fellow junior doctor to request the scan instead.

C. Go and request the scan from the radiologist, but ask them to contact your registrar for more information if they start to ask you questions.

D. Ask the registrar for more information about the patient's clinical history and what sort of issues they would like the radiologist to rule out with a scan.

E. Ask your senior house officer to clarify why the scan is required.

Question 42

You are a junior doctor working in the emergency department. You see a patient who has sustained a head injury but who cannot speak any English. He is accompanied by his cousin who is translating for him. However, you notice that the cousin is not translating everything the patient is saying. You note that the history about how the patient sustained the head injury is very vague. The patient seems to be talking a lot but the cousin keeps saying "he doesn't know how it happened" when you ask how the patient was injured.

Rank in order the following actions in response to this situation (1= Most appropriate; 5= Least appropriate):

A.   Politely ask the cousin to leave the consultation room and see if you can obtain an interpreter to discuss this matter with the patient.

B.   Ask the cousin to carry on translating while awaiting an official interpreter.

C.   Obtain an interpreter to discuss this matter with the patient.

D.   Attempt to communicate with the patient using non-verbal methods.

E.   Obtain a CT head scan without bothering to translate the circumstances of the head injury as getting a history will not change your immediate investigation plan anyway.

Question 43

You are a junior doctor on a GP rotation. One of your patients recurrently presents with abdominal pain and is deeply concerned that he is suffering from cancer. He has had numerous investigations for the pain, including several abdominal ultrasound scans, which have been normal. The patient insists that he be referred to the on-call surgical team for admission to hospital immediately.

Rank in order the following actions in response to this situation (1= Most appropriate; 5= Least appropriate):

A.   Tell the patient that he is wasting your time and apologise that you cannot help him.

B.   Reassure the patient that all the investigations have excluded an organic cause, and it is unlikely that he has cancer.

C.   Contact your senior colleague to come and reassure the patient about these episodes.

D.   Explain to the patient that it may be more appropriate for him to be seen as an outpatient and refer him to a general gastro-intestinal clinic.

E.   Refer the patient to the chronic pain team to help control his symptoms.

Question 44

You are a junior doctor working in general medicine and on the ward round you realise that you had prescribed antibiotics for the wrong patient. They have already started the course of antibiotics despite not having an infection, and the patient who needed the antibiotics has not had any prescribed!

Rank in order the following actions in response to this situation (1= Most appropriate; 5= Least appropriate):

A.   Try and cover up your mistake by rewriting both drug charts with the correct medications.

B.   Do not inform anyone about your mistake and continue as normal.

C.   Inform and apologise to both the patients for your mistake and correct this on the drug charts.

D.   Inform your senior colleagues regarding the mistake and get their advice.

E.   Inform your fellow junior doctors about the situation so that they can learn from your mistake.

Question 45

You are the junior doctor in the emergency department and are seeing a patient who you clinically diagnose with a pulmonary embolism. A CT pulmonary angiogram has been requested but due to portering issues, the patient is left waiting for some time before she can have her scan. She becomes rather impatient and tells you that she cannot wait any longer and needs to go home as she has childcare issues.

Rank in order the following actions in response to this situation (1= Most appropriate; 5= Least appropriate):

A.   Allow her to leave as she has mental capacity, but ensure she signs a self-discharge form.

B.   Take her to a side room and explain what may happen if she self discharges without proper medical work-up of her presenting symptoms.

C.   Explain to the patient that a pulmonary embolism can be lethal and her life may be at risk.

D.   Contact the patient's GP for a follow-up appointment should she continue to feel unwell.

E.   Encourage the patient to wait at least for the CT pulmonary angiogram scan and results so that the team can be completely sure that nothing worrying is present.

Question 46

You are a junior doctor on a urology rotation in a teaching hospital. One of the medical students asks you if they can help to catheterise a patient. They have never watched or performed one before. They have only learnt the theory behind the procedure in lectures but seem eager to be involved.

Rank in order the following actions in response to this situation (1= Most appropriate; 5= Least appropriate):

A.   Do the procedure yourself while the student watches, and explain to them what you are doing as you go along.

B.   Ask the student to insert the catheter under your supervision and tell them you will talk them through it.

C.   Explain the procedure to the student first, then, at a convenient time ask them to get some practice on mannequins first before practising on a patient.

D.   Ask the student to try their best and to insert the catheter unsupervised.

E.   Explain the procedure to the student when you next get a free moment.

PART TWO – Multi-Action Questions

Question 47

You are on-call and carrying the general medical bleep when a patient's family member confronts you. He states that he is not happy with the level of care his wife is receiving and says he will make a complaint to the hospital. The patient is under the care of a different medical team. You do not know the patient and therefore have no idea of their progression nor any mismanagement. You are very busy with other on-call duties and feel the relative's attitude is rather rude.

Choose the THREE most appropriate actions to take in this situation:

A.   Threaten to call security and tell the relative that you do not like the tone of their voice.

B.   Tell the patient that he should be grateful for the level of care his wife is receiving.

C.   Explain to the relative that you are very busy and the best you can do is to return later in the evening (if you have time) to discuss this matter further.

D.   Tell the relative that you have just been bleeped and really need to answer the call. Try to find an excuse to leave the ward and not return until the relative has left the hospital.

E.   Advise the relative that if he would like a frank discussion with a member of his wife's medical team, it would be better to wait until the morning when they are back on duty again.

F.   Tell the relative that you are too busy to deal with his concerns and ask him to find another doctor to complain to.

G.   Offer the relative the chance to speak to the head nurse in charge as she will have a better grasp of all the patients on the ward and may be able to answer and deal with any complaints.

H.   Apologise to the relative and explain that you are unfortunately unfamiliar with his wife's condition or treatment on the ward.

Question 48

Your team has just reviewed a young teenage boy who was admitted with diabetic ketoacidosis and has been newly diagnosed with type 1 diabetes mellitus. The patient's parents are due to visit him in a few hour's time and your consultant would like you to discuss the results with the family and answer any questions they may have.

Choose the THREE most appropriate actions to take in this situation:

A. Explain in depth the pathophysiology of diabetes and the differences between type 1 and type 2 diabetes mellitus.

B. Encourage the family to ask questions or to get you to repeat any information they do not understand. Ask the patient if he has any particular concerns to address.

C. List in detail all the potential complications that may result from untreated diabetes and the likelihood of each of these occurring.

D. Arrange and encourage the patient to visit the diabetic specialist nurse.

E. Briefly explain to the family that diabetes is a complicated disease and hand them an information leaflet. Tell them to contact you after reading the leaflet if they do not understand.

F. Advise the patient that he should not be allowed to drink any alcohol or eat any sugary foods from now on as this will make his diabetes worse.

G. Explain that diabetes will require lifestyle changes, insulin injections and regular checkups but that it is a very manageable disease.

H. Tell the patient that there are worse diseases to be suffering from than diabetes and he should not be too depressed.

Question 49

You are a junior doctor working in a GP practice. A 17 year old girl attends your clinic session in tears and breaks down sobbing in front of you. She is very worried that she may be pregnant after only one episode of unprotected intercourse the day before with an older man in his thirties and would like to book in for a termination.

Choose the THREE most appropriate actions to take in this situation:

A. Call up her parents and request that they schedule an appointment to see you as soon as possible.

B. Inform the school that she will need time off due to medical sickness.

C. Ask her to contact the possible father and explain the situation.

D. Offer the patient advice on longer term contraception and give the patient leaflets on safe sex and sexual health.

E. Suggest that she has a test to confirm pregnancy with a view to a termination of pregnancy if the test is positive.

F. Commend her for seeking medical advice promptly. Enquire sensitively whether the intercourse was consensual and that the patient was not abused or coerced.

G. Take a full menstrual and gynaecological history from the patient, and if clinically appropriate, offer the patient the option of taking an emergency contraceptive pill.

H. Encourage the patient to confide in her parents for emotional support.

Question 50

You are a junior doctor working on the medical assessment unit (MAU). A patient has been recently admitted with multiple non-specific symptoms of fatigue, weight loss, recurrent infections and fever. As you review the blood tests and imaging findings that have been completed for your patient, your registrar notices that a test for HIV has not yet been performed. He asks you to obtain a blood sample and send this off for HIV testing.

Choose the THREE most appropriate actions to take in this situation:

A.   Prepare your usual equipment to take blood and do not inform the patient what the tests are for unless he specifically asks you.

B.   Discuss the potential consequences of a positive HIV result and how this test result may alter his management.

C.   Explain in clear detail to the patient why you are performing a test for HIV.

D.   Tell the patient that it is routine to perform an HIV test on all patients in the hospital and try to make the test seem less daunting than it might otherwise.

E.   Explain to the patient that you think he probably has HIV and ask him if this has been confirmed before. Tell him that this is the reason you are doing the test.

F.   Document in the notes that consent has been taken and that the patient understood the request.

G.   Instruct the nurses to consent the patient while you prepare the equipment.

H.   Call the haematology laboratories and ask them to add on a 'retroviral HIV test' to the blood sample they already have from earlier in the day without speaking to the patient.

Question 51

You are a junior doctor working on a general surgical firm. Mr Josephs has been in hospital for 3 days post-open appendicectomy and is recovering very well. He approaches you on the ward and explains he needs to go home urgently as his pregnant daughter has just been taken to a different hospital in labour. You remember the consultant on the morning ward round was happy for him to go home but decided to keep him in one more day to observe him. Your senior house officer and registrar have been called to a trauma call in the emergency department and you cannot get hold of them.

Choose the THREE most appropriate actions to take in this situation:

A.   Explain to Mr Josephs that if he leaves he does so against medical advice.

B.   Ask Mr Josephs to wait until you can get hold of your seniors to check whether it is safe for him to leave.

C.   Discharge the patient and document that the consultant did mention keeping the patient in hospital for an extra day for precaution's sake.

D.   Tell Mr Josephs if he leaves the hospital you cannot help him if he has any complications.

E.   Let the patient leave after contacting your consultant to double-check that he is comfortable about the patient leaving.

F.   Ask security to restrain the patient until you have found your seniors.

G.   Discuss this scenario with your educational supervisor at your next meeting together.

H.   Reassure Mr Josephs that he will be able to leave soon but you need to get a senior doctor to see him first.

Question 52

As a junior doctor, you are expected on your medical firm to take part performing on-call duties one weekend in every two months. Unfortunately your department has been poorly staffed recently and you have been asked to cover more on-call shifts. As a result you feel that when you return to your normal duties you are not up-to-date on the progress of your patients and in addition you are staying at work for longer hours to complete your jobs. You are starting to feel over-worked, tired and poorly supported.

Choose the THREE most appropriate actions to take in this situation:

A. Come into work an hour earlier and stay on afterwards to try and read up on the patients you know little about and finish all the work you have been given.

B. Prioritise your workload. Do whatever jobs you feel you can to the best of your ability and handover any urgent unfinished jobs to the night team.

C. Report the situation to your consultant and medical staffing in the hope that they may be able to arrange cover for the time you are away or better, to cover the extra on-calls you have been made to do.

D. Raise the issue during the week to your clinical and educational supervisor to try to come to an agreement on how the logistics of the team can be better managed.

E. Discuss your situation with other junior doctor colleagues to see if they are experiencing the same problems on their rotations.

F. Do nothing as previous Foundation doctors have informed you that they have had similar experiences and that this is normal.

G. Ask your senior colleagues to spend more time on the wards to assist you in ward cover rather than clerking in new patients.

H. Write a letter of complaint to the trust and ask for immediate change and compensatory salary for the overtime you have been putting in.

Question 53

Mr Wells is a 54 year old gentleman who has just been diagnosed with type 2 diabetes. Your registrar has just seen him in clinic but he has a lot of other patients still to review. He asks you to help him by speaking to Mr Wells and giving him some advice regarding lifestyle changes he can make to control his diabetes. Mr Wells appears relaxed about discussing lifestyle changes with you so long as you don't bring up his smoking habit. He tells you that smoking is something he is not going to be happy to quit!

Choose the THREE most appropriate actions to take in this situation:

A.   Prescribe nicotine replacement therapy and offer the patient a leaflet with instructions to read himself.

B.   Explain to Mr Wells the importance of healthy eating and compliance with medical treatment. Regular exercise, as well as stopping smoking, both have a role in controlling diabetes.

C.   Apologise for bringing up smoking cessation with him but encourage him to try to quit or cut down this habit, even if it is just by a little bit to start off with.

D.   Increase all of the doses of the diabetic medication Mr Wells has been prescribed by the consultant saying that this way he can eat more sugary foods whilst still being 'extra' controlled by the medicines and will not need to make such big lifestyle changes.

E.   Encourage Mr Wells to buy a dog to motivate him to go running or walking in the park.

F.   Refuse to speak to Mr Wells as you do not feel you have enough expertise to discuss lifestyle matters with the patient.

G.   After briefly discussing the main points of lifestyle change with the patient try to refer him to a dietician, his local GP 'Stop Smoking' services and specialist diabetic nurse clinic for further ongoing monitoring of his diabetes and lifestyle changes.

H.   Review Mr Wells' medical history and discuss the pathophysiology of diabetes and how it causes health complications.

Question 54

You are the junior doctor on an obstetrics and gynaecology rotation. A young woman presents at 41 weeks gestation to the labour ward. Her labour is not progressing naturally and the cardiotocogram (CTG) readings suggest signs of foetal distress. She has been assessed by your registrar who recommends an emergency caesarean. The patient is clearly distressed and upset at the thought of this news as it was not part of her birthing plan. She is refusing to consent to the procedure.

Choose the THREE most appropriate actions to take in this situation:

A.   Get her husband to sign the consent form instead as he appears to have a better grasp of the situation.

B.   Proceed with the caesarean anyway in the best interests of the baby.

C.   Contact the registrar or consultant on-call for advice and explain that the patient is having concerns regarding the operation.

D.   Explain to the patient that this is an emergency and that without a caesarean there is a high chance that the baby may be severely compromised or in the worst case scenario, not survive the delivery.

E.   Assertively describe the importance of swift action to the patient and say that time is not on their side at the moment.

F.   Consider prescribing the patient tocolytic medication to speed up a natural delivery.

G.   Suggest to your registrar that they may be able to use forceps or a ventouse for an assisted vaginal delivery.

H.   Give an anxiolytic to the patient to calm her down and then try to consent her again in about 20 minutes when she is a bit more relaxed.

Question 55

You are a junior doctor working on a medical oncology firm. One of your patients is very ill with pancreatic cancer. His niece, who lives in Australia, has contacted the ward and would like to speak to you. She sounds extremely anxious on the phone and keeps asking you lots of questions about her uncle's condition and prognosis.

Choose the THREE most appropriate actions to take in this situation:

A.   Answer her questions to the best of your ability.

B.   Explain that the best thing to do would be to contact her uncle directly via his mobile.

C.   Ask the niece to call your registrar for more detailed answers about her relative's condition.

D.   Apologise to the niece but explain that in the interests of patient confidentiality you are not able to divulge any information over the telephone.

E.   Suggest that the patient contact their uncle directly and ask him to tell her all the information personally if he is happy with this.

F.   Suggest that the niece should take time off work to come in to the hospital if she wishes to know more information.

G.   Tell the niece that she needs to be officially listed as a patient's next of kin for the hospital to divulge any private personal details about the patient.

H.   Speak to the patient and ask him if he is happy for you to speak to his niece and if so, tell her all the details of his treatment so far including his medical management plan.

Question 56

You are a junior doctor working on a gastroenterology firm. The consultant is reviewing a patient and as part of his examination he would like to perform a rectal examination on the patient. He asks you to help him get some gloves and lubricating jelly whilst he positions the patient. On returning with the equipment the nurse in the bay rudely refuses to let you back into the patient's bed space saying that the consultant is about to perform a private examination and doesn't want too many unnecessary doctors watching.

Choose the THREE most appropriate actions to take in this situation:

A.   Demand the nurse allow you into the bed space and push her aside as she is wasting time.

B.   Explain the situation clearly to the nurse. She may not have understood that the consultant sent you to get some equipment for him and expects you in the bed space.

C.   Stay outside the bed space with the gloves and jelly. Wait for your consultant to call you in or just explain to him what happened later.

D.   Ask the nurse why she is refusing to let you pass.

E.   Shout to your consultant through the curtain telling him that you are not being let back in.

F.   Show the nurse all the equipment you have gathered and explain that this is necessary for the consultant to perform the rectal examination.

G.   Complete a clinical incident form.

H.   Arrange to talk to the nurse later to discuss your clinical relationship and in particular her obstructive attitude towards you.

Question 57

You are a junior doctor on a general medical firm. One of your patients has taken a turn for the worse and you have been performing daily blood tests to monitor the progress of the patient's health. On your way home after work, you suddenly remember that you have forgotten to check the blood result for this particular patient and did not hand this task over to any of your colleagues who are on-call. You are due to meet a friend for dinner and are running late so would rather not head back to the hospital.

Choose the THREE most appropriate actions to take in this situation:

A.   Make plans to attend hospital early the next morning to check the blood results.

B.   Rely on the hospital laboratory to call the ward if any of the results are abnormally high, which will hopefully trigger the nurses to call the on-call doctor if needed.

C.   Contact the on-call doctors via the switchboard and ensure that this task is handed over.

D.   Go back to the hospital to review the patient and bloods yourself.

E.   Give the on-call doctor a brief history of the patient should any issues relating to the blood results arise.

F.   Request that the on-call doctor document the bloods in the patient's notes.

G.   Call your registrar and explain your mistake.

H.   Call the ward and ask the ward sister to check the blood results.

Question 58

You are a junior doctor on a general medical firm and notice that one of your patients is having difficulty swallowing. A nasogastric tube has been inserted this morning and the dietician has drawn up a feeding regimen for the patient. Your registrar asks you to request a chest radiograph to ensure that the tube is correctly sited before the feeding regimen is started.

You receive a bleep from the radiographer later in the evening who tells you that she does not believe the patient needs the chest radiograph as they had one performed yesterday.

Choose the THREE most appropriate actions to take in this situation:

A. Accept that the patient did have a chest radiograph already and start the feed as you don't want the patient to be exposed to more radiation than necessary.

B. Try and aspirate contents from the nasogastric tube. If you are able to aspirate gastric contents, then you will cancel the chest radiograph request.

C. Explain to the radiographer that the radiograph is for assessment of a nasogastric tube placement and is therefore essential.

D. Tell the radiographer that they should be performing the radiograph as you requested it and if not, you will be filling in an incident form.

E. Document in the notes your conversation with the radiographer mentioning that they are refusing to perform the radiograph.

F. After the chest radiograph has been obtained, assess the position of the nasogastric tube. If appropriately sited, commence the feeding regimen for the patient.

G. Contact the registrar to ask for his assistance in explaining the situation to the radiographer.

H. Convince the radiographer to take the chest radiograph. If the nasogastric tube is found to be incorrectly sited then attempt to re-site the tube.

Question 59

A young woman attends the emergency department late one night with her 9 year old son who appears distressed and complains of severe abdominal pain. Your senior colleague diagnoses the patient with diabetic ketoacidosis and you discover from his previous medical history that he has had several similar admissions in the past month. The mother apologises and complains that her stressful job and irregular working hours prevent her from attending her local GP surgery where she needs to obtain a repeat prescription for her son's insulin injections. She is well aware of the consequences of poorly managed diabetes.

Choose the THREE most appropriate actions to take in this situation:

A. Consider contacting social services after consultation with your senior and the paediatricians.

B. Stabilise the patient according to the ABC algorithm and ensure the patient is well resuscitated.

C. Contact the on-call paediatrician for specialist advice and to admit the patient.

D. Call the police as you feel this parent is guilty of child abuse by neglect.

E. Do nothing. It is not your place to intervene in this situation and you are sure that a more senior colleague will handle this instead.

F. Discharge the patient and give the mother a repeat prescription for her son's insulin.

G. Discharge the patient and ask the mother to see the GP for a repeat prescription of her son's insulin in the morning.

H. Ask the diabetic specialist nurse to speak to the mother.

Question 60

You have just completed your first surgical on-call shift when you suddenly realise that you have accidentally given an increased dose of an anti-hypertensive drug to one of your patients. As this incident was earlier on in the morning the drug has already been administered to the patient. You have not been bleeped about the incident yet today.

Choose the THREE most appropriate actions to take in this situation:

A.   Fill in a clinical incident form regarding your mistake.

B.   Discuss the event with your team during the ward round the following day.

C.   Review the possible side effects that could result from an overdose and correct the prescription error on the drug chart.

D.   Be honest with the patient and inform them of what has happened. Ensure that you have documented the event in his medical notes.

E.   Contact a senior colleague to inform him of the event, and ask him how to proceed.

F.   Do nothing. It is probably only a mild overdose and if you haven't been bleeped by now by the nursing staff then the patient is probably all right.

G.   Hand it over to the on-call night team to sort out without mentioning it was you who had written up the overdose by accident.

H.   Contact the on-call pharmacist.

Question 61

You are the on-call junior doctor for general medicine. You are asked to see a 45 year old female patient who has just been admitted with abdominal pain. She reports that she is in "unbearable agony". Of note, her past medical history includes chronic back pain, multiple sclerosis and rheumatoid arthritis. She claims that she regularly takes oramorph (morphine) 30 mg four times a day and wants you to prescribe this for her.

Choose the THREE most appropriate actions to take in this situation:

A.   Contact the patient's GP to confirm whether she is meant to be taking regular oramorph.

B.   Ask the patient to arrange for someone to bring in her regular oramorph from home as you are hesitant to prescribe such strong controlled drugs yourself.

C.   Prescribe the patient simple analgesia such as paracetamol and codeine with a low dose of oramorph to take when required until you can contact her GP to confirm her regular medication.

D.   Prescribe her the usual 30 mg qds oramorph as you sympathise with the patient and cannot bear to see her in such agony.

E.   Inform the patient that she will be unable to receive such a high dose of oramorph whilst in hospital and that you do not believe that she is able to have such high doses at home.

F.   Ask the specialist pain nurse to review the patient and give you advice about pain relief.

G.   Contact the on-call medical registrar to review the patient. Seeing a patient in such agonising pain could signify a serious medical problem and you don't want to be missing a serious medical diagnosis.

H.   Arrange an urgent ultrasound scan of the patient's lumbar spine as you believe there must be something severely wrong and an urgent imaging investigation is warranted.

Question 62

You are a junior doctor working in the emergency department. You have just reviewed a 20 year old female who you suspect is suffering with appendicitis. During a senior review your consultant, tells the patient that it would be in her best interests to be admitted to hospital and she will require an appendicectomy. The patient is unhappy with the management plan and demands to self-discharge claiming that she will lose her job if she takes any more days off work and that she would rather go home and take painkillers.

Choose the THREE most appropriate actions to take in this situation:

A.   Ensure that she understands that appendicitis is a surgical emergency and what the risks are of leaving the condition untreated.

B.   Convince the patient to stay in hospital explaining that if she self discharges and things get worse, the surgical team will not treat her as she has refused their advice.

C.   Inform her that if she were to go home, it would be against medical advice. If she is worried about work, the consultant may be able to contact her boss or write a letter explaining the gravity of the situation if needed.

D.   Call the hospital security to watch the patient and prevent her from self-discharging.

E.   If the patient continues to refuse to be admitted, allow them to go home but suggest they return to hospital should the abdominal pain worsen.

F.   Tell the patient to "stop being silly" and to stay in hospital as the consultant has requested it and "he knows best".

G.   Book the patient on the emergency surgery list anyway as you know this is for her own good and you are acting in the patient's best interests.

H.   Call the patient's family and friends and try to convince them to persuade her to follow medical advice.

Question 63

You have just started your first job as a junior doctor. You were initially quite disappointed as you had hoped to be offered jobs with the chance of doing a lot of general medicine but instead were given a job with a heavy surgical slant. You are still keen to get an insight into general medicine but you are not sure how to go about this with the jobs you have been allocated.

Choose the THREE most appropriate actions to take in this situation:

A.   Accept that you will not get any experience of general medicine this year and leave the rest of your rotations to fate.

B.   Try to spend some time hanging around in the general medicine department during your surgical rotations and try to get involved in the medical patient care.

C.   Complain to your supervisor that you do not want to do any of the rotations you have been given and would rather quit.

D.   Keep an eye out for patients with general medical problems on the surgical wards that you can be actively involved in.

E.   Try to help with jobs on the general medical rotations that your colleagues are working on at the expense of your surgical ward commitments.

F.   Try to determine whether there is a chance that you can apply for a Foundation year 2 post in more medical rotations and continue with the firms you have been allocated for your first hospital jobs.

G.   Complain that the way in which you were allocated your hospital jobs was extremely unfair.

H.   Try to see if it would be possible to swap one of your surgical rotations with another junior doctor who may be more surgically minded and allocated more medical jobs than they would have liked.

Question 64

You have just started your first job as the junior doctor on a general surgical firm. You are interested in surgery and delighted when the consultant asks whether you would like to come to theatre to help scrub up for an emergency laparotomy. To do this, however, it is your duty to ensure another junior doctor can 'cover you' and deal with any medical emergencies that arise for the duration you will be in theatre. You try to ask a junior doctor colleague but they tell you that they are already too busy and can't possibly accept the extra workload.

Choose the THREE most appropriate actions to take in this situation:

A. Go into surgery anyway and tell the scrub nurse that if your bleep goes off they should contact your other colleague, even though they have already told you they are very busy.

B. Tell your colleague to stop complaining and just get on with the workload as you really need to get experience of the surgery.

C. Tell your colleague that you will help him cover some of his shift next time if he wants to get involved in a case interesting to him.

D. Tell the surgeon that you unfortunately cannot scrub in and blame your junior doctor colleague as the reason.

E. Inform the senior house officers about the situation and ask them to support the other junior doctor if the workload becomes too heavy. Only go to surgery if they are comfortable about this.

F. Tell the surgeon that you cannot come this time (but might be available later on during your on-call shift) as there are too many sick patients and ward jobs at the moment to complete.

G. Ask the surgeon to tell your registrar to help with the ward tasks so that you can come and scrub in.

H. Complain about your junior doctor colleague to their educational supervisor.

Question 65

As part of your Foundation training programme you are expected to complete a 'multi-source feedback' assessment where you ask different healthcare professionals to complete an anonymised online feedback assessment form relating to their opinion of you as a doctor. The results are now available and you find that one person has written comments on the form that you believe are unfair. Although you are uncertain who this person is, you think you have a good idea and feel that their comments may be unfair.

Choose the THREE most appropriate actions to take in this situation:

A.   Accept you cannot get along with everyone and try to see if you can use whatever comments that have been made about you to improve your future clinical practice and dealings with colleagues.

B.   Ask your supervisor to release the feedback forms so you can see who and what was written even though you know that this is not allowed.

C.   Approach the person you believe wrote the comments on the feedback form even though you cannot be sure that this is actually the person in question.

D.   Tell your supervisor that the comments stated were unfair and the person who wrote them probably had an ulterior motive.

E.   Reflect upon the comments made and write about them in your 'reflective comments' section of the portfolio.

F.   Make a formal complaint against the person you believe wrote the comments because you think that person has been unprofessional and unfair.

G.   Try to understand why the comment has been made and take up any concerns with your educational supervisor.

H.   Refuse to do anymore assessments for the rest of the year citing that they are all rubbish and do not accurately reflect your performance as a doctor.

Question 66

Whilst doing an on-call shift you walk past a patient on the ward who appears distressed, short of breath and has a red rash over their torso. On examination the patient is tachycardiac, tachypnoeic and also has a very low blood pressure. You suspect the patient is having an anaphylactic reaction and feel this is beyond your competency to deal with. You are not sure what dose of adrenaline is needed. You are also uneasy about leaving the patient to call your senior and do know not what to do.

Choose the THREE most appropriate actions to take in this situation:

A.   Find the nearest resuscitation trolley and give the pre-drawn adrenaline intra-muscularly immediately.

B.   Shout for help and ask the nurse or healthcare assistant to dial 2222 for the cardiac arrest team.

C.   Try and see if the patient has a secure airway and administer high flow oxygen.

D.   Attempt to do an arterial blood gas (ABG) to see if the patient is hypoxic.

E.   Wait and see what happens as the reaction may die down of its own accord.

F.   Ask the nurse to bleep the on-call anaesthetist to come as soon possible.

G.   Try to take some blood from the patient.

H.   Try to obtain intravenous access.

Question 67

Your registrar has asked you to perform a routine ABG (arterial blood gas) on one of your patients. Despite having done many ABGs before, you seem to be struggling with this patient. You have already tried three times with no result. The nurse suggests that someone more senior should perform the examination as the patient now appears a little distressed. You are embarrassed and think that your registrar might humiliate you for struggling with such a standard procedure.

Choose the THREE most appropriate actions to take in this situation:

A. Apologise to the patient for hurting them and ask them whether they are OK for you to continue or if they would like you to stop.

B. Politely ask the registrar if they might be able to help you with the ABG even though you feel rather embarrassed about asking for help.

C. Ignore the nurse and keep trying as many times as possible. It is very important you obtain a blood sample.

D. Ask if the registrar could help to supervise you doing the ABG and step in if needed or give you some advice on how to perform the procedure better.

E. Ask the nurse to perform the ABG.

F. Leave the patient alone and stop trying to get an ABG. It could probably wait until tomorrow.

G. Bleep the on-call respiratory registrar and ask them to come and do the ABG on your patient.

H. Attempt to do a femoral arterial stab.

Question 68

You are one of the junior doctors on the medical team and have just finished a busy ward round. After the ward round you sit down to split all the jobs generated with your senior house officer colleague. You have been asked to obtain a blood sample from a patient who is notoriously difficult to bleed and who in the past has needed a femoral venepuncture. You have never performed or witnessed this procedure in the past.

Choose the THREE most appropriate actions to take in this situation:

A. As there are many jobs that have been created by the busy ward round, you prefer not to make too much of a fuss and will try to attempt the procedure to the best of your ability.

B. Read up online about how to perform a femoral venepuncture. Give it one go and if you are unsuccessful then contact a senior colleague.

C. Leave this task to the end of the day and if it doesn't get done then pretend you just didn't have time to do this rather than admit you weren't sure how it is performed.

D. State your concerns immediately to a senior member of your team.

E. Ask whether you might be able to watch someone else perform the task first then attempt it under supervision on the next occasion.

F. Attempt to bleed the patient using their arm veins rather than a femoral venepuncture. If it looks like you will need to do a femoral venepuncture then find a senior to help you.

G. Ask to be talked through the procedure by your colleague and then attempt to perform it on your own.

H. Accept that being a junior doctor is a steep learning curve and that you will be doing procedures that you may not be entirely comfortable with.

Question 69

You are a junior doctor working in obstetrics and gynaecology. The mother of a patient who had just given birth to a healthy baby girl asks to see you privately on the ward. She expresses her gratitude for the care you have given to her daughter and gives you an envelope with £30 cash in it.

Choose the THREE most appropriate actions to take in this situation:

A.   Thank the relative for their generosity but tell them that this really is not necessary.

B.   Thank the relative for her kindness and request that she does not tell anyone else about this gesture.

C.   Suggest that she donate the money to the ward staff and midwives who also took care of her daughter if she refuses to take back the money.

D.   Suggest that she donates the money to a charity instead.

E.   Take the money and go out and buy everyone snacks.

F.   Take the money and inform the rest of the staff about her gratitude.

G.   State that you are happy that you could help and that you were only doing your job.

H.   Ask the relative to give the money to your consultant instead.

Question 70

You are a junior doctor working in general medicine and one of your medical students asks you to sign off his clinical attachment book which says that he is competent at examining the abdomen. You know this student is competent and have seen him perform an abdominal examination on several occasions but next to the space where you should sign there is some small text that clearly states the book can only be signed by a senior house officer or above.

Choose the THREE most appropriate actions to take in this situation:

A.   Sign the form as you have seen him competently carry out an abdominal examination.

B.   Persuade your senior house officer to sign off the medical student as you have seen him perform the examination well even though they have not witnessed this.

C.   Tell the medical student that you are not officially allowed to sign the form therefore he should contact a senior member of your team.

D.   Sign the form, but clearly document that you are only a junior doctor.

E.   Advise the medical student that he is more likely to gain structured feedback from a senior colleague and it would therefore be beneficial for him to be seen doing the examination by a senior member of the team.

F.   Contact your senior house officer and request that he make time to observe the medical student examine an abdomen.

G.   Forge your senior house officer's signature as you know that he won't mind you doing this and you have seen his signature several times in the patient's notes and are pretty good at forging a true likeness.

H.   Tell the medical student that you cannot assist him and apologise.

Answers to Examination 2

PART ONE – Answers to the Ranking Questions

Answer Question 1

BADEC

An important conversation like this one will require documentation so that any family or patient views and wishes can be recorded and so this information can be relayed by the team. A good junior doctor will only document the major points discussed and the overall plan (bullet points will suffice). The next best thing would be to document everything that is mentioned, although this can be cumbersome to read through and does not convey the key information in a clear way. It is important to note the views of the patient, family members and the team, not just the main outcome of the discussion. Writing down nothing and coming back later to document leaves room for error as crucial details may be missed out or inaccurately remembered. An alternative to writing everything down could be to write down what you can and then clarify with the consultant as you go along. The only downfall of this method is that it would interrupt the discussion.

Answer Question 2

BDCEA

Seeing as the team is managing with the workload well without much strain, it would appear that there should be no harm in expressing the fact that you want more hands-on opportunities to your consultant. Alternatively, you could ask your colleagues to kindly handover interesting cases to your attention for personal interest and learning. This may avoid any confrontational issues unlike option A, whereby all three junior doctors may be competing for some surgical exposure, although it does rely on your senior colleagues having an interest in teaching. The next appropriate option could be to arrange a taster week of pure surgery within the department where you could obtain further first-hand experience of surgery. However, if you do feel strongly about surgery and the current job does not allow for any opportunities, then perhaps switching to a job that does (after speaking to your educational supervisor and consultant) is a feasible option.

Answer Question 3

BCDEA

Taking leave can be an issue if not arranged properly and adequate cover is not ensured. You are entitled to take all of your leave but you also need to make sure that some members of the team are around to care for your patients. The best option is to ask the consultant for his opinion as he will have an idea of how busy things may get in the coming month and keeping him informed and 'in the loop' will prevent any unpleasant repercussions later on. If the consultant appears not to show much interest, then organising leave with the whole team present is the next best option. It is unreasonable for everyone to cancel their leave and even if you do not get your ideal time, a compromise that benefits everyone, whilst maintaining high standards of patient care, should be made.

Answer Question 4

CDAEB

Initially you should speak to your colleagues about their feelings and encourage them to discuss the situation with their consultant or educational supervisor. Speaking to a senior colleague on your firm (such as the registrar) is better than speaking to a consultant on a different firm. Involving the programme director could be an option if the situation escalates and requires input from the Foundation Programme or deanery level. Your parents may be interested in the matter but their input will not do much to help your colleague and may stir up more trouble.

Answer Question 5

ABCDE

If you believe that the absence of your colleague for this brief period of time would not endanger your patients by leaving you without support, then it would be kind of you to help your colleague to get the experience that would be useful in their career progression. You must ensure, however, that should you require extra support that they can be contacted easily and are willing to come back to the ward, should this be necessary.

Answer Question 6

BECAD

All patients who are not British citizens may be required to cover the full cost of their medical treatments in the NHS. Even though this could result in a large amount of money to some patients, you should offer the patient the option of paying for their treatment on the NHS if this is what they would prefer. If the patient finds surgery unaffordable on the NHS, an alternative option would be to enquire whether they would consider having their surgery in their home country. If this is also not a possible option, alternative therapies that may be more affordable could be entertained, providing there is clinical need for this and the patient understands the risks and prognosis of not undergoing surgery as other options such as chemo/radiotherapy will probably be of limited value. Despite having good intentions, surgery should not go ahead if the patient cannot pay for the option unless this happens to be urgent life-threatening emergency treatment.

Answer Question 7

CDABE

The GMC's *Good Medical Practice* guidance states that "wherever possible, you should avoid providing medical care to anyone with whom you have a close personal relationship". Your friend should therefore register with a local GP.

As a junior doctor you are technically not given prescription rights until you have been working in a clinical environment for at least one year and have gained 'full' (as oppose to 'provisional') GMC registration. You are only allowed to prescribe on the wards and within the hospital under the supervision of a senior colleague who has full registration. Therefore you cannot ask your friend (option A) or write a private prescription (option D) yourself. Option D, however, is probably the most appropriate of the remaining four options though as you are still encouraging your friend to see a GP. Although you should not put your colleague in a difficult position by asking them to prescribe the medication, it is worse to just take medication from your hospital ward drugs' cupboard. In option B, it is suggested that you are asking for some sort of permission but in option E, the actions are akin to stealing from the wards, which is a serious offence. Stealing from the hospital could result in being reported to the GMC for probity issues.

Answer Question 8

CBADE

In this situation you are dealing with a complicated patient. Although it seems reasonable that that patient may be started on the Liverpool Care Pathway, this is not your decision to make and your registrar, consultant or the palliative care team should be consulted. In the meanwhile, however, the patient is experiencing some symptoms which you could easily be resolved by intravenous medication. Simple analgesia and anti-emetics can be prescribed until a formal decision has been made. If it is difficult to get a formal opinion, then you should continue to write up the medication that the patient usually takes. It is unreasonable to not give any treatment or medication until a biopsy is taken as the patient is clearly suffering and it may be some time before a biopsy can be performed.

Answer Question 9

ADCEB

This is a difficult case and ultimately if you feel out of your depth you should contact your senior colleagues for help. Initially you should discuss with the patient her reasons for refusing the transplant and thoughts behind this. You should assess her competence and understanding of the consequences of her actions and then contact your senior colleague for back up. Family members, if aware of the patient's situation and if the patient is happy to have them involved, can be consulted. It is wrong to tell the patient that they must go through with the operation after signing the consent form – it is the patient's prerogative to refuse the operation up until right before they are anaesthetized, even if they have already signed their consent form. A consent form is not legally binding.

Answer Question 10

CAEDB

Always have a holistic approach to patient care and alert colleagues to any problems the patient may be suffering, even if they are more senior than you are as they could be preoccupied with other thoughts. Before speaking to your consultant, you should thoroughly assess the situation to ensure you are not mistaken. Only once you have discussed the patient with your seniors can an appropriate referral to another speciality be made.

Answer Question 11

BDEAC

Patient confidentiality must be maintained at all times and personal information should never be given out over the telephone. Even if you have obtained consent from the patient, it is difficult to be certain that the person on the telephone can prove who they say they are.

Answer Question 12

ABECD

Patient confidentiality is paramount. Even by removing patient names, close relatives will be able to work out who you are referring to. To be safe it is better to refrain from any talk about patients outside the hospital setting.

Answer Question 13

DCABE

Consent for medical treatment or surgery in a minor is required from the patient's parents except in an emergency situation. Therefore in this case, you should not withhold live-saving treatment even if you are unable to obtain parental consent. In a non-urgent setting, only a parent or a legal guardian can give consent for a minor.

Answer Question 14

BCEDA

Attending teaching is a key part of Foundation year training. If you are having problems with this you should talk to someone who can help. It may be that your consultant doesn't realise you have teaching so they should always be your first point of contact. Your educational supervisor or Foundation Programme director are alternative senior colleagues you can contact if you are still having problems with your consultant releasing you from clinical duties for your teaching sessions. You shouldn't struggle alone and under no circumstances ask a colleague to forge your signature.

Answer Question 15

CDABE

This is a brilliant learning opportunity for both the students and yourself, and so the ideal option would be to refresh your knowledge of this condition before seeing the patient with your students. If you do not have time to review the condition, you can ask your consultant to teach you quickly about the vital points so you can relay this information to the students. Reading the medical notes may help you understand the presenting complaints and subsequent treatment options, but if the patient is not presenting in a classical way then it may be confusing to the students. It would be unwise to miss a teaching/learning opportunity by cancelling the session.

Answer Question 16

CBDAE

This question probably boils down to individual choice, as some people function better than others with differing amounts of sleep. However, if you feel exhausted and assisting in theatre would be unsafe, it is important you say this and try to find alternative cover. If this is not possible, your consultant should at least be aware of how you feel. Agreeing is acceptable only if you are happy to stay and feel safe to work.

Answer Question 17

BCDAE

Teamwork is one of the key competences that junior doctors should demonstrate on the Foundation Programme. You should offer your services to another team if you notice they are struggling with their workload and may not be able to complete all their jobs. If possible you can also try to fit in working on your audit, as this is also an important skill to learn and will check whether the correct standards of care are being maintained.

Answer Question 18

EACDB

Assessment of an acutely unwell patient in a medical emergency should occur without delay. Once you have carried out initial assessment and management, as a junior doctor you should never be afraid of contacting senior help. If a patient has a low blood pressure or other early warning scores (e.g. tachycardia, tachypnoea) each hospital will have a system in place of who to contact. This should be your priority first before continuing to work through your jobs list. Calling your seniors if you feel overwhelmed or unable to manage is always acceptable, but ideally it should be after you have assessed the patient initially yourself and started life-saving treatment such as giving the patient oxygen.

Answer Question 19

EBCDA

The initial best step would be to try and resolve the issue internally. It could be that your colleague is having personal issues, and discussing these with him may help you reach an understanding. If this fails, discussion with your supervisor should be the next step as they may be able to get through to your colleague or recommend that he steps down from the audit. Continuing your own share of the work is important and audit work is an important part of training and CV building. Replacing your colleague may be an option but it may not be your decision to make. Withdrawing from the audit is the worst option as both the opportunity and the findings will be lost.

Answer Question 20

BACED

This particular patient could easily have fallen and injured himself. If possible you alone can take the patient back to his bed, but a professional trained in manual handling may also be required. The ward manager should be alerted as to the unfolding of these events and the physiotherapists should also be informed so they can offer their input. The patient should be counselled and advised to stay on the ward until he is steadier on his feet.

Answer Question 21

CDABE

Here there is an evident patient safety issue. You first priority is to stabilise the patient and carry out initial management steps. It is appropriate to call your registrar to ask for advice regarding further management.

Answer Question 22

CABDE

The law clearly states that a minor under the age of 13 is not competent to enter into a sexual relationship, and thus the situation would be considered rape. In this case, patient confidentiality must be breached and this must be reported. As you are a junior, it may be out of your depth to call the police immediately, and hence it may be better to get a senior colleague involved before you do so. It would be most appropriate to contact the child protection lead of the hospital, who would be able to coordinate the necessary people to investigate the matter further.

Answer Question 23

BACDE

This scenario requires you to take responsibility for an error that is ultimately your own fault as you should always double-check the expiry date on the vial of local anaesthetic that you administer. It is best practice to be honest with the consultant and the patient and check with a senior colleague whether any further changes to the patient's management will be required. To prevent further harm to other patients, it is appropriate to check the expiry dates of all the vials of local anaesthetic in stock and also to fill out a critical incident form.

Answer Question 24

ABEDC

As the patient is not acutely unwell or requiring emergency treatment, there is no urgency or need for you to return to the hospital to complete the task. It is better to handover the task to another, doctor who will be present in the hospital and who is capable of carrying out the task. In this instance, handing over the task to the on-call junior doctor is appropriate, however, if they cannot be reached, you may wish to speak to the senior house officer as well. Option D is vague and does not state whether you have asked the night team to prescribe the fluids. Option C is the worst as it clearly puts the patient at risk.

Answer Question 25

ABCDE

To avoid awkward situations like the one in this scenario, it is advisable to discuss such sensitive matters with family members when the decisions are made rather than to let them find out by themselves through other means. The family and patient should be allowed to ask questions freely and you should document your discussions in a detailed manner in the notes. Your team should be made aware of the discussion so that they can understand what has been said to the family for future reference. The decision to place a 'do not resuscitate order' is a medical one and not one that the family members can overturn. If they are displeased with the order, they should be referred to a senior colleague who can try to discuss the situation further.

Answer Question 26

BCAED

You should at first apologise to the patient. You can try again in a while but three attempts is already quite a few. Documentation is vital so that people know why a line is not in place. If another doctor is available then try and get them to have a go. If at all preventable, the patient should not be left without a line. If there is no other option for administering the antibiotics, you may wish to consider altering the dose to an oral dose so that at least it does not get missed, but this should be discussed with a senior colleague first.

Answer Question 27

BCDEA

It is important to stabilise the patient you are seeing before you attend to the next patient. In the meantime, you should contact the senior house officer on-call to ask him to help to review the patient with chest pain if he is available as he may be able to review the patient sooner than you can. It is also wise to ask the referring nursing staff to perform any appropriate investigations in the interim and to obtain as much history from the senior sister as possible. This will allow medical management plans and decisions to be made quickly and appropriately.

Answer Question 28

AEBCD

Patient care is always the top priority in good medical practice. If a patient is unwell and needs urgent medical attention you must always offer your assistance regardless of job boundaries. However, having said this you should still act within your limitations and not perform any procedures that you have not been trained in. Never ignore a bleep as you never know when an emergency can arise or when your help is urgently required.

Answer Question 29

BCDAE

In this case the patient is being violent to staff but due to his history of alcohol abuse and acute confusion it is difficult to hold him accountable for these actions. As you have not assessed the patient yet, you should not dismiss him from the hospital as he may need medical treatment. In the first instance, you should try to calm the patient down and if that does not work, the hospital security can assist in restraining him in order to prevent harm to other doctors and patients. Sedation should be a very last resort as it can worsen the patient's confusion.

Answer Question 30

CDBEA

Patients have the right to the most appropriate medical care. In the acute presentation, your role should be to direct the patient to the most appropriate place of care, which would be the emergency department. If you are unsure then it is acceptable to contact a senior colleague for advice. In this scenario you could also encourage the patient to see their GP for follow-up. You should not prescribe any medications to patients not under your care or without having assessed them fully to rule out any underlying serious conditions.

Answer Question 31

CBAED

Always maintain civility in difficult situations and contact a senior colleague for support as soon as you feel out of your comfort zone. Your last resort should be to medically sedate the patient.

Answer Question 32

ACEDB

The consultant in charge should be made aware of the incident in the first circumstance on ward round so that they may alter their medical management of the patient if appropriate and not misdiagnose any condition which is not present and can easily be explained by a lack of the patient's normal treatment. As part of demonstrating good communication skills, you should never automatically jump to conclusions about a colleague's ability, and always attempt to discuss the matter with the person in question first. There may be a perfectly reasonable explanation why the patient has been omitted from receiving their usual treatment which has not been relayed to the medical team.

Answer Question 33

DABCE

Good clinical care must include providing appropriate advice. Although you can provide some information for the patient, dedicated smoking cessation clinics will have the required expertise and resources to help patients quit smoking and can offer support groups to encourage patients further.

Answer Question 34

CDABE

Continued education is an essential aspect of good medical practice. As long as a thorough handover is done and that if needed, you can both return to the ward, then doctors should be encouraged to take these learning opportunities as they arise.

Answer Question 35

DEBCA

Tokens of appreciation are a difficult area of medical ethics and law. Ideally you should not accept anything of significant value from a patient. If you do, then this should be declared. Ideally it should be shared with all members involved in the patient's care. Never take any money without informing other staff members as this could easily be misconstrued as bribery. Always be aware that it is a tricky situation that requires a lot of care and due diligence.

Answer Question 36

EDCBA

Although consistently staying late is unadvisable, in this case it is needed to ensure an adequate handover. Handovers should be done face-to-face where possible with adequate time to fully explain any outstanding jobs, putting patient safety at the forefront. It should never be done at a patient's bedside due to the compromise of patient confidentiality.

Answer Question 37

ECBDA

It is important to maintain patient confidentiality but sometimes situations like this can occur. Getting the list returned to you is your primary concern, as is ensuring the patient understands the confidential nature of the material he may have read. The patient may have read something about himself which could cause distress and it is important to account for that.

Answer Question 38

CADEB

The decision to undergo sterilisation should be a fully informed one, so you should run through all treatment options for long-term contraception with the patient first. You should also note her young age and appreciate she may change her mind later on in life. However, if she is adamant, you should refer her to a gynaecologist as they will also fully consent and explain the alternatives to the patient. You cannot make the patient talk to her husband, but you could explore her reasons behind not doing so. Vasectomy is a quicker procedure and is actually safer. You should by no means break patient confidentiality by informing her husband yourself.

Answer Question 39

CBEDA

All patients should be reviewed by a senior colleague on the ward round or at least have their clinical issues declared once reviewed by a junior doctor. In this case it is advisable that you involve a multidisciplinary approach for a difficult patient with a complex history and re-review any abnormal findings or investigations in the hope this will throw up some new leads on where to take the management further. If a patient is genuinely unwell and a cause cannot be found for their condition, it is unsafe to discharge them without a proper follow-up or management plan in place.

Answer Question 40

BCDAE

Option B would be the best option although it may appear to be confrontational if handled wrongly. You can report the incident to the registrar and discuss the issue directly with your colleagues. By doing this you take decisive action and at least then someone senior can deal with the situation through the correct channels. Option A does not take any immediate action and option E is worse as no action at all is taken.

Answer Question 41

DEBCA

Asking for more information is clearly the best option. Speaking to the radiologist and then asking them to contact your registrar for more information is not ideal, but it is better than guessing at answers, as this could compromise patient care and is unsafe.

Answer Question 42

ACBDE

In this case it is important that you obtain an accurate history from the patient, and ascertain what has happened. It is best not to use a family member as an interpreter as you cannot necessarily rely on them interpreting the whole situation clearly without any prejudice. It would be most appropriate to obtain an interpreter and ask the cousin to leave the consultation room. Attempting to communicate with the patient non-verbally using body language and diagrams is clearly better than refusing to see the patient at all.

Answer Question 43

BCDEA

This patient is clearly very anxious and hence it is most appropriate in such a situation to explore the patient's concerns and reassure him that he does not have cancer. Contacting your senior colleagues and referring the patient to the surgeons as an outpatient would be appropriate. Referral to the chronic pain team is also a good idea.

Answer Question 44

CDEBA

It is important to be honest, apologise to the patients and rectify your mistake. Informing other members of staff is better than not telling anyone. Trying to cover up the mistake is unprofessional and is gross misconduct.

Answer Question 45

BCEAD

The patient should be reviewed in a quiet environment with the potential consequences of a diagnosis of pulmonary embolism explained. She should be encouraged to wait for her CT scan so that she can be given treatment if required. If she still decides to leave, then a self-discharge form should be signed and her GP should be made aware of the events that have occurred so that a follow-up can be arranged if the patient continues to feel unwell.

Answer Question 46

ACEBD

The best way to teach the student how to perform a catheterization is to let them watch you and to explain in real time what you are doing. As the student is familiar with the background theory, he/she should be able to attempt the procedure after watching you a few times. Such a procedure can only be learnt from practical exposure so if the first option is not possible, then they should practise their skills on a mannequin instead. Although not ideal, explaining how you would perform catheterization can help with improving their technique. Students should in no circumstances undertake procedures without having seen it being performed properly before and must be supervised at all times.

PART TWO – Answers to the Multi-Action Questions

Answer Question 47

EGH

Unfortunately, there may be occasions where patients or their relatives are not happy with their level of care or wish to make a complaint. According to the GMC's *Good Medical Practice*, "Patients who complain about the care or treatment they have received have a right to expect a prompt, open, constructive and honest response including an explanation and, if appropriate, an apology."

In this scenario you are not the doctor most familiar with the patient's current circumstance and may have several other acutely unwell patients to deal with. If the patient in question does not require emergency treatment, you should speak to the relative and honestly explain who you are and why you may not be completely aware of the current situation (option H). Explain that they may get a better explanation from the patient's usual medical team (option E) or arrange for someone who is familiar with the situation (option G) to meet the relative who may be able to help deal with the matter.

In an ideal situation, where you do not have other duties to attend, you may wish to try to understand the situation, note the relative's complaints and relay these concerns to the patient's usual medical team the next day, but this is not one of the options listed. Option C is not one of the most appropriate responses here as there is the danger that you may not have time to return to speak to the relative and they may feel even more upset at being ignored or not having their concerns taken seriously.

Answer Question 48

BDG

Good communication skills are crucial to being a good doctor. You should listen carefully to your patients, respect their views and encourage them to ask questions. If patients do not understand what is being explained then you should make arrangements to meet their language and communication needs.

In this scenario we know the patient has presented for the first time with a new diagnosis and will have many questions to ask which should be encouraged (option B). An explanation of lifestyle changes (option G) and referral to a specialist (option D) can help the whole family take in the situation better.

Although leaflets (option E) are a good method of communicating a large amount of information, they should not be a substitute for good verbal communication. Listing multiple complications (option C) or going into depth about diabetes (option A) are not appropriate at this early stage. Telling the patient that they should not drink alcohol or eat any sugary drinks is inaccurate information as it is not necessary to completely cut out these foods entirely in the diet (option F).

Answer Question 49

DFG

In this situation, the patient appears to fully understand her situation and has attended the GP surgery for advice on termination of pregnancy. As her only episode of intercourse with the older man was one night previously it is impossible to determine whether the patient is pregnant or not at this stage (therefore performing a pregnancy test is futile as in option E). If the patient is competent and certain that she would not want to continue with the pregnancy should it occur, you may wish to counsel her on taking the morning-after pill or advise her to have a copper coil inserted straightaway (option G).

To prevent the patient from finding herself in a similar situation in the future, advice on safe sex should be given (option D). In addition, patients view clinicians as trustworthy members of society and in delicate issues regarding sexual intercourse, especially younger patients; it is always worth asking whether the intercourse was consensual (option F). You may be the first and only person the patient has confided in about this issue and the first person to potentially discover whether the patient is being abused by their partner.

Encouraging the patient to confide in family and friends (option H) may be appropriate but in the immediate situation, this is not the most appropriate action.

Answer Question 50

BCF

When screening a patient for HIV, it is important that you realise you cannot just take blood without telling the patient specifically what it is for or without their consent. You should clearly explain to the patient why they are being tested for HIV (option C), including the potential change and consequences to their management (option B). The patient should also be told that he will be informed as soon as the results are back and that all information will be kept confidential. It is important not to jump to conclusions regarding the results of the test before they are finalised (option E) given the sensitive and chronic nature of the disease.

In some hospitals there is a specific consent form that needs to be signed when consenting a patient for HIV. If you are uncertain regarding the type or amount of information you should be giving the patient you can always ask for advice from your senior colleagues or the HIV specialists within your hospital (who may sometimes also be covered by the infectious diseases specialists if there is not a dedicated HIV specialist).

Answer Question 51

BEH

According to the GMC's *New Doctor* publication, "Foundation doctors should always have senior support available to them." You are not in a position to discharge ward patients without senior advice and if you cannot get hold of your senior house officer or registrar then you should attempt to speak to your consultant to double-check the current situation (option E). Despite what the consultant may have said on the ward round, if he decided to still keep the patient in hospital, it was for a valid medical reason.

If you feel that the situation is not urgent and that your senior house officer and registrar will be available for advice soon, then you may be able to persuade the patient to remain in hospital until this time (options B and H). If you cannot get the patient to wait or get hold of any seniors then you should inform the patient they are discharging themselves against medical advice (option A).

Answer Question 52

CDE

The current situation is clearly compromising patient care and safety and is a matter for medical staffing to rectify due to poor staffing levels.

It is important that you do not ignore the situation and raise the issue to your senior colleagues, if they have not already recognised this issue already. The first port of call would be your clinical and educational supervisors (options C and D) who may be able to relay the issue to more senior hospital management and the staffing department.

You should try your best to continue with your daily tasks and prioritise your workload to the best of your abilities (option E), but coming into work earlier or working later (option A) will only worsen your tiredness and may further compromise patient care.

Answer Question 53

BCG

This scenario is centred on communication skills and promoting patient health. Although the patient may not want to discuss the issue of smoking, it is important to make them realize that even cutting down the number of cigarettes (option C) can be beneficial and very effective at reducing the risk of cancer and heart disease. You may wish to suggest he should take nicotine replacement patches (option A), although seeing as the patient has not been thinking about quitting, this action may be slightly premature until further discussion has taken place.

Referral to a diabetic specialist nurse (option G) and a dietician are good initial steps and allow for a more holistic management approach. Buying a dog (option E) does not take into account the patient's other accommodation circumstances or the views of his family members who may be against such a decision.

Increasing the medication doses that the patient is taking (option D) is an unsuitable decision for a Foundation doctor to make without having a more complete history or discussion with senior colleagues.

Answer Question 54

CDE

This scenario is centred on understanding your clinical limitations as a Foundation doctor and elements relating to patient consent. There is no reason in this vignette to suspect that the patient lacks the capacity to consent for a caesarean section and you should not ask her husband to consent on her behalf just because you believe he understands the situation better (option A). It may be that she requires extra explanation about the procedure and the urgency of the situation (options D and E). The most appropriate doctor you seek help from should be the registrar or consultant who will be carrying out the operation (option C).

Your senior colleague has already assessed the patient and implemented a management plan. As a junior doctor, it is not your place to change the plans by prescribing tocolytics (option F) or sedatives (option H), which may interfere with the anaesthetic that will be administered unless you have discussed this beforehand.

Answer Question 55

DEH

This is a scenario relating to patient confidentiality and communication. As a junior doctor, you will be required to frequently liaise with families and keep them updated about their relative's condition, however, you must be wary of divulging information inappropriately and breaking confidentiality.

The most appropriate actions would be to apologise to the niece (option D) for not being able to give the information straightaway, take a contact number and speak to the niece after obtaining consent from the patient (option H). Alternatively you may let the patient know that his niece is concerned and if he wishes to discuss his health matters, he can speak to his relatives directly himself (option E).

The relative does not need to be officially listed as a next of kin (option G) or be present in the hospital (option F) to obtain information about the patient if the patient has specifically expressed consent for the relative to be informed. Asking the niece to contact her uncle directly by mobile (option B) may be a good alternative, but on certain wards, mobile phones are not permitted to be used if they interfere with equipment and sometimes network services may be erratic.

Answer Question 56

BDF

This scenario is concerned with dealing with colleagues and communication skills. It is important to bear in mind that whatever conflicts you encounter at work, they should not interfere with patient care.

The most likely explanation in this scenario is that the nurse in question is trying to maintain patient dignity and has not recognised that you have been given a task by the consultant. It is important that you explain this to her (options B and F) and if there is still some conflict, enquire why she is not letting you pass (option D). Rudeness or trying to undermine the nursing staff in question before any proper explanation or reasoning has occurred will only serve to escalate tension on the medical ward.

Answer Question 57

CEF

This scenario is testing your ability to communicate and delegate tasks to your colleagues. As a doctor caring for a patient, it is your duty to check the results of any tests that you order and act upon these should they be abnormal.

Although you have not checked the blood result for the patient in question, it is now past your working hours and you have already left the hospital. It is important that the task is performed, but not essential that you return to hospital if there is a responsible and capable doctor able to carry out the task for you.

You should contact the on-call doctor (option C) and clearly explain the situation and task (option E) including what should be done with regards to patient management (option F). Calling other members of your team to explain that you made a mistake when they have already left the hospital (opinion G) is not useful and asking the ward sister to check the results is less than ideal as she may not be the most suitable person to deal with any abnormal results (option H).

Answer Question 58

CFH

This situation is assessing your communication skills with other members of the healthcare profession and clinical judgement. If the radiographer is refusing to perform the chest radiograph, it may be that they have not been made aware of the clinical need for the investigation. The indication for the radiograph should be clearly explained. Although a chest X-ray was performed the previous day, that was prior to the nasogastric tube insertion and therefore a further X-ray is required now (option C). Miscommunication is often the stem of issues in a working environment.

Once the radiograph is obtained, it is vital to assess the results of this and act appropriately (options F and H). You must not start the feeding regimen without confirming the correct position of the nasogastric tube as the patient may be put at risk of aspiration.

Answer Question 59

ABC

This scenario deals with the sensitive issue of child abuse. Your first priority is to patient care and the young child should be resuscitated (option B) and referred within the hospital for specialist care regarding their diabetic treatment (option C).

Although the mother gives a credible excuse for not picking up the insulin prescriptions, the clinical case states that this is a recurrent problem and the parent is not ignorant of the long and short-term consequences of her actions. As a junior doctor, you may feel out of your depth in this situation and you should enlist the help of a senior colleague prior to contacting the social services (option A).

Unfortunately, child abuse is not an uncommon situation and paediatric doctors are generally well informed and knowledgeable about how to coordinate the necessary services required in investigating the matter further.

Answer Question 60

CDE

It is important to be honest about your mistakes and take steps to correct these as soon as you recognise they have occurred. According to the GMC's *Good Medical Practice* guidelines, "If a patient under your care has suffered harm or distress, you must act immediately to put matters right, if that is possible. You should offer an apology and explain fully and promptly to the patient what has happened, and the likely short-term and long-term effects."

To this end, you should review the patient to ensure they have come to no harm and explain the situation to them (option D). In addition, you should check that the appropriate measures are put in place to prevent the situation recurring and rectify any mistakes (option C). Involving a senior colleague (option E) will make sure that you are taking the appropriate steps.

Although discussion with your team during the ward round (option B), filling in a clinical incident form (option A) and contacting the on-call pharmacist (option H) are all suitable actions, they have the least immediate impact on the patient's current health and safety.

Answer Question 61

ACG

GMC guidelines clearly state that doctors must "prescribe drugs or treatment, including repeat prescriptions, only when there is adequate knowledge of the patient's health, and that the drugs or treatment serve the patient's needs".

Giving the patient the high dose of morphine she suggests without confirming that it is indeed her regular medication is dangerous and could potentially lead to an opiate overdose if the patient is not accustomed to such high doses. You should treat the patient with adequate pain relief for their presenting complaint, and when writing up their regular analgesia, it is recommended that the 'WHO ladder of analgesia' is adhered to by initially prescribing a lower dose of a regular non-opiate drug with stronger analgesia to take as required for 'breakthrough pain' (option C). The medication may be titrated to higher doses to help alleviate the patient's increased pain if necessary.

As pain is a subjective response to a stimulus, not all 'agonising' pain may signify a serious medical illness. However, in this situation the patient does have a rather extensive complicated past medical history and complains of pain that is not usual or expected for her situation. If you feel out of your depth and unable to handle a medical condition, senior advice should always be sought (option G). Advice from the patient's GP (option A) can help confirm the patient's regular prescriptions. Urgent imaging may be warranted, and if this is the case the most appropriate imaging may include a plain radiograph of the lumbar spine to identify an acute fracture or MRI imaging to identify neural involvement. Ultrasonography of the lumbar spine (option H) is not an appropriate indication for severe back pain of this nature.

Answer Question 62

ACE

In cases where the competence of a patient is not questioned, one must respect patient autonomy, even if the medical situation is an emergency. The GMC's *Good Medical Practice* guidelines state that "you must be satisfied that you have consent or other valid authority before you undertake any examination or investigation, provide treatment or involve patients in teaching or research."

The most appropriate action to take would be to inform the patient of the risks of leaving hospital against medical advice and consequences of untreated appendicitis in addition to the potential benefits and risks of having an appendicectomy (option A). By engaging the patient in this discussion, you empower them and allow them to reach a balanced and informed decision themselves. By acknowledging the patient's ideas, concerns and expectations (as suggested in option C), you can help maintain patient confidence, trust and alleviate their anxieties. This may make them more open to following your suggestions.

You are not allowed to force or detain a competent patient to undergo a medical procedure against their wishes (options D and G) and you should not breech patient confidentiality by speaking to their friends and family members without patient consent (option H).

If despite giving the patient all available information, they still intend to leave, you should ensure that they understand what to do if their situation worsens including 'warning symptoms' to look out for. It is wise to also advise them that they should be accompanied at home by a responsible adult in case they deteriorate and are not be able to call for help themselves.

Answer Question 63

DHF

Unfortunately it is not always possible to get the ideal rotations you apply for in Foundation training. However, the jobs are all designed to provide junior doctors 'balanced' training in general medical and surgical management.

If you are interested in a specific field of medicine, you can maximise your learning opportunities by getting involved in audits, case reports or research in topics that interest you (option D). If this is not feasible then the next best option could be to apply for a future job in your second year of Foundation training in the specialty you would like, otherwise if done well in advance, there are chances to swap jobs with other colleagues if you are both doing jobs that you would rather swap out of (options F and H).

Answer Question 64

CEF

Despite having such a good learning experience presenting itself to you, your primary responsibility is to complete your general ward duties. If you cannot find a colleague willing to cover you, you could try to negotiate a way in which you might be able to both gain from the situation (i.e. by agreeing to cover for them next time, option C) or arranging a more senior doctor to help cover (option E).

It would be wrong to ask the surgical registrar to help with the ward tasks as they are required in theatre with the consultant in most cases (option G) and also wrong to go to theatre without adequate cover for your ward patients (option A). If you really cannot arrange to go to theatre, you should apologise to your consultant and if still interested, ask that they continue to inform you of future learning opportunities (option F).

Answer Question 65

AEG

According to the *New Doctor* publication, "feedback about performance helps to identify strengths and weaknesses, both in Foundation doctors and in the training provided, allowing changes to be made." It is therefore important that no matter how irrelevant you believe the feedback you receive, that you reflect upon the comments (option E) and try to understand why these have been made (option G).

If you find that such comments are unfair, you should speak to your educational supervisor (option G) regarding the matter and use it as a way of improving and changing your future practice (option A). The feedback forms are purposely anonymised so that they cannot be traced back to the person who wrote them, thereby encouraging honest suggestions for improvement. Involvement in completing academic assessments are compulsory in Foundation and specialty training and refusal to participate (option H) will not allow you to complete and proceed to the next stage of your training.

Answer Question 66

ABC

This scenario is concerned with understanding your clinical limitations and asking for help. You have correctly identified the problem with the patient but are uncertain how to go about resolving this emergency situation.

As the patient is in shock and in a peri-arrest situation, you should dial for the cardiac arrest team (option B). You can also begin by instigating emergency resuscitation by assessing the airway, breathing and circulation of the patient as well as administering oxygen (option C).

The correct dose of adrenaline in cases of anaphylaxis is 0.5 mg of 1:1000 adrenaline administered intra-muscularly. This medication can be found in pre-drawn aliquots in the resuscitation trolley and is the single most important agent to administer in this situation (option A). Obtaining blood (option G) and intravenous access (option H) is less important than the administration of adrenaline in the setting of anaphylaxis.

Answer Question 67

ABD

There will be times where for no apparent reason you cannot do a procedure despite having performed this before. You should make the care of the patient your primary concern and should refrain from hurting the patient further and apologise if you feel that this is the case (option A). After trying your best to perform the procedure, the best option would be to seek senior advice and help (option B and D).

Asking the nurse to perform your duties (option E) or asking someone from another medical team (option G) are not appropriate as the nurse may not be trained to do this procedure and members of another medical team may have their own duties to attend to. A femoral stab (option H) can be an alternative to obtaining arterial blood gas, but is more intrusive and in some cases can be more painful.

Answer Question 68

DEF

It is important for any doctor of any level to be aware of their clinical limitations and know when to ask for advice and help. According to the *New Doctor* publication, "Foundation doctors (should) only undertake tasks in which they are competent or are learning to be competent in with adequate supervision." Therefore you should not under any circumstance attempt a procedure you have never performed or seen (unlike in options A, B, G or H).

You should state your concerns about performing the procedure (option D), ask if someone might be able to supervise you (option E) or attempt a different method of gaining a venous sample of blood (option F).

Answer Question 69

ACG

According to the GMC *Conflicts of Interest* guidelines, "You must not encourage patients to give, lend or bequeath money or gifts that will directly or indirectly benefit you, nor must you put pressure on patients or their families to make donations to other people or organisations."

By thanking the relative, you are acknowledging that they are grateful for your help and care (options A and G) but you should not accept the money or suggest other members of staff to accept the money (option H). If the relative is still insistent on donating the money to the healthcare professionals, you may suggest that the money be put towards the ward fund (option C), but you must not place any pressure on her to do this if she does not wish to.

Answer Question 70

CEF

This scenario is based upon the theme of honesty and probity. The GMC states on this issue that "Probity means being honest and trustworthy, and acting with integrity: this is at the heart of medical professionalism."

Although you have seen the student carry out a competent abdominal examination, the form states that the supervision should be that of a senior house officer or above. You should therefore advise the student to ask your senior house officer (option C) to sign the form and if the senior colleague has not witnessed the student perform the examination, to suggest that they repeat this in the presence of a senior colleague (option E). You may be able to help the student contact your senior colleagues on their behalf if they do not know how to get hold of them (option F). Signing the form but explicitly stating your rank as a junior doctor (option D) is another alternative, however, it is less appropriate than the other correct options listed as this may make the student believe they have been 'signed off' for the task and as a result become less likely to seek the approval of a more senior clinician. In all other options, you would not be acting with honesty.

Examination 3

PART ONE – Ranking Questions

Question 1

Your hospital has received some criticism lately from the local newspaper following a patient's death, of which you are aware. This has led to several changes in the hospital and many consultants unhappy with working conditions. Whilst working in a busy emergency department you get called by the senior sister to take a phone call from the same journalist who wrote the article. You ask someone senior to take the call but they are too busy and tell you to just hang up or swear at him, considering how his article has made things worse.

Rank in order the following actions in response to this situation (1= Most appropriate; 5= Least appropriate):

A.   Get the doctor who told you to hang up or swear at him to speak to the journalist himself, despite them saying they are too busy.

B.   Tell the journalist that someone will address his questions when they are free.

C.   Hang up on the journalist and tell him to stop calling.

D.   Tell him that you are not in a position to comment and put the phone down.

E.   Ask him to go through the official channels such as the trust press officer if he wants a reaction about the criticism.

Question 2

A fourth year medical student has asked you for a favour. He only has one more day until he has to hand in his sign-off sheet and needs one more DOP (directly observed procedure) to complete the sign off. He says that he has inserted a cannula but the doctor (your colleague) who observed him has already left the hospital and now he wants you to sign it. You have a few cannula insertions which need to be done and you are happy for him to do these, but he is eager for you to sign his sheet now and wants to go home.

Rank in order the following actions in response to this situation (1= Most appropriate; 5= Least appropriate):

A.   Tell him that you are in no position to help him and ask the student to find the relevant doctor who supervised him when the doctor next gets into work tomorrow.

B.   Find out if your colleague can sign the sheet for the student before the deadline, even though they have already gone home for the day.

C.   Tell the student you would be happy to sign them off but you want to first observe him do the procedure yourself and then sign the form accordingly.

D.   Sign off the DOP with your signature despite your colleague observing him and not you.

E.   Ask him to try and get another procedure done before the deadline and get it signed by one of the other doctors he is attached to instead.

Question 3

After finishing a lengthy ward round you sit down with your two senior house officers to split the jobs. There is a whole array of jobs to be done in a short amount of time including checking results, organising investigations, taking bloods and making referrals. What is the best way to organise the jobs considering your expertise as a junior doctor and that of your two senior house officers?

Rank in order the following actions in response to this situation (1= Most appropriate; 5= Least appropriate):

A.   Get the most experienced senior house officer to do most of the jobs as they are the most senior and hence least likely to make a mistake.

B.   Prioritise the jobs and do the tasks that need to be done urgently, splitting them according to each of your expertise and competency.

C.   Try to take on more complex jobs such as difficult procedures by yourself as that can ease the workload of your senior colleagues.

D.   Try to take on the routine jobs yourself and let the two senior house officers do the more demanding ones such as complicated referrals or difficult procedures.

E.   Do all the routine jobs (i.e. taking blood from stable patients) later on as they are less urgent and might not affect patient care, and help the senior house officers with the more complex tasks.

Question 4

Whilst writing up a patient's drug chart, a patient confronts you requesting nicotine replacement patches. You are aware that the patient has a 20 pack year history of cigarette smoking. On reading the notes, he has tried patches on numerous occasions, each time failing to quit smoking and he even continued to smoke whilst taking patches on a previous admission.

Rank in order the following actions in response to this situation (1= Most appropriate; 5= Least appropriate):

A.   Prescribe the patches, but ensure the patient is aware of how to use them properly.

B.   Do not prescribe the patches as you feel they are not helping, but ensure that the patient is aware of the dangers of smoking.

C.   Discuss with the patient his previous experiences with the patch and why he finds it hard to stop smoking.

D.   Explore forms of nicotine replacement therapy other than a nicotine patch.

E.   Do not prescribe the patch as clearly it has not helped the patient so far and will be a waste of resources. Tell the patient to try his best to manage without.

Question 5

You have just started your first day as a junior doctor on a busy surgical rotation. One of the senior sisters on your ward bleeps you regarding a patient who has developed a fever and has become tachycardic and tachypnoiec whilst being transfused blood. You are feeling very anxious, and are concerned that the patient may be having a transfusion reaction. However, you feel out of your competency to deal with this.

Rank in order the following actions in response to this situation (1= Most appropriate; 5= Least appropriate):

A.   Ask one the nurses to bleep your registrar urgently. In the meantime, stop the transfusion and stabilise the patient.

B.   Gather as much information about what has happened, stop the transfusion and try to stabilise the patient. When you get a spare minute, bleep your registrar to come to the ward urgently.

C.   Do not seek further help as you will be admitting to everyone that you do not know how to handle the situation and lack competence.

D.   See the patient and contact one of the other junior doctor colleagues on the ward for advice and help.

E.   Tell the senior nurse to stop the transfusion and say that you will come and see the patient once you have managed to get hold of your registrar.

Question 6

A patient with metastatic prostate cancer presents with chest pain. His troponin was only slightly raised and he tells you that he has been recently started on a new cancer drug called abiraterone, which is known to cause chest pain as a side effect. The pain only began when he started taking the new drug.

Rank in order the following actions in response to this situation (1= Most appropriate; 5= Least appropriate):

A.   Do an ECG and hold off the abiraterone for now until you have sought senior approval and further advice from the oncologist.

B.   Carry out an ECG and treat the patient for an acute coronary syndrome.

C.   Do nothing further for the patient as the information he has told you confirms this is just a side effect of the drug.

D.   Send off a 12 hour troponin level to check if there is any rise in his blood levels.

E.   Do a chest X-ray to look for bony lytic lesions or evidence of any rib fractures causing chest pain.

Question 7

Your best friend has gone abroad while his mother has been admitted under your team's care. Your friend rings you from his hotel to enquire about his mother's condition and wants to know if he should return home to be with his mother.

Rank in order the following actions in response to this situation (1= Most appropriate; 5= Least appropriate):

A.   Divulge as much information as he wants seeing as he is a direct relative of the patient.

B.   Ask what your best friend has been told so far about his mum's situation.

C.   Discuss the matter with your seniors and obtain consent from the patient before giving out any information.

D.   Do not discuss anything as you will breech patient confidentiality and tell your best friend to try to understand your difficult position.

E.   Obtain consent from the patient first before giving any information to her son/your best friend.

Question 8

During a post-take ward round the consultant has asked you to carry out multiple complicated tests for a patient with suspected Cushing's syndrome and then liase with the endocrinology registrar to arrange a review of the patient. You read the patient notes but all the diagnostic blood tests and scan results seem too complicated for you to fully understand. The endocrine registrar asks you to give a summary of what has been done so far.

Rank in order the following actions in response to this situation (1= Most appropriate; 5= Least appropriate):

A.   Only tell him the results of the investigations that you understand and leave out the others.

B.   Admit to the registrar that you do not fully understand the notes and work through it with him.

C.   Just read out everything done with no real understanding of the purpose or relevance of the investigations.

D.   Make up what has been done as it will be time-consuming to read through all the notes.

E.   Tell the endocrine registrar what you understand some of the results but ask him to personally read the notes as you are unsure about a few aspects.

Question 9

Your team is seeing a patient who has been admitted with a lower gastrointestinal bleed. During the ward round the consultant quickly examines the patient, requests that you book her for a flexible sigmoidoscopy and then moves onto the next patient. As the rest of the team moves on, you finish writing in the notes. As you leave the patient asks you "What's going on, Doctor?"

Rank in order the following actions in response to this situation (1= Most appropriate; 5= Least appropriate):

A.   Explain to the patient about the reasons as to why she needs a flexible sigmoidoscopy.

B.   Apologise to the patient for not having had this explained fully and then explain the reasons as to why she needs a flexible sigmoidoscopy.

C.   Explain what a flexible sigmoidoscopy is and the likely sequence of events, and explain why she needs this investigation.

D.   Suggest that if she would like, you will come back later in the afternoon to talk in more depth about her progress and her stay in hospital.

E.   Inform the consultant that you were delayed on the ward round because the patient wanted to know more about her management plan.

Question 10

A 98 year old patient is gravely unwell. Due to lack of intravenous access, the registrar informs you that the only way to provide him with the necessary medications is through a central line. She mentions to you that even with the medications his prognosis is very poor. As you are on-call and she is busy attending to other sick patients she requests that you talk to the family to explain the situation and the likely prognosis. She also would like you to ask if they would want an invasive central line or would rather that he was not aggressively treated.

Rank in order the following actions in response to this situation (1= Most appropriate; 5= Least appropriate):

A.   Fully explain what a central line is, the reasons behind inserting one and the prognosis of the patient.

B.   Explain to the family the current poor condition of the patient.

C.   Offer the family the opportunity to ask questions while you explain the situation to them.

D.   Approach the family and request that you speak with them in a private, quiet side room with adequate senior supervision.

E.   Offer them time alone to talk to each other.

Question 11

You are a busy on-call surgical junior doctor and have just started your night shift at 8pm. You get bleeped to speak to the relatives of Mr Smith, who is a 95 year old gentleman that you have not met before. His relatives are concerned about his discharge as he was meant to be going back to his nursing home 10 days ago and they are very annoyed to find him still in hospital. They are insisting that they speak to a doctor.

Rank in order the following actions in response to this situation (1= Most appropriate; 5= Least appropriate):

A.   Explain to the relatives that it may be better for them to discuss this in the morning with the patient's regular team.

B.   Look through the last entries of the patient's medical notes and explain to the relatives that you are happy to speak to them but can only go by what has been documented in the notes as you are not the patient's regular doctor. Document what has been discussed afterwards.

C.   Explain to the patient's relatives that you are not Mr Smith's regular doctor and are therefore unable to answer any questions. Advise the relatives to make a complaint against Mr Smith's doctors for the delayed discharge.

D.   Tell the nurse that you refuse to see Mr Smith's family as there isn't much you can help them with.

E.   Call the registrar looking after the patient to ask them for more information in the hope that he will know something about this.

Question 12

You have just started your first surgical rotation as a junior doctor. You have repeatedly noticed that your consultant never rolls his sleeves up or wash his hands in-between examining patients. This particularly concerns you as some of the patients are MRSA positive.

Rank in order the following actions in response to this situation (1= Most appropriate; 5= Least appropriate):

A.   Inform the clinical director of the hospital.

B.   Speak to your consultant in private regarding this issue.

C.   Discuss the matter with another consultant and hope that they can bring it up delicately.

D.   Turn a blind eye to the situation. It is not a serious issue and there is no proof that he has caused any infections to his patients so far.

E.   Tell the patients to be aware of him and get them to ask him to wash his hands as he will not be able to refuse if they ask him instead of the other doctors.

Question 13

During the first few months as a junior doctor, you start to think that the handover process (in the morning and evening) can be improved in numerous ways. You feel that there is poor representation from each medical team and that not all information is relayed appropriately.

Rank in order the following actions in response to this situation (1= Most appropriate; Least appropriate):

A.   Make a list of ways that the system could be improved and then discuss this with your senior colleagues.

B.   Re-audit the outcome of handovers after you make improvements to the handover process.

C.   Present the results of your audit regarding handover to all the doctors who normally attend the handover meetings.

D.   Start a quality improvement project to audit the handover system without involving senior colleagues – you don't want to involve them when they are already so busy.

E.   Discuss your irritations and misgivings with senior colleagues who run the handover.

Question 14

One of the patients on your list needs a lumbar puncture on recommendation from the neurologist. You feel that you have had little exposure to procedures such as chest drains and lumbar punctures as your two senior house officers are given priority within your team to do them.

Rank in order the following actions in response to this situation (1= Most appropriate; 5= Least appropriate):

A.   Ensure the patient consents to you doing a lumbar puncture despite your lack of experience and document this in the notes.

B.   Do the lumbar puncture when there is a spare moment on the ward before the other senior house officers have got round to it, despite your lack of previous experience. You don't mention your lack of experience to anyone (including the patient).

C.   The next time there is a lumbar puncture to be performed offer to perform this under supervision to improve your confidence.

D.   Express your desire on the ward round to learn to do the lumbar puncture and politely ask if you can observe a senior colleague this time.

E.   Politely ask the other members of the team if you would be allowed to try to do the lumbar puncture and tell them that you have done them before, despite not having done so.

Question 15

You are in your weekly 'bleep-free' junior doctor teaching session. As you were busy on the ward and scared of being late, you were in such a rush that you forgot to check-in your bleep at the postgraduate centre. It is 20 minutes into the teaching session and your bleep is going off. Your colleagues and the consultant delivering the teaching are giving you unpleasant, irritated looks. They are not impressed.

Rank in order the following actions in response to this situation (1= Most appropriate; 5= Least appropriate):

A.   Answer your bleep and leave teaching to attend to any jobs that need to be done.

B.   Answer your bleep and write down the jobs (which are all non-urgent) without telling the person that you cannot attend to these for the next hour as you are in a mandatory teaching session.

C.   Answer your bleep and explain to the person who has bleeped you that you are in a mandatory teaching session and ask them to bleep another person in your team.

D.   Answer your bleep and explain to the person who has bleeped you that you are in a mandatory teaching session and that you will call them back in one hour when the teaching session has finished.

E.   Go straight to the ward that is bleeping you as it could be an emergency.

Question 16

You are a junior doctor on a busy respiratory rotation. It is two months into the rotation and you do not feel that you have learnt much during the rotation. You are upset that your registrar has given several opportunities to the other Foundation doctors to practise procedures such as a pleural tap, and has never once asked you. Every time you have asked her to do a mini-CEX (clinical exercise) assessment for you, she always says that she is too busy and gets frustrated with you.

Rank in order the following actions in response to this situation (1= Most appropriate; 5= Least appropriate):

A.   Discuss this matter in private with your registrar.

B.   Do nothing as you do not want to cause conflict with a colleague.

C.   Be proactive and ask your colleagues to inform you whenever they are performing a procedure so that you can learn by watching.

D.   Escalate your concerns to your consultant (clinical supervisor) if your registrar fails to respond to your concerns.

E.   Ignore the situation with the registrar and speak to your educational supervisor who will probably be able to carry out any assessments for you instead.

Question 17

It is 8.20pm and you have just finished your on-call shift, which was officially meant to end at 8.00pm. You are eagerly waiting for the night junior doctor to turn up so that you can handover to him, but no one has arrived. After another 10 minutes you are informed that he has called in sick. You are keen to leave as you have to be at a friend's birthday party in an hour and no one has come to replace your colleague.

Rank in order the following actions in response to this situation (1= Most appropriate; 5= Least appropriate):

A. Contact another member of the on-call night team such as the registrar to inform him of the situation. If there are no urgent tasks that you can help with, then handover to the registrar and go home.

B. Wait another hour for the junior doctor in case he has a change of heart and gets better. If not, contact the on-call night registrar to handover.

C. Cover the night junior doctor shift as it is unlikely that there will be enough time to arrange locum cover at such late notice.

D. Contact the on-call night registrar informing him of the situation and offer to stay for a few more hours regardless of whether there are any urgent tasks you can help with.

E. Contact the night junior doctor at home and tell him that it is unacceptable for him to have given such late notice and that he should come in to do his shift even if he is feeling ill.

Question 18

The third year medical students on your firm tell you that the amount of teaching that they get varies according to the firm they are on. They feel that they have learnt lots as your team has been very helpful but their colleagues are yet to cover basic topics.

Rank in order the following actions in response to this situation (1= Most appropriate; 5= Least appropriate):

A. Thank the students for their valuable feedback and then follow-up on it.

B. Suggest arranging a weekly tutor session by each junior doctor covering the basic topics for all the third year undergraduates.

C. Discuss the problem raised with the undergraduate teaching coordinator at the medical school.

D. Relay this issue to the dean of the medical school.

E. Ask the students how they think each firm can be improved and to write you a list.

Question 19

You want to pursue a career in ENT (ear, nose and throat) surgery. Unfortunately you do not have an ENT rotation and are struggling to get much exposure to the specialty as a junior doctor. You have tried discussing the situation with senior members of your team, but they do not seem to be providing much advice.

Rank in order the following actions in response to this situation (1= Most appropriate; 5= Least appropriate):

A. Make a visit to the hospital's ear, nose and throat team.

B. Ask to speak to one of the registrars or consultants working in the specialty to see if there are any projects that you could get involved with.

C. Negotiate time off with your team when you are not busy to go to the ENT (ear, nose and throat) department to observe their clinical practice.

D. Discuss career progression with your educational supervisor and see if they can offer you advice.

E. Look into which exams you must sit to pursue a career in ear, nose and throat surgery.

Question 20

During your on-call, one of the patients that had recently been admitted following a paracetamol overdose threatens to self-discharge. He has been treated with N-acetylcysteine and his paracetamol/salicylate levels are now normal. The patient is mentally competent but the day team have clearly documented that they are keeping him in as an inpatient so that he can be reviewed by the psychiatry team.

Rank in order the following actions in response to this situation (1= Most appropriate; 5= Least appropriate):

A. Allow the patient to leave without any intervention as he is competent.

B. Allow the patient to leave if still insistent, after signing a self discharge letter.

C. Calm the patient down. Explain to him why you want to keep him in.

D. Contact the patient's GP to inform him of the situation.

E. Document in the notes your discussion.

Question 21

You are walking up to the third floor of the hospital when you notice one of the patients struggling to come down the stairs the opposite way. It is clear that he is finding it difficult to cope with stairs and appears unstable while trying to do so. When you ask him if he would like some help, he mumbles odd sounds and appears confused.

Rank in order the following actions in response to this situation (1= Most appropriate; 5= Least appropriate):

A. Discuss with the ward manager how this patient was allowed to get so far on his own, when it is clear he cannot cope.

B. Support and walk the patient back to his ward with extra help if needed.

C. Discuss with the physiotherapists the patient's ongoing mobility plans.

D. Document in the notes the events and your discussions.

E. Advise the patient that he should not be doing things that he does not feel that he can cope with.

Question 22

You are the on-call junior doctor on a busy orthopaedic ward. You have been handed over by the day team to review an elderly female who is day 1 post-total hip replacement and has developed acute renal failure secondary to urinary retention. You have been asked to monitor her urine output and ensure that she is catheterised, which you instruct the nurse to do immediately. However, when you return later that night the patient has still not been catheterised. The patient is now complaining of unbearable pain in the suprapubic region and is acutely confused.

Rank in order the following actions in response to this situation (1= Most appropriate; 5= Least appropriate):

A.   Fill in a clinical incident form.

B.   Call your senior colleague and ask him for advice about what to do and how to manage the patient.

C.   Ensure that the patient is catheterised immediately.

D.   Speak to the nurse in private regarding the consequences of her not following your instructions.

E.   Turn a blind eye to the situation. It is acceptable for people to make mistakes.

Question 23

You are a junior doctor working in the GUM (genitourinary medicine) clinic. You have just seen a 9 year old girl who has been diagnosed with a sexually transmitted infection. On taking a more extensive history she tells you that she has been having a sexual relationship with a 13 year old boy.

Rank in order the following actions in response to this situation (1= Most appropriate; 5= Least appropriate):

A.   Call social services and the police.

B.   Inform the girl's parents and let them deal with the situation.

C.   Discuss the case with the child protection lead of the hospital.

D.   Inform the boy's parents about the situation.

E.   Assess whether the girl is competent to make the decision to enter into a sexual relationship. If you feel she is competent, ensure that you advise her on safe sex and contraception.

Question 24

You are a junior doctor in the emergency department. You realise that you have just administered a vaccine to a patient that is out-of-date.

Rank in order the following actions in response to this situation (1= Most appropriate; 5= Least appropriate):

A.   Check the expiry dates of all the vaccines in the fridge to ensure the other vials are not out-of-date.

B.   Inform the patient what has happened and reassure him not to worry as the vaccine is only two months out-of-date.

C.   Inform the patient what has happened and apologise. Monitor the patient for any signs of them developing a reaction and tell them to return to hospital if any adverse effects occur.

D.   Fill out a critical incident form.

E.   Do not say anything to the patient.

Question 25

An elderly woman presents to the emergency department with long standing tiredness and intermittent episodes of mild epigastric and right-sided abdominal pain. She also reports that her skin sometimes turns 'yellow' but has never seen the doctor for this. After a thorough examination you conclude that that although not acutely unwell, she may have gallstones but cannot exclude malignancy. You plan to order some blood tests and an abdominal scan but she refuses. She is due to fly abroad the next day to attend her son's wedding and cannot stay in hospital to wait for the results.

Rank in order the following actions in response to this situation (1= Most appropriate; 5= Least appropriate):

A. Admit her urgently and arrange as many investigations as soon as possible.

B. Tell her that she can leave but arrange for your consultant to see her in outpatients' clinic in a few weeks time.

C. Carry out the urgent abdominal scan and blood tests but ring her back before she travels with the result.

D. Discuss with a senior colleague contacting the on-call radiologist and pathology laboratory to arrange an urgent scan and blood test giving the patient the result before she leaves hospital.

E. Inform her that she can travel only if she lets her travel insurance company know about her current situation.

Question 26

On top of your normal day-to-day duties you are carrying out a major audit for your team. In view of your workload you realise that you cannot go through all the relevant patient notes by the end of the day. The department offices are closed for the weekend and the project needs to be handed in early next week.

Rank in order the following actions in response to this situation (1= Most appropriate; 5= Least appropriate):

A. Photocopy the relevant notes, making sure you leave out any personal details, and finish the project at home.

B. Take the notes with you and continue the audit at home.

C. Ask your consultant to extend the deadline as you need more time to finish the audit.

D. Ask the secretary to go through the notes with you and help gather the information.

E. Take a rough guess at what the data may be by looking at the results you already have.

Question 27

You have just finished a long week of being on-call and are due to hand in an application form by tomorrow noon for a taster week in a specialty you want more experience in. You realise that it will take you a good few hours to complete and feel exhausted from the long week you have had. You have a consultant ward round tomorrow but this application is very important for your next hospital job.

Rank in order the following actions in response to this situation (1= Most appropriate; 5= Least appropriate):

A. Ask the other junior doctors to hold your bleep after the ward round so you can do your form.

B. Try to stay up late to complete the form even if it means having a lot less sleep.

C. Ring a senior team member and ask whether you can finish the form after the ward round tomorrow. Say you will ask the other junior doctors to cover your bleep during this time.

D. Call in sick the next day and stay at home to complete the form.

E. Ask one of your friends to give you their application form and copy it.

Question 28

A young mother brings her 2 year old son into the emergency department. He is crying and on examination appears to have a fractured femur. He also has several bruise marks across his back. On questioning the mother she just says that he is clumsy and tends to fall off the sofa and bump into things. She didn't bring him in initially as she thought his excessive crying was normal for that age. The mum starts being aggressive stating that you are accusing her of being a bad mother.

Rank in order the following actions in response to this situation (1= Most appropriate; 5= Least appropriate):

A. Tell her off for neglecting her child and not bringing him in any sooner.

B. Call social services straightaway.

C. Call the police straightaway.

D. Discuss the situation with someone senior, ideally the on-call paediatric registrar, as to what to do.

E. Carry out a basic examination of the child and bleep the orthopaedic registrar to examine and treat the suspected fracture.

Question 29

You are the on-call medical junior doctor. It is 17:30 and you have been handed over plenty of jobs by the medical day teams. These include checking blood results for numerous patients, a few reviews of fluid status and adjusting warfarin dosing for several patients. While you are trying to complete these jobs, you are also getting bleeped consistently from various ward sisters requesting that you review their patients for different reasons.

Rank in order the following actions in response to this situation (1= Most appropriate; 5= Least appropriate):

A.   Obtain an accurate summary of the current clinical picture and observations of each of the patients that you have been bleeped about.

B.   Request help from your senior colleagues if you feel that you cannot cope with the workload.

C.   Prioritise each case in order of those that need the most urgent attention.

D.   Seek senior advice only about the certain clinical scenarios you feel to be beyond your limitations.

E.   Keep a clear list of the ward jobs at hand so that you are able to systematically work through them and handover appropriately the next day if they do not get done overnight.

Question 30

You are the on-call junior doctor over the weekend. You have been asked to review a patient who has become slightly short of breath and has a productive cough. You examine him and find that he has bronchial breathing at the right base. His observation chart shows that he is regularly spiking temperatures. You suspect he has hospital-acquired pneumonia.

Rank in order the following actions in response to this situation (1= Most appropriate; 5= Least appropriate):

A.   Wait until the handover at the end of the shift and ask the night doctor to perform the blood cultures, sputum cultures and X-rays.

B.   Send the patient for a chest X-ray.

C.   Start the patient on broad spectrum antibiotics according to trust protocol, after sending off sputum for microscopy, culture and sensitivity.

D.   Send off urinary legionella antigen tests for atypical pneumonia.

E.   Take blood cultures when the patient spikes his temperatures.

Question 31

A patient with known heart failure is experiencing shortness of breath. You review his notes and chest radiograph and see that he has bilateral pleural effusions. On global assessment including the analysis of the fluid in/output chart, you diagnose that the patient is fluid overloaded. He is currently on furosemide 40 mg once a day.

Rank in order the following actions in response to this situation (1= Most appropriate; 5= Least appropriate):

A.   Increase the furosemide diuretic dose to 40 mg twice a day after senior advice is sought.

B.   Examine the patient's fluid status thoroughly including full cardiological and respiratory examination.

C.   Ensure a urinary catheter is inserted for accurate urine output recordings.

D.   Request the nurses document daily weights.

E.   Ask the nurses to put up a sign that states '1.5 L fluid restriction'.

Question 32

You are the on-call surgical junior doctor. One of the patients (who has had abdominal surgery a few years ago) has been admitted complaining of abdominal pain. He has not passed stool or flatus in the last 12 hours, has vomited six times and has noticed his abdomen getting larger.

Rank in order the following actions in response to this situation (1= Most appropriate; 5= Least appropriate):

A.   Contact the on-call surgical registrar immediately.

B.   Examine the patient (including listening for bowel sounds).

C.   Ask the nurses to prepare an NG tube and gain intravenous access for fluids.

D.   Request an abdominal X-ray.

E.   Take bloods (including FBC, U&Es, group and save).

Question 33

A young Afro-Caribbean gentleman presents with chest discomfort lasting for a few minutes. The only other symptom he noticed was some minor palpitations. On admission, his troponin was negative, CXR clear and his heart rate was high. After a few hours his chest discomfort seems to have disappeared. The only thing of concern is that the patient's ECG (done 20 minutes ago) shows sinus tachycardia. He is otherwise asymptomatic.

Rank in order the following actions in response to this situation (1= Most appropriate; 5= Least appropriate):

A.   Add the patient to the coronary angioplasty list for tomorrow.

B.   Repeat the patient's ECG again.

C.   Discharge the patient as sinus tachycardia can be normal for him.

D.   Get a repeat troponin.

E.   Start the patient on ACS protocol.

Question 34

Yourself and two fellow junior doctor colleagues have been asked to present a paper at an international symposium. Due to a busy schedule, your consultant has asked for all three of you to do the majority of work which you have no problems doing. While one of the junior doctors also seems keen to put in the work, the other is known to be lazy and has a bad reputation amongst his peers. How would you go about preparing for the presentation?

Rank in order the following actions in response to this situation (1= Most appropriate; 5= Least appropriate):

A.   Only work with the junior doctor colleague who is keen to put the effort in and exclude the third 'lazy' member from the presentation.

B.   Arrange a discussion with you and your colleagues concerning everyone's contribution and how to split the workload.

C.   Let the other 'lazy' member only have a minimal role as both you and your colleague cannot afford for any mistakes to happen.

D.   Approach the third member and state that they will have to change their ways if they want to be part of this presentation.

E.   Delegate the tasks but checkup on the third colleague to ensure that they are not falling behind.

Question 35

On a ward you notice that one of your patients, Mr Smith, complains that the patient in the next bed, Mr Yeti, is frequently rude and constantly swears to the staff and patients on the ward. Mr Smith is quite annoyed by the situation and wants to move to a different ward. Mr Yeti is also under your care and has been acting this way since the death of his son two weeks ago.

Rank in order the following actions in response to this situation (1= Most appropriate; 5= Least appropriate):

A.   Tell Mr Yeti that he could be asked to leave the ward if he continues to verbally abuse staff and patients on the ward.

B.   Explain to Mr Smith that Mr Yeti is acting this way as he has just recently received news about his son's death.

C.   Speak to Mr Yeti about his behaviour and try to reach some understanding about how his words are affecting other people around him.

D.   Ask Mr Smith about Mr Yeti's behaviour and obtain information from the ward staff concerning the circumstances around the death of his son.

E.   Tell Mr Smith that you are powerless to do anything about the situation and he just needs to 'put up' with it for now until he is discharged.

Question 36

You are the junior doctor in the emergency department and see a patient with a distal radius fracture which is visible on X-ray. You speak to the orthopaedic registrar who assesses the patient, reduces the fracture and puts it in a cast. The orthopaedic registrar asks you to arrange a repeat X-ray and says to call him when this is done. An hour and a half later you see the X-ray has been done, so you call the registrar who reviews it from theatres and says that the bone is in a good position. He says you can discharge the patient and asks that you arrange for the patient to come back to fracture clinic in one week. When you go to tell the patient this, the patient says they are in a lot of pain and have been since the cast was put on. The patient says he told a few of the nurses, who gave him analgesia, but this has not helped. He is now starting to get a tingling sensation in his fingers.

Rank in order the following actions in response to this situation (1= Most appropriate; 5= Least appropriate):

A. Give the patient analgesia, discharge him and advise him to come back if it continues to hurt.

B. Ask one of your senior colleagues in the emergency department for urgent advice about whether you should remove the plaster.

C. Call the orthopaedic registrar immediately and inform them of this new development and seek advice about whether you should cut off the plaster.

D. Arrange a repeat X-ray in case the reduced fracture has slipped out of position.

E. Discharge the patient and tell them there is nothing wrong with them anymore as the fracture has been reduced successfully and pain is normal in this situation. Reassure them the sensation will pass.

Question 37

You are on a hepatology attachment and go out to the pub one evening with a few of your colleagues. You see a patient there who you know has a history of alcoholic liver disease and is on the liver transplant waiting list, clearly drinking a pint of beer. You know that this is strictly forbidden if patients are on the waiting list. She sees you and begs you do not tell anybody, explaining that this is a one-off as it is a birthday celebration.

Rank in order the following actions in response to this situation (1= Most appropriate; 5= Least appropriate):

A. Discuss the situation with your consultant and the transplant coordinators the next day.

B. Pretend you have not seen the patient, as you know that if she gets taken off the transplant list she will probably die from the complications of end-stage liver disease within the next year.

C. Strongly advise her to stop drinking, and say that you will have to report her if you see her drinking again.

D. Ask the patient to come to the ward tomorrow to get a more detailed history in regards to her drinking, where there will be more seniors to advise you.

E. Speak to her in length at the pub to try and ascertain if she is telling the truth.

Question 38

You are a junior doctor and have just started a busy orthopaedic job. One of the senior nurses on the ward approaches you to consent a patient for a lumbar discectomy. You are not aware of the risks involved in this operation. The patient is next on the operating list.

Rank in order the following actions in response to this situation (1= Most appropriate; 5= Least appropriate):

A.   Advise the patient not to have the operation. This way you will not need to consent him.

B.   Ask the senior nurse to contact your registrar and inform him of the situation, asking him to consent the patient.

C.   Contact your registrar directly and inform him of the situation, asking him to consent the patient.

D.   Do not consent the patient and document in the notes why you are not happy to consent the patient.

E.   Try and consent the patient to the best of your ability without involving any seniors.

Question 39

You are approaching the end of a busy night shift when you sustain a needlestick injury whilst trying to cannulate a patient. You are quite anxious as this is your first needlestick injury, and you cannot remember whether or not you have had your hepatitis B booster. You are due to go to handover in 15 minutes, following which you have to go on the post-take ward round with the consultant.

Rank in order the following actions in response to this situation (1= Most appropriate; 5= Least appropriate):

A.   Contact the registrar and consultant and explain that you won't be able to attend handover straightaway as you need to report the incident to the Occupational Health department, as well as ensuring that the patient is consented and bled by someone else for a needlestick injury screen.

B.   Go to handover and the post-take ward round, and then come back and ask the senior sister on the ward to arrange for the patient to be consented and bled for a needlestick injury screen.

C.   Do not tell anyone what happened as you feel stupid.

D.   Ask the senior sister on the ward to arrange for the patient to be consented and bled for a needlestick injury screen whilst you go to handover and the post-take ward round.

E.   Only inform your team about the needlestick injury the following day, as you want to go home and check the date of your hepatitis B booster first.

Question 40

You notice that your fellow junior doctor has been coming late into work for the past few weeks. This means that you have to prepare for the morning ward round alone, which gets very hectic. You initially thought this was just a phase and after a while they might notice that you are taking on quite a lot of the work, but so far they don't seem to have changed their ways.

Rank in order the following actions in response to this situation (1= Most appropriate; 5= Least appropriate):

A. Speak to them and find out why they are late. Try and find out if there is anything wrong and suggest they speak to a senior if required.

B. Speak to your registrar about this and ask them to speak to the other junior doctor.

C. Speak to your consultant about this and explain you are feeling a bit overwhelmed.

D. Tell the Foundation Programme director about this and mention that your colleague is not completing their competence on 'teamwork' very effectively.

E. Do nothing as this is none of your business and just hope that you will have more considerate colleagues on your next rotation.

Question 41

You are the surgical junior doctor and have been asked by your registrar to consent a patient for a procedure that you know nothing about. The registrar tells you to look it up and do the consent as he is needed in theatre to assist the consultant and can't help you.

Rank in order the following actions in response to this situation (1= Most appropriate; 5= Least appropriate):

A. Tell your registrar that you will try and consent the patient and ask him to quickly summarise what you need to tell the patient.

B. Ask the scrub nurse, who has seen the procedure in theatre performed several times, what to write on the consent form and then consent the patient.

C. Tell your registrar that you are not happy to do this and ask that he consents the patient despite needing to go to theatre urgently.

D. Look up on the internet what you should put in the consent form.

E. Tell your registrar that you are not happy to do this, and ask that he consents the patient – offer to go to theatre to assist the consultant instead while he is consenting the patient.

Question 42

You are running late for work due to a tube strike that means you needed to take a longer route on your way to work than normal. You are rather flustered and nervous as your consultant is not the most forgiving sort of man around.

Rank in order the following actions in response to this situation (1= Most appropriate; 5= Least appropriate):

A.   Call in sick as you do not want to be late. You were late last week and would rather pretend that you intended not to come in.

B.   Do not contact anyone and try and sneak onto the ward round without anyone noticing.

C.   Contact the ward and say you will be late but are on your way.

D.   Contact your fellow junior doctor and say that you will be late. Apologise and tell them to tell the consultant on your behalf.

E.   Contact your registrar and apologise saying that you will be late. Tell him that you can stay late to finish some of the outstanding jobs if this is necessary to make up for your delay.

Question 43

You are a junior doctor on a medical firm. After the morning ward round you and your fellow junior doctor meet in the office to split up the jobs. Your colleague says they will bleed Mr Adam and send the samples off to the haematology laboratory. On the evening ward round the consultant asks what the bloods results showed for Mr Adam. Your colleague says that you were meant to do this and denies any knowledge about the task.

Rank in order the following actions in response to this situation (1= Most appropriate; 5= Least appropriate):

A.   You get angry with the other junior doctor in front of the consultant and accuse them of lying.

B.   You tell the consultant that you were not meant to be doing this job – it was the other junior doctor who was meant to do it and they have just forgotten.

C.   You politely tell the consultant that you thought your colleague was going to bleed this patient, apologise for any communication errors between the junior doctors and say you will bleed this patient now. You then later speak to the other junior doctor about this.

D.   You tell the consultant that you took the blood and are not sure why the result is not back. Attempt to blame the haematology laboratory as you want to protect yourself and your colleague from getting into trouble.

E.   You tell the consultant that you took the blood and make up the blood results.

Question 44

You are feeling unwell at work and have a fever. You feel rather nauseated and are finding it very hard to concentrate on the tasks you have been allocated to do.

Rank in order the following actions in response to this situation (1= Most appropriate; 5= Least appropriate):

A. Inform your team that you feel unwell and handover any jobs to your colleagues then go home.

B. Inform the rota coordinator and ask them to get someone to cover your absence at short notice, then go home.

C. Inform the medical staffing department and then go home.

D. Struggle through the day and do not tell anyone. It is only 4 hours until the end of the day and you are sure you can try to cope.

E. Do not tell anyone about this and quietly sneak off the ward and go home. If there are any urgent jobs the nurses will get hold of the senior house officer if you cannot be contacted anyway.

Question 45

You are the on-call junior doctor and have been handed over by your colleague a patient on the ward that is due to have a blood transfusion and you are asked to arrange this. While you are writing up the prescription for the blood, the patient tells you they are a Jehovah's Witness and refuses to accept the blood.

Rank in order the following actions in response to this situation (1= Most appropriate; 5= Least appropriate):

A. Cancel the prescription and inform the registrar of the situation.

B. Cancel the prescription but do not inform anyone else.

C. Leave the prescription but tell the nurses not to give the blood.

D. Cancel the prescription and inform your registrar of the situation, and also document it in the patient notes.

E. Tell the patient that they need blood and it is in their best interests, you are obliged to give the blood and they should take it.

Question 46

You are the on-call junior doctor and are in the middle of taking blood from a patient, but your bleep keeps going off from the same number. You are almost done with bleeding the patient but they look rather annoyed at you because you keep getting distracted by the bleeping noise.

Rank in order the following actions in response to this situation (1= Most appropriate; 5= Least appropriate):

A. Ask the nurse attending to the patient to answer your bleep and write down any messages.

B. Ask the nurse to answer your bleep and let you know what it is about.

C. Ask the nurse to answer your bleep and tell the person on the other end to stop bleeping you.

D. Ignore the bleep and answer it after you finish bleeding the patient.

E. Ask a different patient in the bay to answer your bleep.

PART TWO – Multi-Action Questions

Question 47

You are a junior doctor working on a respiratory ward. You review a chest X-ray for your patient, Mr Epstein, and notice a large lesion that looks suspicious of lung cancer. As you turn around, you notice one of his relatives standing directly behind you. He has been looking over your shoulder the whole time. Before you have the chance to say anything they ask you, "Do you think that could be cancer, Doctor?"

Choose the THREE most appropriate actions to take in this situation:

A.   Politely ask them to refrain from looking at confidential information and continue looking at the X-ray in public.

B.   Explain that you cannot talk to them about Mr Epstein's care due to patient confidentiality issues.

C.   Call your senior to talk to the patient's family about the cancer.

D.   Talk to the family about the results of the chest X-ray.

E.   Explain the results of the chest X-ray to the family and then apologise to Mr Epstein for allowing his family to see the chest X-ray.

F.   Explain to Mr Epstein and his family that you are unsure of the diagnosis but will ask one of your senior colleagues to talk to him when they have a diagnosis.

G.   In the future, ensure no one is looking over your shoulder.

H.   In the future, look at radiology films in the doctor's office.

Question 48

During your general medical mid placement review with your educational supervisor, it has been noticed that you have not completed any DOPS (directly observed procedure) assessments. Despite being involved and active in performing many clinical procedures you just have not had any opportunities to perform the activities in front of a senior who can assess your performance. The firm looks after many sick patients, is understaffed and your educational assessments tend to be the last priority during the busy day.

Choose the THREE most appropriate actions to take in this situation:

A. Complain to your educational supervisor and tell them that your job is too busy and that your training is not factored into the job at all.

B. Inform your consultant and registrar of your problem and ask them if there is any chance they can fit in 5 minutes of their time to help complete an assessment for you.

C. Ask your team if, within the coming next few weeks, they could involve you in any practical procedures so that you may be supervised performing these.

D. Ask a member of a different medical team if they can quickly watch you perform a procedure and sign you off for a DOP.

E. Go to the Accident and Emergency department and ask one of the doctors to observe you performing a procedure.

F. Ask to swap hospital jobs so that you can be part of a team where your training is better supported.

G. Decide not to perform any DOP assessments during this job and try to make up for it by doing more assessments in the next job.

H. Try to make it as easy as possible for your team to fill out a DOP by remembering your online portfolio password and ensuring there is a free computer to log onto so that your assessments can be completed straightaway.

Question 49

You are a junior doctor working in general medicine. Although you feel you are coping with all the work on the firm, you can't help but feel that you are not learning or gaining much medical training on the job. You don't feel anyone is offering you teaching sessions or explaining the rationale behind patient management and care. You worry that if you raise this issue with your seniors, you will be seen as a 'trouble maker' by adding an extra workload to their already hectic schedule.

Choose the THREE most appropriate actions to take in this situation:

A.   Write a complaint to your educational supervisor telling them that the job you are doing is rubbish and that it should not be included on the Foundation Programme if it doesn't provide the proper training.

B.   Try to come up with topics that you feel you would like to learn more about and ask the seniors if they might be able to spare a few minutes to teach you about some of these.

C.   Ask your seniors lots of questions on the ward rounds in the hope that this may make them talk to you a little bit more about the rationale behind patient care during the rounds.

D.   Do some background reading yourself and try to incorporate this knowledge in your daily routines such as in ward rounds.

E.   Do nothing as providing a service comes before your own educational needs and patient care must come first.

F.   Switch to another hospital job and don't mention your dissatisfaction to your team.

G.   Inform your consultant how you feel and see if he has any ideas on how you may go about gaining more teaching/training as you would like to.

H.   See if you can choose an interesting ward patient each week to discuss in further detail with the consultant or registrar. Ask to use this as a case-based discussion (CBD) assessment which will aid your understanding of patient management and also help towards completing your ePortfolio.

Question 50

You have clerked a patient in the pre-assessment clinic who is scheduled to have day case surgery next week. His medical history includes the diagnosis of epilepsy and his last seizure was two months ago. He has been informed by his neurologist that he must stop driving but he admits to you that he did drive to hospital today to attend clinic. Despite insisting that he should stop driving, he is adamant that he cannot stop because of his employment and tells you that he is completely compliant with his medication.

Choose the THREE most appropriate actions to take in this situation:

A.   Take no further action as his last seizure was a few months ago.

B.   Take no further action as you must respect patient confidentiality.

C.   Inform the patient to notify the DVLA regarding his medical history.

D.   Inform the patient that you will discuss his situation with a senior and notify the DVLA yourself if he doesn't do so.

E.   Inform his GP and his neurologist that he is still driving despite their advice.

F.   Inform the consultant who will be performing his surgery.

G.   Document this fact in the patient's notes so that it is flagged up in the next clinic.

H.   Discuss with a senior about cancelling his surgery.

Question 51

During a busy shift while on-call in general medicine, you review a patient's drug chart. Whilst looking at the drugs you notice that levothyroxine has been prescribed with the dosage in milligrams (mg) rather than micrograms (mcg). When you highlight the issue to the nurses they tell you that they already noticed the mistake and have been dispensing the dosage in micrograms anyway and that the patient has been receiving their correct dose. You know the handwriting and signature of the doctor who prescribed the medication wrongly.

Choose the THREE most appropriate actions to take in this situation:

A.   Stop the incorrect medication and rewrite the drug as it should be prescribed.

B.   Document in the patient medical notes the mistake that was made and that this has been corrected.

C.   Do nothing for now as the correct dose is being administered, but notify the prescribing doctor about it so they can correct it when they next rewrite the drug chart.

D.   Inform your colleague of his mistake at the next available opportunity so that they will remember not to make the same mistake again.

E.   Write up a clinical incident form.

F.   Assume that this is a one-off mistake and take no further action as patient safety is not being compromised.

G.   Raise the issue at the next morning handover in front of the whole medical team so that other doctors will be aware of the medications they have been prescribing.

H.   Tell all your other colleagues about the mistake that this junior doctor has made so that they can look out for mistakes that the doctor may be making elsewhere.

Question 52

You are a junior doctor on a general medical attachment. You are worried that you have not completed very many case-based discussion (CBD) assessments and have come across an interesting patient who would be good to discuss for the assessment. You try to ask your registrar on several occasions to go through your assessment with you but at each occasion she comes up with an excuse not to do this and complains that she is too busy and doesn't have any time.

Choose the THREE most appropriate actions to take in this situation:

A.   Take down details of the case and try to find another more appropriate time to go through the case with the registrar.

B.   Try to find out if the patient's consultant might be able to go through the main learning points of the case with you instead and help you complete your assessment.

C.   Send off the ticket request on the online ePortfolio system to the registrar now and ask them to complete it online in their own time despite not having discussed it in person with them.

D.   Do some background reading regarding the differential diagnosis of this particular case to aid your learning and development.

E.   Give up trying to ask your registrar and accept that you may just need to find a different interesting case another time and forget about this interesting patient.

F.   Continue to interrupt your registrar to complete the CBD even though you can see them becoming increasingly annoyed.

G.   Get the CBD done by the senior house officer instead.

H.   Get the CBD done by another registrar even though they may not know the patient.

Question 53

An adult male is admitted into the emergency department following a road traffic accident. He is haemodynamically unstable and will require a blood transfusion. After informing him of this fact, he tells you that he is a Jehovah's Witness and refuses the transfusion despite knowing the consequences of possible death. His wife confirms his religious beliefs but is adamant that you should transfuse him anyway stating that the accident has made him delirious and he is not talking any sense.

Choose the THREE most appropriate actions to take in this situation:

A. Transfuse the patient as it is in his best interest to be kept alive no matter what.

B. Transfuse the patient because you agree with his wife that he is incompetent to make any decision regarding his health.

C. Do not transfuse the patient as doing so would go against the patient's wishes.

D. Look for alternative ways to resuscitate or stabilise the patient.

E. Look for some form of documentation to prove that the patient really is a Jehovah's Witness.

F. Bleep the psychiatric team on-call and persuade them to section the patient before transfusing him anyway.

G. Explain to the patient's wife in a calm and clear manner that you should not transfuse the patient.

H. Wait until the patient loses consciousness before transfusing the patient so he will not know that this has happened.

Question 54

A 60 year old gentleman is under your care suffering from an infective exacerbation of chronic obstructive pulmonary disease (COPD). He has copious amounts of upper airway secretions and has a past medical history of stroke which has left him hemiplegic. He is looking weak and is not tolerating his normal amounts oral intake.

Choose the THREE most appropriate actions to take in this situation:

A. Do not prescribe any medications for the patient as he is not tolerating oral intake.

B. Prescribe a further 2 week course of the patient's current antibiotic medication. He appears to be taking longer than usual to recover from his infection and needs a longer course of medication.

C. Contact the dietician to review potential methods of increasing the patient's calorie intake.

D. Involve the chest physiotherapists in the patient management. They may be able to help him bring up more secretions by special exercises to help clear his airways.

E. Perform regular arterial blood gases to monitor his response to treatment.

F. Discuss the patient's situation with a senior from your team, reviewing the antibiotic prescribed according to results of his sputum culture that you sent off for microbiology.

G. Prescribe regular large volumes of intravenous fluids for the patient to keep him hydrated.

H. Request a barium swallow investigation to examine the patient's swallowing.

Question 55

The senior house officer on your medial team has just passed his postgraduate medical examinations and was out until the late hours of the evening celebrating. The following morning at work he arrives looking disheveled and smelling of alcohol. He has not changed his clothes from the night before and appears disinterested in the patients on the ward.

Choose the THREE most appropriate actions to take in this situation:

A.   Your colleague has made it into work and is fit enough to continue with his duties. Having passed his postgraduate examinations, he is clearly a competent and knowledgeable member of the team. He will sober up without any intervention from yourself.

B.   Advise your colleague that it may be better for him to go home and tell the consultant that he is feeling unwell.

C.   Advise your colleague that he should not carry out any ward tasks whilst hung-over and should instead hand them over to other team members.

D.   Contact the clinical director and inform them of the situation.

E.   Inform the GMC of your colleague's actions.

F.   Inform your consultant of the matter if your colleague does not heed your concerns.

G.   Ask medical staffing to find a locum doctor to cover your colleague today.

H.   Advise your colleague to curb their alcohol intake and suggest that they attend counselling for their 'alcohol problem'.

Question 56

You are a junior doctor working in a GP clinic. A fully competent 15 year old girl attends clinic stating that she missed her last few periods and has had a positive pregnancy test. Her boyfriend is also 15 years old but since finding out this news has left her. The patient would like an abortion. You have encouraged her to discuss the situation with her parents but she refuses and insists that if her parents are told then she will just have an abortion elsewhere.

Choose the THREE most appropriate actions to take in this situation:

A.   Tell her that you will have to inform her parents about the situation.

B.   Report her to the police as she is having sex before the legal age.

C.   Try to convince her to tell her parents as this is a stressful process and family support would be useful in these difficult times.

D.   After discussion with the GP, agree to refer the patient to an abortion clinic but only with parental consent.

E.   After discussion with the GP, agree to refer the patient to an abortion clinic without parental consent.

F.   Suggest that the patient practise abstinence until she is ready to start a family to prevent unwanted pregnancies in the future.

G.   Suggest the patient should repeat the pregnancy test to confirm that she really is pregnant.

H.   Counsel the patient on different forms of contraception to prevent future unwanted pregnancies and convince her to undertake a full checkup for sexually transmitted infections as well.

Question 57

A patient who is admitted under your team has undergone an abdominal ultrasound scan for suspected pancreatitis secondary to gallstones. The patient is a busy businessman and has already spent a number of days as an inpatient. The ultrasound scan results are unremarkable and although the blood results have not yet returned to normal values, the patient decides to self-discharge after the scan. He says that he has already stayed in hospital for too long and that he has important work-related matters to attend to. His wife is present during the consultation and appears uneasy with this decision.

Choose the THREE most appropriate actions to take in this situation:

A.   Advise him to not attend work for the next few weeks.

B.   Allow him to self-discharge but to re-attend hospital if his symptoms worsen.

C.   Inform his wife of the potential consequences of him self-discharging in the hope that she can persuade him to stay.

D.   Discharge the patient on painkillers and antibiotics.

E.   Call security to prevent the patient from self discharging.

F.   Advise the patient to attend his local GP surgery if his pain recurs.

G.   Tell the patient that he can leave but it will be against medical advice as his pancreatitis can flare-up again.

H.   Allow the patient to self-discharge but arrange an outpatient follow-up appointment for him in six weeks time.

Question 58

You are a junior doctor working on a busy medical ward. One of your patients is due to be discharged home and you have sent a prescription to pharmacy with a list of his discharge medications. The patient, however, keeps trying to persuade you to add an anti-hypertensive drug and statin onto his prescription chart as his friend died from a myocardial infarction and he would like to eliminate any risk factors for heart disease. His blood pressure has persistently been normal and his cholesterol levels are not raised.

Choose the THREE most appropriate actions to take in this situation:

A.   Explain to him that his blood pressure is normal and that he does not require any anti-hypertensive or statin medication. If he is still concerned, he can discuss this with his GP.

B.   Explore his concerns about exactly why he feels he needs an anti-hypertensive and statin drug. Reassure him that his blood pressure is normal and explain that just because his friend may have had risk factors for heart disease it does not mean that he is at risk.

C.   Give him one week supply of an anti-hypertensive drug and statin to 'try out'. Ask him to see his GP next week to address this issue further.

D.   Assertively tell him that he is being silly and refuse to prescribe it.

E.   Explain to him that his blood pressure is normal and that he does not require any anti-hypertensive medication. If he still concerned, contact your senior house officer or registrar to reassure the patient.

F.   Ask him to discuss his concerns with the on-call pharmacist.

G.   Refer him to a cardiologist for a 'general checkup'.

H.   Prescribe him a regular anti-hypertensive and statin drugs on discharge.

Question 59

One of the senior sisters asks you to "have a word" with your junior doctor colleague who constantly has her hair loose, is always wearing short skirts, high heels and frequently ignores the ward infection control policies of rolling her sleeves up or washing hands in-between patients. The nursing staff are concerned that her demeanour is neither professional nor hygienic but feel it would be best if you spoke to her first as you are both good friends.

Choose the THREE most appropriate actions to take in this situation:

A. Acknowledge the senior sister's concerns and agree to have a sensitive word with your junior doctor colleague regarding the matter.

B. Sensitively discuss the matter with your colleague, explaining what the senior sister has said and giving specific examples of situations that have particularly concerned the nursing staff.

C. Turn a blind eye to the situation as there is nothing wrong with your colleague's dress code and the nurse is just being picky.

D. Sensitively tell your colleague that she should change her dress code but do not tell her that the senior sister had asked you to speak to her as it may upset her.

E. Tell the senior sister it is not her place to tell your colleague how she should dress.

F. Tell the senior sister that if she is so irritated by the junior doctor's attitude then she should speak to her herself and that you do not want to be involved in this drama yourself.

G. Discuss with the other junior doctors whether they feel your colleague's dress code is inappropriate or not.

H. Try to find a moment when you and your colleague are both relatively free at work and ask to have a private word with her away from other members of the team to avoid any embarrassment.

Question 60

You notice that many of your junior peers (i.e. the medical students) are approaching their first clinical and practical examinations but feel underprepared for them. Despite being on clinical attachments throughout the year, you notice they are still unsure of what to learn for the examination. You decide that you would like to run a mock OSCE session for them to help improve their confidence before their test but news spreads quickly and before you realise it there are too many students to accommodate for your mock OSCE!

Choose the THREE most appropriate actions to take in this situation:

A. Do nothing, their learning has nothing to do with you and you need to focus on your own learning as well.

B. Try and set up another mock OSCE session by yourself even though you have a lot on your plate already.

C. Email the medical school and let them know that they are not teaching the students properly as many of them are feeling underprepared.

D. Set up a group of junior and senior doctor colleagues and formulate a plan to organise your own mock OSCE ensuring that tasks are shared out so no one doctor is overwhelmed by the preparation involved.

E. Inform the clinical skills staff members that perhaps a mock OSCE or teaching session is needed before the clinical exam itself as it is something lots of students are receptive towards and would find useful.

F. Tell some of the more senior clinicians, for example your consultant, that the students are underprepared and encourage them to arrange more formal clinical revision sessions.

G. Only offer to help some and not all of the students who you feel would have the most benefit.

H. Set up the OSCE even if you know that it may affect your daily duties on the ward.

Question 61

You are the junior doctor on a busy general medical firm. Under the supervision of a medical registrar you perform a lumbar puncture and then ask her to help you complete a DOP (directly observed procedure) assessment. The registrar is happy to do this but starts to spend ages on discussing with you the relevant learning points about lumbar punctures, indications and the complications of the procedure. You are aware that the cerebrospinal fluid you have obtained from the lumbar puncture needs to be sent off to the laboratories quickly but your registrar seems more interested in teaching you and you can't seem to get a word in edgeways.

Choose the THREE most appropriate actions to take in this situation:

A. Thank the registrar for their time and help in teaching you the procedure. Reflect upon the procedure and your background reading in your ePortfolio later on at home.

B. Take the opportunity to teach your fellow junior doctor colleagues the same procedure.

C. Ask the registrar if you can now do all the future lumbar punctures unsupervised.

D. Go and find some information about lumbar punctures and read up about it straightaway before you forget. You can send off the cerebrospinal fluid later.

E. Organise some time with the registrar to evaluate what you have learnt.

F. Ask the registrar if there are any more procedures to be done and send the cerebrospinal fluid to the laboratories after your shift with all the other samples together.

G. Ensure that the fluid is sent off and the results are chased and followed-up immediately.

H. Document the procedure in the notes legibly and with accuracy as soon as possible.

Question 62

You are a junior doctor on a busy general medical rotation. During lunch, a final year medical students expresses his concerns to you about the poor teaching he has received whilst being attached to your team for his clinical rotation. He has six weeks until his medical finals and is disappointed he has not had the chance to examine patients or to observe any good clinical signs. He is very worried about failing his examination.

Choose the THREE most appropriate actions to take in this situation:

A. Suggest that he should discuss his concerns with the consultant in charge of his training. Perhaps the consultant knows of other interesting patients in the hospital.

B. Tell the medical student to speak to his medical school and request that he gets moved to a different firm where he will get better teaching.

C. Ask the student to speak to his medical school and make a formal complaint so that this problem does not happen in the future.

D. Speak to your team and inform them of the situation and how the student is feeling, asking them to call him whenever they come across any good clinical signs.

E. Offer to give him some bedside teaching sessions when you get time and also examine him on his clinical examination skills on relatively fit patients so that he can practise his practical skills even if there aren't any interesting cases.

F. Offer to make a complaint to the consultant in charge of his training on his behalf.

G. Request for the medical student to be moved to your colleague's firm where he will get better teaching.

H. Offer to make a complaint on the student's behalf to his medical school.

Question 63

You are a junior doctor working on a general medical firm and are about to see a well-educated 65 year old gentleman on the ward who was admitted overnight. You review the patient's medical notes and note that his liver enzymes are abnormal and that he has had a 4 week history of substantial weight loss. Your team are eager to rule out an underlying malignancy but have not mentioned this to the patient. He is refusing to undergo any tests as he is scared of what the results might show.

Choose the THREE most appropriate actions to take in this situation:

A. Discuss with the patient the relevant investigation findings and tell him that the reason you want to perform further tests is to find the cause of the abnormalities. You avoid using the word 'cancer' or 'tumour' as far as possible in order to try not to upset the patient.

B. Avoid performing any investigations as you feel it would take too much effort and time to explain every detail.

C. Do not carry out further investigations, as even if there is evidence of malignancy, the prognosis is poor, and treatment would be palliative care.

D. Explore his concerns and the reasons for him not wanting any further investigations, re-assuring him as much as possible and explaining that there may be options for treatment if an abnormality is found.

E. Inform him of the benefits and disadvantages of having the investigations, how they will help and the consequences of doing nothing now. Give him time to make his mind up as he is competent.

F. Telephone his next of kin to get their consent for further investigations.

G. Telephone his next of kin to come into the ward to 'reason some sense' into him.

H. Inform him that you are going to carry out further investigations whether he wants this or not as it would be in his best interests.

Question 64

You are the only junior doctor on the respiratory ward for the day as your senior house officer and registrar are away on a course. The consultant asks if you are free as he would like to teach you how to insert a chest drain and would also like your help collecting the equipment for it. You know it would be a great learning opportunity but have so many jobs to do before the end of your shift you are worried this will take a lot of time out of your day.

Choose the THREE most appropriate actions to take in this situation:

A. Thank the consultant for the opportunity and help him with collecting equipment for the chest drain.

B. Make a list of all the jobs that need doing and if you cannot perform all of these in your shift, hand them to the night staff.

C. Keep your bleep on you so you can be contacted and leave in the middle of the teaching if you get bleeped.

D. See if any of your junior doctor colleagues can cover you for the brief period you are assisting with the chest drain insertion.

E. Try to prioritise the most important jobs that require doing before your shift ends so that you can make sure these get done after the teaching session.

F. Pass up on this opportunity but arrange some alternative teaching for later in the week.

G. Ask the nurse at the bedside to answer your bleep if you get called and give you any messages later after the consultant has finished teaching you.

H. Explain the workload to your consultant and ask him if it is possible to perform the chest drain tomorrow.

Question 65

You are a junior doctor working in a GP surgery and are asked to see a newly registered patient who is visiting the surgery for the first time. The patient tells you that the reason he is attending the surgery is for a replacement prescription for methadone. He was a heroin addict in the past and is now on methadone replacement therapy. You do not have any of the patient's past medical history on the computer.

Choose the THREE most appropriate actions to take in this situation:

A. Take a full medical, surgical and psychiatric history from the patient including details of past heroin abuse and doses of methadone he has been taking.

B. Give the patient their usual does of methadone for the day and tell them to return when you have the old medical records from his last GP surgery.

C. Do not prescribe anything until you have the notes from the other GP the patient has transferred from.

D. Tell the patient you will need to discuss the matter with the senior GP in the practice as you are only a junior doctor and cannot prescribe the methadone yourself.

E. Prescribe the patient a week's worth of methadone to help ease his symptoms.

F. Call the patient's old GP surgery and try to gain as much information about the patient as possible.

G. Refer the patient for an outpatient psychiatric appointment to help him deal with his drug addiction.

H. Tell the patient that you are not willing to prescribe methadone for him and if it is an urgent matter he should go to the hospital emergency department.

Question 66

You are the junior doctor on a busy surgical firm. There are no other junior doctors on your firm and your workload is very high but you are gaining lots of valuable experience and theatre time. Once a week you are scheduled to help in the outpatient clinic but this coincides with your compulsory junior doctor weekly teaching. You have missed several teaching sessions already, but your team is insistent that you continue to attend clinic and you don't want to annoy anyone.

Choose the THREE most appropriate actions to take in this situation:

A. Continue to miss teaching as clinic is also a good learning opportunity for you.

B. Go to clinic and teaching on alternate weeks as a compromise so you can have the experience from both areas.

C. Explain to your team that teaching sessions are mandatory and you need to have a higher attendance level otherwise you will not get signed off for Foundation training.

D. Try and make up your teaching attendance during your next attachment but continue to miss it whilst you get the opportunity to attend the surgical clinics.

E. Speak to the education coordinator about rescheduling the day of the weekly teaching as the current situation is not convenient for you.

F. Miss clinic to attend teaching and if your team ask why you were not around just apologise and explain that teaching takes priority.

G. Talk the matter over with your clinical supervisor/consultant and discuss whether there may be other clinics on different days you can be involved in instead.

H. Try and attend the surgical clinics as soon as teaching finishes. The clinics are generally overbooked and run late into the afternoon.

Question 67

You are a junior doctor working on a busy medical ward. You never get a moment to yourself, you are usually left on your own to deal with complex patients and often don't have time to stop for lunch. When you reach home every night you are too tired to cook dinner and just make yourself a slice of toast and go to bed. Your friends are all commenting on how much weight you have lost and are seriously worried about your health.

Choose the THREE most appropriate actions to take in this situation:

A. Discuss the issue of the high workload with the other members of your medical team. See if there is any way that the jobs might be able to be shared out more equally so no one is left staying too late after hours.

B. Handover your bleep to a colleague every day during the lunch hour so that you can have some personal time to eat properly.

C. Acknowledge your friends' concerns. Make an effort to look after your health by ensuring your diet is healthy, even if you are too tired to cook dinner, and by seeking help at work whenever you feel you cannot handle a situation.

D. Refuse to answer your bleep during your lunch hour in the future so that you can have some personal time during the day.

E. Arrange a meeting with your educational supervisor and ask if they can recommend any methods by which you can improve your efficiency on the ward so you do not end up feeling so drained every day.

F. Ask a colleague to take a blood sample from you to make sure that you have not got any abnormalities that might be causing you to be so tired all the time such as low haemoglobin or low thyroid hormone levels.

G. Start eating high calorie foods for breakfast and dinner so you will put on more weight and your friends stop making a fuss about how thin you are.

H. Continue as normal. Your friends care about you but as none of them are medical doctors, they don't understand the stresses of your job.

Question 68

You are working as part of the on-call medical 'crash team' and have been administering cardiopulmonary resuscitation (CPR) on a 17 year old boy who collapsed suddenly whilst playing football. Your team has been administering external cardiac massage for at least 45 minutes and the team is physically and mentally exhausted. There is no electrical activity on the ECG monitor. Nobody seems willing to stop their efforts but you strongly believe that the patient should not be put through anymore futile treatment.

Choose the THREE most appropriate actions to take in this situation:

A. Continue external cardiac massage in turns among members of the team whilst you gently raise the issue with the registrar leading the 'crash call'.

B. Call time of death and make an announcement to the others that everyone should stop.

C. Continue until a more senior member of the team makes a decision. It is not the role of the junior doctor to make this call.

D. Suggest to other members of the team (whilst still continuing to deliver cardiopulmonary resuscitation) that the patient does not appear to be recovering. Involve all team members by enquiring how much longer everyone feels the process should continue for.

E. When it is your turn to administer cardiac massage, refuse to take part and say that you believe this has gone on for long enough. You should not take part in a process that you feel strongly against.

F. Find more people to relieve the exhausted members of the crash team so that external cardiac massage can continue.

G. Check for a reversible cause for the arrest by analyzing a blood sample for electrolyte and glucose levels in the arterial blood gas machine and requesting urgent blood analysis from the haematology laboratories.

H. Ask the family members present whether they think cardiopulmonary resuscitation should be discontinued.

Question 69

You are the junior doctor on a general surgical ward at the end of your night shift. You have been asked to take blood from a patient but as you were very tired and not paying attention, you accidentally put the needle into the brachial artery instead of the median cubital vein and a large haematoma forms.

Choose the THREE most immediate actions to take in this situation:

A.   Place a dressing over the wound and apply pressure for at least 10 minutes or longer if the bleeding continues.

B.   Document in the medical notes what has happened but don't mention this to the patient as it will be too difficult for them to understand and will cause them anxiety.

C.   Call a nurse to attend to the patient and apply a suitable dressing whilst you remove all sharps from the area.

D.   Explain fully to the patient what has happened and document your actions in their medical notes.

E.   Ask a senior colleague to take the blood instead and refuse to have anything further to do with the patient.

F.   Avoid taking blood from the same patient in the future as you presume they will not be too impressed by this incident.

G.   Apologise profusely to the patient and reassure the patient that although there may be bruising it will soon settle down.

H.   Reassure the patient that you did nothing wrong and sometimes taking blood causes a lot of bleeding.

Question 70

A 37 year old patient comes in to the emergency department with a rash over his limbs. You have seen a similar rash before on AIDS patients whilst you were on elective in Africa and believe the rash to be Kaposi's sarcoma. The patient has never had an HIV test and becomes angry when you suggest that you would like to test for this. He refuses to consent for the test.

Choose the THREE most appropriate actions to take in this situation:

A.   Test his blood for HIV anyway as this is an important diagnosis to make.

B.   Explore the patient's concerns and fears behind a possible positive HIV result. Reassure the patient regarding current options for treatment and management.

C.   Offer the patient some moisturising cream for his rash.

D.   Admit the patient and obtain all other relevant blood results (apart from an HIV test) to determine whether the patient is suffering from any other AIDS defining illnesses such as pneumocystis pneumonia or intracerebral fungal infections.

E.   Inform the patient's partner about your suspicions and try to ask the partner to convince the patient to have the blood test.

F.   Commence anti-retroviral therapy immediately even if the patient will not consent to a blood test as you are confident about the diagnosis.

G.   Do not perform the HIV test as the patient has not consented for this.

H.   Tell the patient that if he is not willing to take medical advice then he should not have come to the hospital.

Answers to Examination 3

PART ONE – Answers to the Ranking Questions

Answer Question 1

EBDAC

Despite how good your intentions may be, as a junior doctor you are not entitled to speak on behalf of the hospital trust. In this case, doing so can cause your words to be taken out of context, making the situation worse than it already is. Thus going through the official channels is the best option. Clearly more criticism is not needed so perhaps if you do have to say something, just state that you cannot comment on anything or someone will ring him later, which is better than simply hanging up the phone. In this case the senior doctor is clearly annoyed at the journalist and it is wise for him to also avoid speaking to the journalist.

Answer Question 2

CBEAD

As you have a few cannulas that need to be done there is no harm in asking the student to do this as it means the student gets signed off, the patient gets the cannula they need and one of your outstanding jobs is completed. If this is not possible, then asking your colleague to sign the sheet before the deadline is the next best option. Alternatively, there is a vast array of DOPS for medical students and getting one done within his allocated team really should not be a problem. Offering him no help whatsoever is bad practice and unnecessarily puts the student in a difficult situation. Signing his form without you seeing the procedure is unprofessional, and the student may also be performing the procedure incorrectly.

Answer Question 3

BDEAC

Splitting jobs is crucial in making sure that everything is done properly. The key is to split them in such a way that everything is done and nobody has jobs they feel they cannot do. As a junior doctor you may find it harder to make referrals and do certain procedures due to your lack of experience. You could try them but it would be more efficient to let your senior house officer do such jobs when you are pressed for time as in this situation. Routine jobs should be done later in the day whereas urgent tasks (e.g. requesting urgent scans), will need to be done now. Taking on difficult tasks can seem rewarding, but if you are unsuccessful in completing the job then this wastes even more time and creates more work for everyone.

Answer Question 4

CDABE

Option C is the best answer. The patient wishes to stop smoking but is experiencing difficulties. A discussion about any issues preventing him from stopping smoking may help in making the next attempt more successful. Option D is also a good response but it assumes the nicotine replacement therapy is not suitable for him, whereas it may be the right approach if used effectively. Option A is a possible approach but given his previous failures with the patches it may need more than this for him to succeed. Option B is unlikely to help the patient and option E does not help him at all.

Answer Question 5

ABDEC

It is most appropriate to stabilise the patient first, and ask the nurse to bleep your registrar immediately. The next best option is bleeping the registrar after you have seen to the patient. Asking other colleagues for help (e.g. other junior doctors) is also acceptable although not ideal. It is not appropriate to only see the patient once you have found your registrar and it is even more inappropriate not to seek help when you need it. This situation highlights the importance of being honest and seeking senior help when you feel that a situation is beyond your competency, thus minimising risks to patient safety.

Answer Question 6

ABDEC

Given the pain only started once taking the new drug, it is sensible to do an ECG and hold off the drug until further advice is given. Doing an ECG only is the next best option, followed by sending off a 12 hour troponin. It would also be sensible to look for any metastatic deposits in the ribs/chest that can cause chest pain. It is not appropriate to do nothing.

Answer Question 7

CEDBA

This question tests your integrity as a clinician. Although the patient is your best friend's mother, you still should not treat this case any differently than that of any other patient and confidentiality should remain. The best option is option C as you are involving senior colleagues and can discuss any confidentiality issues directly. Option E follows this closely as you would still not be breaching confidentiality. Although option D is a blanket rejection of divulging any information (thereby still maintaining confidentiality), here you could risk coming across as unhelpful or straining the doctor-patient relationship. As a result it is placed as the third option and not higher in the levels of appropriateness. Option B allows you to gauge what the son knows, which you could relay to the team and then decide how much information needs to be given. Nevertheless, you may risk divulging patient information as the son could try to push you to fill him in on any missing information he has not given you or ask you to correct him on his understanding of the situation. Option A is clearly the worst option as you are breeching confidentiality without speaking to the patient first.

Answer Question 8

BCEAD

As a junior doctor you are not expected to understand every biochemical test or be able to interpret complicated scans. However, in this scenario these happen to be very important pieces of information for the registrar. Despite it being embarrassing you should admit your lack of knowledge in the relevant area. This way you do not give any false information and can even learn more. If this is not possible then it would be better to just read everything out rather than miss out information. It is unprofessional to make up information which can lead to unnecessary treatment or further investigations.

Answer Question 9

BCADE

Although you are busy on a ward round and the rest of the team has moved on, it is important that the patient does not feel poorly informed as this could result in poor adherence to medications, lack of trust in the admitting team and possibly even refusal for consent of the investigation. One should apologise, explain and offer more of your time at a later point. The consultant should be made aware of why you were delayed for his learning purposes as well as yours.

Answer Question 10

DBCAE

All five options are valid and necessary. You should therefore be listing them in order of importance and in order of what you would do first. The correct environment is vital, followed by an explanation. The opportunity for them to ask questions should be provided throughout. Information should be given in simple terms so that it is fully understood and adequate time should be allowed for them to discuss the matter in private.

Answer Question 11

BAEDC

This patient's relatives are clearly very annoyed with Mr Smith's discharge progress. It is therefore important that you address the relatives' concerns as soon as you can, provided that you are not meant to be attending to any urgent tasks. However, you must be honest and explain that as you are not the patient's regular doctor, you may not be able to answer all their questions. It is not appropriate to contact the patient's team out of hours regarding this issue as they are not on-call; but this is better than simply refusing to see the patient's family when they are clearly upset. It would be better to advise the relatives to talk to the patient's regular team the following morning. It is also inappropriate to advise the patient's relatives to file a complaint against Mr Smith's doctors.

Answer Question 12

BCAED

This case highlights the importance of protecting patient safety whilst maintaining professional courtesy towards our colleagues. It is best to sensitively address this first with the consultant concerned so as not to undermine him. If the situation does not resolve then it would be appropriate to approach another consultant and then the clinical director if required. Moreover, as a junior doctor it is best to involve a senior colleague such as another consultant before approaching the clinical director so that you do not feel out of your depth when dealing with the situation. It is not appropriate to inform the patients to be aware of the consultant, and it is even more inappropriate to turn a blind eye.

Answer Question 13

AEDCB

Making a list of problems with the system will enable you to address each one individually. Discussions with senior colleagues will help determine their opinions on flaws and possible improvements. You could then start a quality improvement audit, initiate change and then re-audit to complete the cycle.

Answer Question 14

CDEAB

If you politely state that you would like the opportunity to learn to perform a lumbar puncture as you have never previously done so, the other members of the team are likely to respond to your enthusiasm. You must, however, not perform a procedure that you are not competent to do and must not lie to your patients or senior colleagues either.

Answer Question 15

DCABE

Learning is an integral part of being a Foundation doctor. The idea behind 'bleep-free' teaching is that it should be uninterrupted and your team members are supposed to cover your absence on the ward whilst you are in teaching. You are meant to hand in your bleep to a receptionist, who informs anyone who bleeps you that you are in teaching. It is your responsibility to check-in your bleep. As you have forgotten to hand in your bleep in this case, you are obliged to answer your bleep and ask the person bleeping you to contact another team member. If it is regarding an urgent task, it is more sensible to bleep a team member yourself to ensure that the task is attended to.

Answer Question 16

ADECB

It is most appropriate to discuss this issue directly with your registrar and then express your concerns to your consultant if the situation has not been resolved. Your consultant is responsible for overseeing your learning and can address this sensitively with your registrar. It may also be useful to voice your concerns to your educational supervisor who may be able to organise some teaching for you, or advise you about other measures to further your learning. In the meantime, it is good for you to take responsibility for your own development and be willing to learn from other colleagues whenever possible.

Answer Question 17

ADBCE

In this case it is best that you immediately inform a senior colleague in the night team about the situation and directly handover any tasks. This gives them sufficient time to make any necessary arrangements (e.g. contact medical staffing to organise a replacement etc.). It is important that you ensure that any urgent tasks are attended to immediately. However, in this case, the night team is understaffed and the registrar may be busy with ill patients in the emergency department. If there is no one else to handover urgent tasks to, you may to have attend to them yourself to ensure that there is no risk to patient safety. This demonstrates the importance of prioritising tasks by clinical urgency and delegating tasks to other colleagues where suitable, whilst ensuring that you do not abandon your own personal commitments unnecessarily.

Answer Question 18

ACBED

Student feedback is an important way of improving the teaching that is provided to undergraduates. A simple conversation with the undergraduate teaching coordinator can solve these issues and a teaching programme set up by junior doctors would not only help the undergraduates but would also improve junior doctor teaching skills. It would be unnecessary to involve the medical school dean at this time.

Answer Question 19

ABCDE

Most departments are happy to provide advice and opportunities to people who take a special interest in their field. It would be advisable to find a mentor, someone who can guide you through applications and career progression. If you can negotiate time off with your team then you can gain experience within your chosen specialty. It would also be wise to discuss your aims with your educational supervisor who may be able to assist you in fulfilling your aspirations.

Answer Question 20

CEBDA

It is your duty to explain the risks of self discharging. One must clearly document all the risks that have been quoted to the patient. If the patient is deemed mentally competent and all risks and adverse circumstances have been explained then he may be allowed to leave given he signs a self-discharge form. One should provide clear documentation in the notes and the GP needs to be informed in case the patient becomes ill again. If you feel out of your depth dealing with the situation, you may need to contact a senior colleague but you should at least try to see the patient immediately to convince him to stay.

Answer Question 21

BACED

Patients who struggle with mobility and transfer should only be allowed on stairs and in corridors with physiotherapy support. This particular patient could easily have fallen and injured himself badly. If possible you alone can take the patient back but usually a trained professional in manual handling is required as well. The ward manager should be alerted to these events and the physiotherapists should be informed so that they have further input into the patient's care. The patient himself should be counselled and advised about not currently attempting stairs without support. The patient's team should also be informed about this and therefore documentation in the notes is important.

Answer Question 22

CBDAE

Here there is an evident patient safety issue. Your first priority is to stabilise the patient and ensure that she is catheterised. If you feel that the patient is deteriorating, it is appropriate to call your registrar for advice and he may also be able to suggest the best approach to dealing with the nurse's actions. Once you have stabilised the patient, it is appropriate that you speak to the nurse in private regarding what has happened as her actions have put a patient at risk and it is important that she understands the consequences of this. It is wise to fill in an incident form so that the reasons as to why this has occurred can be looked into to prevent future occurrences.

Answer Question 23

CABDE

The law clearly states that a minor under the age of 13 is not competent to enter into a sexual relationship, and thus it is considered rape. Hence in this case, patient confidentiality must be breached and this must be reported. As the patient is a junior it may be out of your depth to call the police immediately, and therefore it may be better to get a senior involved before you do so. In this case it would be most appropriate to contact the child protection lead of the hospital, who would be able to coordinate the necessary people to investigate the matter further.

Answer Question 24

CADBE

This is ultimately your error as it is your responsibility to check the expiry date of the vaccine. It is best practice to be honest with the patient and check with a senior colleague whether he will require a further dose to provide maximum protection. To prevent further harm to other patients, it is appropriate to check the expiry dates of all the vaccines in the fridge and also to fill out a critical incident form to prevent future occurrences.

Answer Question 25

DCAEB

The patient's symptoms may well be due to gallstones but a more sinister cause such as cancer which may need urgent treatment needs to be excluded. By contacting radiology the scan will be done and reported quickly before she leaves. If it is gallstones she can be reassured and if it is malignancy then it has been picked up. It would be sensible to get the results before leaving because she could be in a position where she is given abnormal results but cannot do anything about it. She does not need emergency admission as she is not acutely unwell. Regarding insurance, it would be prudent to let the travel insurance know. Problems could arise if the patient became ill whilst abroad and subsequently filed a claim. The first thing that would happen after a claim would be for the insurance company to request a copy of the medical reports.

Answer Question 26

ACDBE

Option A is the best approach. There is no problem in taking information home for a project as long as identifiable patient details are left out. This way the audit can be completed and the information is anonymised. If this isn't an option then asking for an extension would be the next best answer. Asking the secretary is not appropriate, but it is more inappropriate to take patient notes home. Falsifying the results is a serious offence.

Answer Question 27

CABDE

Involving a senior colleague for advice is the best option as this way your team is informed and you can complete the form without compromising patient safety. Staying up late is far better than lying and calling in sick. Option E is considered plagiarism/fraud and is a serious offence.

Answer Question 28

DEBCA

In your capacity as a junior doctor who may be rather inexperienced in paediatric medicine, option D is the most sensible action as you can then gain advice from someone senior about the best course of action. This should only be brief however as the child is clearly in pain and will need to examined and treated as soon as possible. After getting senior advice it would then be appropriate to contact social services before involving the police. Scolding the mother does not do any good and will just make her angrier.

Answer Question 29

ACEDB

You should obtain an accurate summary of the various clinical situations from the referring healthcare professional who is contacting you. This will help you prioritise each clinical situation so that you can see to the patients who need urgent attention first. Keeping an accurate list of jobs that you have accumulated is useful to structure your own mind as well as to highlight unfinished jobs. You should be aware of your level of competence and request senior help whenever necessary.

Answer Question 30

CBEDA

One can start the patient on broad spectrum antibiotics if clinical suspicion is high. A chest radiograph would confirm the diagnosis. Sputum culture and blood cultures would help narrow down the specific diagnosis. It is unlikely to be legionella, especially as the patient has been an inpatient. However, one can send this test off for completeness.

Answer Question 31

BCAED

A thorough examination is vital. It is evident that the patient is overloaded with fluid. A catheter would help monitor urine output as one can measure this using a urometer. An increase in diuretics would improve symptoms and is a treatment for the heart failure, but you should be cautious in altering the dosage of this medication and seek senior advice prior to doing so. Furosemide can also result in renal failure and hypotension and therefore should not be tampered with without senior advice. Oral fluid restriction would improve symptoms and daily weights would allow regular assessment of patient progress, but these last two options would not cause any immediate effect on the patient's clinical status and so therefore are the least appropriate 'immediate' actions to take even though they are also important.

Answer Question 32

BCEDA

It is clear from the history that the patient is likely to be suffering from bowel obstruction secondary to adhesions. Conservative management usually resolves the bowel obstruction, but surgery is occasionally needed. One should first examine the patient, obtain intravenous access and take blood. An abdominal X-ray can then be requested with urgency. While waiting for this the registrar can be contacted and he/she will advise you regarding further management. The registrar will most likely choose to review the patient himself.

Answer Question 33

DBCEA

Cleary the best option is to repeat the troponin, given that he had an ECG 20 minutes ago. The next best option is repeating the ECG. If all tests come back normal and the patient is stable then he can be discharged. He should not be started on ACS (acute coronary syndrome) protocol without evidence of sustaining an acute coronary syndrome, and he should definitely not be added to the angioplasty list without review from a senior colleague such as a cardiology registrar.

Answer Question 34

BECDA

In working with other colleagues there may be issues regarding people not contributing their fair share. The best option to avoid such problems is to agree beforehand that how much work everyone puts in should be reflected in the authorship of the paper. Another good option is to delegate the tasks but then check everyone's progress. It is not that efficient for a minimum number of people to do the maximum amount of work and being confrontational or excluding the third colleague will not help with team dynamics.

Answer Question 35

DCAEB

In this case, Mr Yeti's behaviour may be put down to the passing away of his son. Thus you should ask Mr Smith about Mr Yeti's behaviour and what exactly he does or says, then speak directly to Mr Yeti to explain to him that despite understanding why he is angry he cannot act like this. This will give him the opportunity to explain himself as well and you may be able to offer him some counselling if necessary. If Mr Yeti still continues to act inappropriately then he may need to move to a side room or another ward to minimise upsetting other patients. Although telling Mr Smith that you cannot do anything is an inadequate response, the most inappropriate response would be to breach confidentiality and inform him about the death of Mr Yeti's son.

Answer Question 36

CBDAE

Although you cannot be 100% sure, the scenario here may be the result of the patient developing compartment syndrome which is a surgical emergency. You should contact the orthopaedic registrar immediately, who will likely advise you to cut off the plaster and come to review the patient themselves. Contacting another senior colleague is the next best option, although they may not be as familiar with orthopaedic issues as the orthopaedic registrar. Arranging a repeat X-ray is better than discharging the patient.

Answer Question 37

ADCEB

Although reporting the patient may have disastrous consequences for her, you are ethically bound to inform your seniors if this occurs as it is a serious contraindication for transplant. Getting a more detailed history from the patient would also be advisable the next day and will allow your seniors to have a chance to speak to her. Option C is the next best option, but means that you have not involved your seniors, which you should do in this situation. You should not ignore the situation completely, nor is the pub a particularly suitable venue for a consultation.

Answer Question 38

CBDEA

In order for the patient to give informed consent he needs to be aware of the benefits and risks of the operation, which can be communicated to him by your registrar. Hence it most appropriate to ask your registrar to consent the patient, and it is preferable that you directly ask him, rather than via the senior nurse, to ensure that it is done. It is not acceptable for you to consent the patient as you are not aware of the benefits and risks of the operation, and hence the patient would not be able to make an informed decision. Consent can only be explained by someone who understands the procedure and/or is able to carry it out themselves. Advising the patient not to have the operation is grossly inappropriate.

Answer Question 39

ADBEC

This question addresses the importance of balancing your duty to patients with your duty to protect your own health. Hence it is most important that you go to the Occupational Health department and receive a hepatitis B booster or receive any HIV prophylaxis if required. The patient needs to be consented and bled by someone other than you. It is not appropriate to wait until the following day to report the injury, though this is clearly a better option than never reporting it.

Answer Question 40

ABCDE

It is best to speak to your fellow junior doctor first, and then raise the issue with a senior colleague. Doing nothing is not acceptable as your colleague being late is already affecting your ward round preparation and this could compromise patient care.

Answer Question 41

ECADB

It is important that you do not consent someone when you do not know anything about the procedure. The next best option is asking the registrar what to put on the consent form. Looking it up on the internet (although still a dubious option) is better than asking the scrub nurse what to write as she may only be able to tell you about the procedure itself but may not be aware of the complications afterwards if she is not directly involved in the post-operative patient care.

Answer Question 42

EDCBA

Contacting someone senior is clearly the best thing to do. It is unprofessional to sneak onto the ward round without first sending your apologies or informing the team you will be late, and it is even more inappropriate to call in sick. Doing this turns the small issue of running late into a probity issue by lying to your colleagues.

Answer Question 43

CBADE

Telling the consultant politely about the situation is the best option. It is unprofessional to get angry with the other junior doctor and accuse them of lying which they may not be aware of and might honestly have forgotten the conversation. It is even worse to lie and say you took the bloods when you didn't even send any off. Making up results is very dangerous to patient safety and is gross misconduct.

Answer Question 44

ABCED

Telling someone you are unwell is important. Your team are the first people to inform, followed by the rota coordinator and medical staffing. You should not struggle through the day without telling anyone, but it is even worse to simply go home without mentioning it to anyone as your firm will be very concerned about your whereabouts.

Answer Question 45

DABCE

You need to follow the patient's wishes as they have explicitly told you they refuse to have the blood. Leaving the prescription but telling the nurses not to give the blood will cause confusion. Giving the blood against the patient's wishes amounts to battery and is gross misconduct.

Answer Question 46

ABCDE

Given that your bleep keeps going off from the same number, it may be an emergency. Therefore it would be prudent to ask the nurse attending to the patient to help you answer your bleep and let you know what it is about so that you can prioritise appropriately. Ignoring the bleep and answering it when you can is better than asking a patient to answer it, as this is grossly inappropriate and would breach patient confidentiality if they were to find out information about another patient on a different ward.

PART TWO – Answers to the Multi-Action Questions

Answer Question 47

BFH

This scenario is centred upon patient confidentiality and communication skills. The mistake performed by the Foundation doctor here is reviewing patient records on the public ward. Whenever you review any information that may be sensitive regarding a patient you should try to do this in private, either in the doctor's office or somewhere where you will not be disturbed or overlooked by other patients/relatives (option H).

Despite the fact that the patient's relatives now might have a good idea about what is going on having seen the chest X-ray, you should still refrain from confirming or denying their beliefs and refuse to disclose any personal information (option B). Although the radiograph appears rather concerning, it does not necessarily confirm the presence of cancer and it would be best if a senior colleague can speak to the family and give them more advice on the further management (option F).

Answer Question 48

BCH

According to the *New Doctor* publication, "assessment systems are in place to ensure that Foundation doctors are fit for purpose." It is mandatory to pass the appropriate number of DOPS and other assessment methods to continue to the next level of medical training.

It is useful to obtain feedback from members of your team in the first instance as they will be most familiar with your abilities and able to give you balanced and accurate feedback on your performance (options B and C) but should there not be any opportunity for this then you may wish to ask members of other medical teams or the emergency department clinicians to assess your practical skills (options D or E). If you really feel that you cannot fit in any opportunity for assessments in your work then it would be necessary to raise this issue with your educational supervisor (option A) rather than to not do any assessments at all.

Answer Question 49

BGH

According to the *New Doctor* publication regarding Foundation training, training should include (amongst other things):

- "learning based on experience that provides clinical training in a range of practices and procedures

- regular, formal educational sessions that cover topics of value and interest to Foundation doctors, who must be facilitated to attend

- opportunities to reflect on learning and practice and to discuss issues with their educational supervisor and other colleagues."

It is therefore important that if you believe your job is not allowing you the opportunity to develop as a doctor and learn new skills you raise the issue with your educational supervisor and/or clinical supervisor (option G). Choosing topics that you believe you would like extra teaching on is a good way to direct your learning (option B) and keeping an eye out for interesting clinical cases on the ward to complete assessments and obtain feedback upon in the form of a CBD (option H) is another way around this problem.

You can always do your own personal reading at home (option D) or ask your seniors to explain their management in more detail to you on ward rounds (option C). However, these are probably less effective methods of gaining extra teaching.

Answer Question 50

DCE

The DVLA guidelines state that "it is the legal duty of the (driving) license holder to notify the DVLA of any medical condition which may affect safe driving", however, there may be cases where the driver may not wish to disclose this information, such as when their job depends upon their ability to drive.

In these cases doctors are expected, where possible, to intervene in the interests of public safety. The GMC have published specific guidelines for doctors that do encounter such patients. These guidelines state:

- if the driver/patient refuses to accept their diagnosis or the effect it may have on their condition to drive, a second opinion may be sought

- if the driver/patient continues to drive every effort should be made to persuade them otherwise, including speaking to their family members, so long as the patient/driver agrees

- if these measures do not work, then the doctor should contact the DVLA about the situation and before doing so, inform the patient of their intention.

The full recommendations with regards to driving, medical conditions and the law are available within the *At a Glance Guide to Current Medical Standards of Fitness to Drive*, published by the DVLA on the http://www.directgov.co.uk website.

In this question, one may be tempted to inform the surgeon performing the surgery (option F), but this is less important than the other choices as it has no direct correlation or contribution towards stopping the patient from driving. Informing the patient's GP and neurologist would be a better option (option E) since these clinicians regularly see the patient and are more able to check his progress and follow-up on the management of his epilepsy. If you do not feel that the patient will inform the DVLA themselves then you should warn the patient that you will do this (options C and D) after giving the patient notice of this.

Answer Question 51

ABD

It is the duty of all doctors to protect and promote the health of their patients, which includes protecting the patient from any harm that may occur from a colleague's mistakes. Although this drug error is a minor error which does not appear the patient has been harmed by, it is still important to correct the mistake (option A) rather than to leave it. You should document why you have crossed off the drug and rewritten it to avoid any confusion with other clinicians looking at the chart and if there is insufficient space on the chart, this should be written in the medical notes (option B).

Feedback to your colleague may be useful as they may not have realized they have been writing the wrong units of measurements for the drug and it will prevent future errors. It is not professional at this stage to advertise the mistake that the doctor has made in front of their medical team (option G) if it really was an honest mistake or to try to turn other doctors in the hospital against your colleague (option H) by undermining their prescribing actions, unless this becomes a serious repeated offense.

Answer Question 52

ABD

The GMC's *Good Medical Practice* guidelines state that "Teaching, training, appraising and assessing doctors and students are important for the care of patients now and in the future. Doctors should be willing to contribute to these activities." Therefore it is a duty of your registrar to assist you in completion of your assessment.

It may be that your senior colleague is overworked with other clinical commitments and if this is the case it would be prudent to try to rearrange a time suitable for the both of you to go though the case (option A), otherwise you may be able to get some feedback from the consultant (option B) who can also complete your assessment. Reading around the case and the management will help to improve your knowledge of the patient's condition and learning (option D).

It is less appropriate to ask a senior house officer to complete the assessments for you (option G) as they may not be as experienced or able to give you as detailed feedback on the patient's management. Emailing the link for the assessment online to the registrar (option C) can mean that you may get the assessment completed more conveniently, but you will not learn anything from the case if this is not discussed with your senior colleague.

Answer Question 53

CDG

This is a scenario assessing your ability to maintain patient autonomy and involve the patient in decisions regarding their health. As the patient appeared to have capacity when he elected to refuse the transfusion, it would be wrong to dismiss his wishes. Despite the wife's protestation, your duty of care is to your patient, and friends or relatives should not make medical decisions on their behalf. You should explain this in a calm manner to the wife (option G) and avoid transfusing blood to the patient (option C).

The most appropriate action in order to help this patient would be to look for alternative methods to resuscitate this patient such as with intravenous fluids (option D). Involving the psychiatric team would be unnecessary and delay life-saving treatment (option F).

Answer Question 54

CDF

The *New Doctor* guidelines state that Foundation doctors should "demonstrate that they recognise personal and professional limits, and ask for help from senior colleagues and other health and social care professionals when necessary."

In this scenario, the patient in question appears weak and their condition is deteriorating. It is important to get senior advice from your medical team (option F) as well as any advice from other healthcare professionals who may be able to treat the patient (options C and D). A common problem in elderly patients with multiple co-morbidities include inadequate nutritional intake and the involvement of a dietician is crucial.

Although prescribing intravenous fluids to rehydrate the patient is important, large volumes of this can cause the patient to suffer from pulmonary oedema (option G) and if the patient is at risk of aspiration a barium swallow (option H) may not be as appropriate as aspiration of barium can cause mediastinitis. If the patient is not on the appropriate antibiotic therapy, continuing the same medication may not be effective in treating the patient's infection (option B). It is tempting to repeat arterial blood gases on the patient to monitor their oxygenation levels, however, without any intervention, this will not help to improve the patient's condition and repeated attempts may thrombose the vessel meaning the next time a blood gas is required, it may be more difficult to obtain (option E).

Answer Question 55

BCF

According to the GMC *Good Medical Practice* guidelines, "you must protect patients from risk of harm posed by another colleague's conduct, performance or health. If you have concerns that a colleague may not be fit to practise, you must take appropriate steps without delay."

In this scenario, there is some question about patient safety being compromised by a colleague who does not appear fit to practise, at least temporarily. You should try to convince your colleague to refrain from seeing patients or making any major clinical decisions (options B and C) and if they do not appear to respond to your concerns and you are still convinced of their state, you should approach your consultant regarding the matter (option F).

The scenario implies that your colleague is normally a responsible doctor and there is no evidence that he has an 'alcohol problem' so counselling may not be necessary (option H) and neither is reporting the doctor to the GMC if they heed your concerns and do not put patient care at risk (option E).

Answer Question 56

CEH

In this particular scenario, the patient is Gillick (or now commonly known as 'Fraser') competent and appears to have an understanding of the full implications of her actions. It would be ideal, although not compulsory, for the patient to inform her parents of the situation as this can be a stressful time and family support may be helpful for some patients (option C). Referral to an abortion clinic does not require parental consent (option E).

Although it is advisable to confirm pregnancy by way of a pregnancy test, this will be performed at the abortion clinic and is over 95% accurate (option G). Offering the patient alternative methods of contraception to prevent the same situation recurring and screening for other potential health problems such as sexually transmitted diseases ensures that you are helping to educate the patient on other aspects of sexual health and are offering a holistic approach to their care (option H). Abstinence will prevent future pregnancies, however, this an unreasonable option and the patient may not be adherent to this suggestion (option F).

Answer Question 57

BCG

In this scenario the patient is perfectly entitled to leave even if it is against medical advice providing he is aware of the potential consequences of this and knows where to go if his medical situation changes (options B and G).

Although the abdominal ultrasound scan is normal, this does not necessarily mean that the patient is 'cured' or does not have pancreatitis as ultrasonography is not the most sensitive scan for identifying the pancreas in detail. It is mainly ordered to rule out a cause for the pancreatitis such as gallstones.

It is tempting to ask the patient to see their GP if their symptoms recur (option F) but a flare-up of the patient's pancreatitis would be more appropriately dealt with in the hospital and not within the community. Persuading the patient's wife to reason with him may convince him to change his mind and reconsider his decision and, if not, at least there is another adult caring for the patient who can look out for the signs of the patient's condition worsening (option C). There is no question regarding patient confidentiality in this situation with informing the wife as she is present during the consultation and the patient is presumably happy for her to be there.

Answer Question 58

ABE

The GMC *Good Medical Practice* clearly states that "you should only prescribe drugs to meet identified needs of patients." It is good practice in such situations to explore the reasons behind the patient's request for certain medication and explain your reasons for not providing treatment if you feel it is not suitable (options A and B). After discussing this, the patient can also be advised to seek a second opinion if he feels dissatisfied (option E).

Asking the patient to have a 'general checkup' with a cardiologist is inappropriate without the patient having a specific medical problem in the acute hospital setting (option G) and although the on-call pharmacist (option F) may be able to give more advice on the complications and side effects of certain drugs, they are not in a suitable position to counsel patients on their treatments or prescribe them medication.

Answer Question 59

ABH

The *New Doctor* publication states that Foundation doctors should "demonstrate that they are sensitive and respond to the needs and expectations of patients, taking into account only where relevant, the patient's age, colour, culture, disability, ethnic or national origin, gender, lifestyle, marital or parental status, race, religion or beliefs, sex, sexual orientation, or social or economic status."

Clearly the dress code adopted by the junior doctor in this scenario is inappropriate and does not take into account a patient's expectations of a member of the medical profession. In addition, there is an issue regarding patient safety that needs to be addressed as your colleague's dress code may be offensive to patients, and by wearing her hair loose there is also a potential infection hazard.

It is most appropriate to discuss this with your colleague in a sensitive manner and privately (options A and H) and if she is defensive about her situation, it can help to give specific examples of cases when her demeanour has been inappropriate (option B). It is important that your colleague understands the importance of the issue and that it is affecting staff and patient perceptions of them. If, however, you feel uncomfortable discussing this issue with your colleague, who is the same grade as you, you could ask a senior colleague to help.

Answer Question 60

DEF

New Doctor publication states that junior doctors should "teach their peers and medical and other health and social care students under guidance, if required to do so, using appropriate skills and methods."

In such a situation, as you have already prepared a mock OSCE for your own medical students, doing another one as long as it doesn't interfere with your work is a good option to further help the students and promote teaching (option D). This will no doubt help the students, and also look good on your medical résumé.

The scenario is that the students seem underprepared so perhaps this is a reflection on how they are being tutored. Therefore informing the clinical teaching staff at the university is a reasonable suggestion (option E). If there are too many students for you to possibly accommodate, then informing a consultant (option F) who can liaise with medical school personnel or provide teaching of their own can help reach out to more students than you yourself alone.

Answer Question 61

GHA

There are multiple appropriate answers in this scenario, but the most important immediate actions to take are those that relate to safety of the patient. This includes accurate documentation of the procedure in the notes (option H) and making sure the fluid is sent off straightaway (option G). Only then should you consider going through the case with your senior colleague. After that one could then reflect on the procedure to aid self development (option A).

Although you have only performed the procedure once, it takes several attempts to be competent. Until you have been deemed to have reached this level, you should not teach your peers or supervise them performing the same procedure (option B).

Answer Question 62

ADE

As a doctor you have a duty to teach and appraise medical students so that they can learn to become competent doctors themselves. In this situation, your medical student has approached you for some help and raises concerns at the clinical experience of his attachment on your firm. The best option is to try to resolve the student's concerns locally first by suggesting they should speak to the consultant (option A).

There are ways in which you can help resolve the situation by involving the rest of the medical team to see if your colleagues have suggestions for patients who would be useful for the student to examine (option D). If you are willing to teach (option E) it will help to develop both your teaching skills and those of your colleagues, as well as supporting the student.

If the student is still not content with their experience on the firm, then it may be worth them submitting a complaint to their medical school or ask to change rotations, however, it is not your place to do this on the student's behalf (options B, G and H).

Answer Question 63

ADE

As a good doctor, it is your duty to communicate effectively with your patients, which includes "listening to patients, asking for and respecting their views about their health, and responding to their concerns and preferences" in accordance with the GMC *Good Medical Practice* guidelines.

In this situation, it is most appropriate to inform the patient of the benefits and risks of having further investigation and explore any concerns they may have, to ensure that he can make an informed decision (options A, D and E).

If after this the patient still refuses to have further investigations, this wish must be respected as he is competent. In time, it may also be suitable to advise the patient to discuss this matter with his family, if he wishes, who may want to be made aware of the situation and who can offer emotional support.

Answer Question 64

ADE

The *New Doctor* publication states that Foundation doctors should learn to "manage their own time under supervision, and develop strategies with other healthcare workers to maximise efficient use of time."

This scenario is asking you to balance your requirements for managing patient care with your need to continue to improve and learn new skills as a doctor. As your consultant has come to deal with a sick patient and asked for your help in assisting with a chest drain, you should help him gather the equipment he requires (option A). If you believe that the procedure teamed with teaching will take a long time and you have several ward tasks, you should arrange for cover during the time you are assisting in case you cannot answer your bleep (option D) and prioritise your workload (option E) to ensure you manage to get all the important tasks done afterwards before your shift ends.

There are several other appropriate options, but the ones stated above ensure that you are assisting your consultant in patient care, improving your own training and skills and ensuring that your workload is being managed.

Answer Question 65

ADF

This is a rather difficult situation and not one that you should be solely involved in as a Foundation doctor. Your role in this circumstance is to ensure that you gain as much detailed history from the patient (option A) and their previous GP (option F) as possible. When deciding on an appropriate management plan where controlled drugs are required to be prescribed, especially in the community, you must involve the help of a senior colleague (option D).

There may be several management options that your senior colleague suggests or be happy instigating, including giving the patient a single observed dose of methadone (option B) or not prescribing any medication for the time being (option C), however, you must not act in this situation alone.

Answer Question 66

CGH

This scenario is centred on balancing training opportunities with clinical responsibilities. Attending Foundation teaching sessions is a mandatory requirement of completing your Foundation training and therefore missing this teaching is not an option. Your clinical team should be aware of this arrangement if they are not already aware (option C) and should support you in allowing you to attend.

If you are finding that your team are not supportive, you should discuss the matter with your educational supervisor (option G) and if you still wish to continue gaining clinical experience from the surgical clinics, you can always try to attend these after your teaching (option H).

It would not be appropriate to re-arrange compulsory Foundation teaching on a different day of the week as this would disrupt the timetable for all the other junior doctors in the hospital (option E).

Answer Question 67

AEC

In this scenario, your personal health is starting to deteriorate as a result of your workload and it is concerning friends close to you. According to the *New Doctor* publication junior doctors should "demonstrate knowledge of their responsibilities to look after their health, including maintaining a suitable balance between work and personal life, and knowing how to deal with personal illness to protect patients."

The issues regarding your workload can be addressed by talking to your clinical or educational supervisor or medical colleagues (option A and E). You should acknowledge any deterioration in your personal health and whether this is affecting your clinical work. You should take measures to try to maintain your health (option C).

Answer Question 68

ADG

This will be an emotionally challenging situation for all involved, particularly in such a young patient. However, it is important to recognise when attempts are futile, and somebody needs to broach the subject. According to the 'Advance Life Support' guidelines published by the Resuscitation Council "resuscitation should be continued as long as ventricular fibrillation persists and it is generally accepted that asystole for more than 20 minutes in the absences of a reversible cause, is grounds for abandoning the resuscitation attempt."

Initiating a discussion, whilst continuing CPR (option A) is important, and CPR should continue until no reversible cause is found (option G) and members of the cardiac arrest team are comfortable with the decision to stop (option D). Even though you are a junior doctor, you will be a valuable member of the cardiac arrest team and your opinion is important. Calling time of death (option B) is not appropriate until efforts have been stopped. Finding people to relieve the crash team (option F) is appropriate if CPR is going to be continued but not if it is merely prolonging the inevitable.

Answer Question 69

ADG

According to the GMC *Good Medical Practice* guidelines, "If a patient under your care has suffered harm or distress, you must act immediately to put matters right. You should offer an apology and explain fully and promptly to the patient what has happened, and the likely short-term and long-term effects."

In this scenario, you should not try to pretend that nothing has happened or try to cover up your mistake (options B and H), but instead be honest and open about the mistake to your patient as well as offer your apologies (options G and D). You should also act to rectify the mistake by using compression and placing a dressing to halt any further bleeding (option A).

After the bleeding has stopped you may wish to ask a senior member of the medial team to help take the blood from the patient (option E) and ensure that no sharps are left around the bedside (option C), but this is not the most immediate action to take.

Answer Question 70

BDG

This scenario is based upon communication skills, consent and patient capacity. Although it is important to diagnose HIV and begin treatment for this, you cannot force a patient to consent for any test or procedure if they have capacity and refuse to consent; you can only offer your medical advice and opinion (option G).

In this case you should explore the patient concerns (option B), and still fully assess the patient by taking other useful blood tests (option D) to identify any other serious illnesses you may be able to treat.

You should not take the patient's blood for HIV without their consent (option A) and commencing lifelong anti-retroviral therapy without a positive HIV diagnosis would not be appropriate (option F). Without definitive knowledge of the patient's diagnosis, you should not break patient confidentiality and discuss your concerns with the patient's partner without his consent (option E), unless the patient is willing for you to do this.

Examination 4

PART ONE – Ranking Questions

Question 1

You are one of the junior doctors on the medical team. You and your senior house officer colleague have just commenced one of your patients on treatment for hyperkalaemia. The time is now 17:30 and you are about to go home when your colleague reminds you that you need to let the on-call house officer know that he needs to take a repeat sample in an hour to gauge improvement.

Rank in order the following actions in response to this situation (1= Most appropriate; 5= Least appropriate):

A. Document clearly in the notes about who you have handed over to and the current situation (dated and timed).

B. Inform the patient of what treatment he has received and the likely forthcoming measures.

C. Ask the nurses to take a repeat U&E sample and to contact a member of the on-call team if no improvement.

D. Provide any member of the on-call team with the patient's details, brief medical history and requested actions.

E. Bleep the on-call junior doctor to inform him about taking the blood test, and give them the patient's details, and brief medical history.

Question 2

The third year medical students on your firm tell you that they have had a good experience on your firm with the exception of their time with one registrar. They say that this registrar has been quite rude to them and refused to teach them as he feels this is not his job. He has even told them to leave theatre every time he operates.

Rank in order the following actions in response to this situation (1= Most appropriate; 5= Least appropriate):

A. Thank the students for their valuable feedback.

B. Discuss the problem of the registrar with the undergraduate teaching coordinator.

C. Discuss the problem of the registrar with the consultant.

D. Do nothing about the students' feedback.

E. Report the registrar's behavior to the medical school.

Question 3

It is approaching 5pm and you have just finished a busy day shift. You are getting your belongings together and are about to leave the ward when you meet your consultant. He asks you to prepare a presentation for the monthly morbidity and mortality meeting tomorrow as the doctor who was meant to be doing it is unwell. You are keen to leave on time today as you have made arrangements to go to your sister's birthday party. What do you do?

Rank in order the following actions in response to this situation (1= Most appropriate; 5= Least appropriate):

A.   Stay behind and prepare the presentation for tomorrow and cancel your plans to go to your sister's birthday.

B.   Prepare the presentation once you come back from your sister's birthday party at midnight.

C.   Make up an excuse to your consultant about why you can't do the presentation.

D.   Inform your consultant of your arrangements tonight and say that you will be unable to prepare a presentation in time for the meeting tomorrow. Offer to help find a colleague to prepare the presentation.

E.   State that you have made plans tonight but are happy to work on the presentation tomorrow if another team member helps you.

Question 4

On the ward round, you are writing up some medication for a patient as instructed by your registrar. While looking at the drug chart you realise that you incorrectly prescribed this patient laxatives the previous day. You were told to do so for a different patient.

Rank in order the following actions in response to this situation (1= Most appropriate; 5= Least appropriate):

A.   Fill out an incident form.

B.   Request that you speak to your team in private to inform them of the mistake.

C.   Apologise to the patient.

D.   Go and prescribe the laxative to the patient that you were meant to.

E.   Assess both patients for implications of receiving/not receiving the laxative.

Question 5

You have been asked by the consultant to deliver a presentation of an audit in front of the entire surgical department within your specialty. This is a big presentation which you have put a lot of work and time into. As you are leaving the ward to set up for the presentation, a nurse bleeps you stating that a patient of yours has been slightly drowsy for the past hour following surgery. You are aware that if you attend to the patient you will miss the whole presentation and will not have another opportunity to present it.

Rank in order the following actions in response to this situation (1= Most appropriate; 5= Least appropriate):

A.   Gather more information from the nurse first and then attend to the patient immediately if it sounds like an emergency.

B.   Get one of your colleagues to give the presentation while you attend to the patient.

C.   Ask one of your colleagues to attend to the patient while you deliver the presentation, ensuring that he has all the patient's details and background.

D.   Tell your consultant that you cannot attend as you have an emergency to attend to.

E.   Ignore the nurse's concerns. If the patient is still drowsy after the presentation you can attend to them at this point.

Question 6

You are a junior doctor on an obstetrics and gynaecology rotation. The consultant has bleeped you to help him assist in theatre. The theatre nurse informs you in passing that the next case is a termination of pregnancy in a 25 year old female. You are very reluctant to go as you strongly believe that termination of pregnancy is "against God's will". What do you do?

Rank in order the following actions in response to this situation (1= Most appropriate; 5= Least appropriate):

A.   Inform the consultant that you are unable to assist in theatre because of your personal beliefs and ask him to find someone else.

B.   Bleep one of your team members to see if they are able to assist in theatre. However, you are obliged to assist in theatre if they are unavailable.

C.   Assist in theatre. You should not let your beliefs affect patient care.

D.   Refuse to assist in theatre and tell the consultant that you are unable to come as there is an emergency on the ward. You do not want him to know that termination of pregnancy is against your beliefs as it may affect the grade he gives you when signing you off.

E.   Inform the consultant that you are unable to assist in theatre as it is against your beliefs and ask him to find someone else. Try and move to a different rotation as it is unacceptable for you to do a job which promotes activities against your beliefs.

Question 7

Whilst on a lunch break you notice a colleague having a couple of pints of beer at the medical school bar before returning to the ward. What should you do next?

Rank in order the following actions in response to this situation (1= Most appropriate; 5= Least appropriate):

A.   Call hospital security as he may be a danger to his patients.

B.   Approach your colleague and express your concerns, and advise him that it is likely he is not in a fit state to continue work that day.

C.   Inform the staff on his ward that he has been drinking alcohol.

D.   Report it to your senior.

E.   Arrange for another doctor to see your colleague's patients.

Question 8

You are having lunch in the hospital canteen, which is also used by the general public. You find the cardiology team's patient list on one of the tables. It is clear that a member of their team has left the list in this communal place.

Rank in order the following actions in response to this situation (1= Most appropriate; 5= Least appropriate):

A.   Remove the list and put it into a confidential waste bin.

B.   Contact your colleagues in the cardiology team and advise them as to what you found.

C.   Raise the issue at the next morning handover, to ensure that the mistake is not repeated.

D.   Encourage the anonymisation of patient details wherever possible.

E.   Suggest to the medical director that signs are put up in communal areas to remind staff not to bring confidential material into such areas.

Question 9

Mr Rajwani is a young Indian gentleman who has been admitted to the ward with jaundice. He speaks poor English and is accompanied by many members of his family and his sister, who is acting as a translator. Investigations reveal that he is HIV positive. His family are increasingly anxious and have many questions regarding his health. How should you manage the situation?

Rank in order the following actions in response to this situation (1= Most appropriate; 5= Least appropriate):

A.   Find a member of staff who can act as a translator to speak to Mr Rajwani in a private setting.

B.   Confirm with Mr Rajwani that he does not mind his sister being there to discuss any medical problems before using her as a translator.

C.   Contact his GP to establish his past medical history and details of any previous diagnoses.

D.   Organise an interpreter to come to the ward and speak with Mr Rajwani in a private setting.

E.   Wait until after visiting hours and try to speak to Mr Rajwani yourself to ascertain his own level of understanding.

Question 10

Mrs Plowman has been diagnosed with rectal cancer. The consultant surgeon has explained the available treatment options to her, but she remains unsure of what to do. When your consultant leaves the room she asks you for your honest opinion as to the best course of action.

Rank in order the following actions in response to this situation (1= Most appropriate; 5= Least appropriate):

A.   Answer truthfully, explaining that you do not have the experience that your consultant does and would defer to their opinion.

B.   Repeat what the consultant has explained and run through her options again without giving any specific opinions.

C.   Explore Mrs Plowman's fears and understanding before giving any of your own opinions.

D.   Give your honest opinion as the patient has explicitly asked for your advice.

E.   Do not give your opinion as this may cloud her judgment and influence the patient into making a decision.

Question 11

You review a child in the emergency department whom you suspect has appendicitis. His parents are extremely angry as they brought their son to the emergency department yesterday with similar symptoms and were discharged with analgesia. The mother is crying hysterically and the father is shouting at you, threatening to sue the hospital.

Rank in order the following actions in response to this situation (1= Most appropriate; 5= Least appropriate):

A.   Find the doctor that treated their son yesterday to explain his mistake.

B.   Inform the parents that if they do not calm down they will be escorted out by security.

C.   Try to find a senior colleague.

D.   Apologise for the situation, and explain the current management plan for their son.

E.   Try to calm both parents down by explaining the current situation.

Question 12

You are on your lunch break and receive a bleep from a nurse asking you to assess a post-operative patient who is complaining of chest pain. His observations are stable and the nurse informs you that an ECG is normal. She also informs you that she does not believe it is anything serious but is "covering her back" by calling you.

Rank in order the following actions in response to this situation (1= Most appropriate; 5= Least appropriate):

A.   Ask the nurse to repeat the observations, give some analgesia and explain that you will be along to assess the patient as soon as you have finished your lunch.

B.   Ask the nurse to closely monitor the patient, repeat the ECG and tell her you will be right there.

C.   Contact a colleague to see if he is free to assess the patient.

D.   Call your registrar.

E.   Ask the nurse to initiate medical treatment for acute coronary syndrome (ACS).

Question 13

You are a junior doctor working in the surgical department, and are finding your workload very light as your consultant is now doing reduced operating lists. You have very few inpatients, and often find yourself spending your days in the doctors' mess and going home early.

Rank in order the following actions in response to this situation (1= Most appropriate; 5= Least appropriate):

A.   Inform your clinical supervisor that you feel the post is not a good learning opportunity for a junior doctor.

B.   Make the most of this attachment as you know your next job is in the emergency department and you will be incredibly busy.

C.   Try and go to theatre as much as possible, get involved with an audit/research and make the most of your free time.

D.   Do nothing as it is nice getting to go home early.

E.   Help your other junior doctor colleagues in other surgery rotations who seem a lot busier than you.

Question 14

You have asked your registrar to assess you for a case-based discussion for your ePortfolio. These must be completed as part of your mandatory training during your first Foundation Programme year, and you have left them until quite late to complete. Your registrar has said he is very busy, but would be happy to simply sign the forms for you without formally assessing you due to time restrictions.

Rank in order the following actions in response to this situation (1= Most appropriate; 5= Least appropriate):

A.   Allow your registrar to complete your assessments this way as you need to complete them before your rapidly approaching deadline.

B.   Speak to your Foundation supervisor about getting an extension on your deadline, explaining the circumstances.

C.   Explain to your registrar that you would rather complete the assessment properly, and arrange a mutually convenient time as the next available opportunity.

D.   Speak to a different registrar or consultant about completing your case-based discussion for you.

E.   Complete the assessment this way and get an extra case-based discussion done at the next opportunity.

Question 15

There are two final year medical students attached to your firm, and your consultant has asked you to arrange teaching for them. Since your junior doctor colleague is on annual leave your workload is very high and you are unsure about whether you have the time.

Rank in order the following actions in response to this situation (1= Most appropriate; 5= Least appropriate):

A. Discuss the situation with your consultant and ask whether the teaching can be rescheduled.

B. Speak to other healthcare professionals on the ward to try and arrange teaching for the students in other disciplines whilst you are busy, enabling you to do your jobs and teach them afterwards.

C. Explain the situation to the students and hope they understand your need to reschedule teaching to the next mutually convenient time.

D. Ask the medical students to help you with your jobs in order to make some time available for bedside teaching.

E. Cancel the teaching and encourage the students to go home early.

Question 16

You are completing an audit for your registrar who has given you a deadline for the data collection as you are both hoping to submit the project for publication in a medical journal. By the day of the deadline you have managed to collect information from 97 out of 100 patients and still have three sets of notes outstanding to collect data from.

Rank in order the following actions in response to this situation (1= Most appropriate; 5= Least appropriate):

A. Make up the last three results to match the trend of the rest of your data.

B. Duplicate three results from three random patients.

C. Omit the patients from the analysis.

D. Try to complete the last three patients today.

E. Speak to your registrar about getting an extension.

Question 17

You are the junior doctor on a renal attachment covering the wards on a weekend. A patient is admitted that needs urgent haemodialysis but has no vascular access. Your registrar asks you to organise this.

Rank in order the following actions in response to this situation (1= Most appropriate; 5= Least appropriate):

A. Confirm with your registrar how to go about organising this, and who to contact.

B. Fully clerk the patient, including a thorough examination and taking routine bloods.

C. Contact radiology to see whether a line can be inserted under ultrasound guidance.

D. Contact the consultant on-call.

E. Speak to another junior doctor for advice.

Question 18

One of your junior doctor colleagues on your endocrinology firm is interested in a career in endocrinology and wants to leave the wards to spend some time in clinic with the consultants.

Rank in order the following actions in response to this situation (1= Most appropriate; 5= Least appropriate):

A.   Suggest that he should spend his spare time reading as his work priorities should be his first commitment.

B.   Suggest that you will cover the wards while your colleague goes to clinic.

C.   Ensure you have a method of contacting your colleague should you need help.

D.   Inform your registrars of your plan.

E.   Refuse to allow your colleague to go to clinic as you would prefer to have support on the ward.

Question 19

You are a medical junior doctor on-call and are called to see Mrs Patel with haemoptysis and night sweats. You are concerned she may have active tuberculosis.

Rank in order the following actions in response to this situation (1= Most appropriate; 5= Least appropriate):

A.   Inform the communicable disease team at the hospital and follow hospital protocols.

B.   Inform your consultant and ensure respiratory isolation from other patients until the consultant can come to reassess the patient and situation.

C.   Await positive sputum samples before placing the patient in isolation.

D.   Inform all the nurses on the ward so they may protect themselves.

E.   Keep the patient in isolation until three early morning samples have returned as negative.

Question 20

You are a medical junior doctor working the night shift when you notice a patient's prescription charts at the nurses' station has a much higher dose of methotrexate than is listed in the British National Formulary. It is not your patient but you recognise the rheumatology consultant's signature on the prescription.

Rank in order the following actions in response to this situation (1= Most appropriate; 5= Least appropriate):

A.   Leave it as it is, the consultant must have a reason for writing it that way.

B.   Phone the consultant and ask whether he would like it changed.

C.   Cross off tomorrow's dose and document it in the notes.

D.   Leave it and arrange to talk to the consultant in the morning.

E.   Cross off tomorrow's dose and handover to the team in the morning to review it.

Question 21

After a very busy surgical night shift you have finished your handover and are leaving the ward. As you walk past the end bay you see Mrs Johnson has fallen out of bed and is not moving. No one else seems to have seen it and the nurse covering the bay is on a break.

Rank in order the following actions in response to this situation (1= Most appropriate; 5= Least appropriate):

A.   Bleep the doctor on duty and inform him of the situation, then return to look after the patient until they arrive.

B.   Raise the alarm and shout for help. Attempt to lift the patient back into bed so you can get good access to perform a primary survey.

C.   Raise the alarm and shout for help. Approach the patient with care and begin assessment.

D.   Ask one of the nurses to get the on-duty doctor, whilst beginning assessment yourself. Once they arrive, handover in an appropriate manner and ensure they are OK to care for the patient.

E.   Go and find one of the medical day team to look after the patient.

Question 22

You are on a consultant ward round and you realise your registrar has written up Tazocin for a patient allergic to this medication.

Rank in order the following actions in response to this situation (1= Most appropriate; 5= Least appropriate):

A.   Politely make the registrar aware of the allergy.

B.   Point out the mistake to the consultant.

C.   Cross the antibiotic off the drug chart and try to find an alternative later.

D.   After the ward round, wait for a quiet time to ask the registrar whether you should be giving this patient Tazocin.

E.   Without involving your team, phone microbiology and ask for their advice. Swap Tazocin for an alternative they suggest.

Question 23

You are the junior doctor on a paediatric attachment. One of your patients is a 6 month old baby who has presented with severe anaemia leading to breathing difficulty and requires an urgent blood transfusion. However, the parents are refusing to consent on behalf of their child as they are Jehovah's Witnesses and do not believe in the transfusion of blood products.

Rank in order the following actions in response to this situation (1= Most appropriate; 5= Least appropriate):

A.   Discuss the situation with your seniors.

B.   Explain the urgency of the blood transfusion to the parents.

C.   Give the child the blood transfusion anyway.

D.   Find out if your hospital has a policy to deal with situations such as these.

E.   Respect the parents' opinion and try to find alternative treatment options.

Question 24

You attend a multidisciplinary team (MDT) meeting to discuss discharging a patient who has had bilateral below-knee amputations. Your team believes he is medically fit for discharge but one of the physiotherapists argues with you that this is not the case. She questions your medical judgment and claims it would be unsafe to discharge the patient now.

Rank in order the following actions in response to this situation (1= Most appropriate; 5= Least appropriate):

A.   Do not discharge the patient at this time.

B.   Stand your ground as this decision has been made by the team.

C.   Ask other members of the MDT for their opinions.

D.   Respect her opinion but explain the reasoning behind your case.

E.   Discharge the patient anyway as the decision ultimately lies with you.

Question 25

You are one of two junior doctors on a surgical attachment. You feel that your colleague is getting preferential treatment from your consultant as he always gets to go to theatre and clinic with your consultant while you are left doing ward work.

Rank in order the following actions in response to this situation (1= Most appropriate; 5= Least appropriate):

A.   Speak to your colleague about this and ask if you can take it in turns to attend theatre.

B.   Speak to your consultant directly.

C.   Speak to your registrar.

D.   Do not say anything as you are wary that your consultant has to sign you off.

E.   Make a formal complaint.

Question 26

You are a junior doctor on a stressful surgical rotation. You find yourself drinking at least a large glass or two of wine when you get home every evening to relax. You drink a little more during the weekends when you are out with your friends but do not consider your drinking excessive.

Rank in order the following actions in response to this situation (1= Most appropriate; 5= Least appropriate):

A.   Keep an alcohol diary to monitor the number of units you drink a week.

B.   Consider alternative ways to relax such as signing up to your local gym.

C.   Continue as you have been for you are sure your drinking falls within the recommended allowance.

D.   Attempt to cut back on your drinking.

E.   Cut back on drinking during the week but make up for it during the weekend.

Question 27

You are asked to review a sick patient with hypotension, tachycardia and who is now spiking a temperature. After your review you write up some fluids and paracetamol and ask the nurse to perform 15 minute observations to monitor any response. The nurse refuses your request stating she is really busy and does not think this patient needs them that regularly.

Rank in order the following actions in response to this situation (1= Most appropriate; 5= Least appropriate):

A. Contact your registrar asking him what you should do.

B. Talk to the nurse about your working relationship and how you can improve it.

C. Ask the nurse why she doesn't believe the patient needs such as regular observations.

D. Review the patient again to determine if you have missed something.

E. Complain to the nurse in charge and ask her to find someone else to cover the patient.

Question 28

You are a junior doctor on a medical placement, and are called by the bereavement office to sign the death certificate of a patient that died over the weekend. The junior doctor working over the weekend is not in today but you saw the patient briefly the week before. The patient had pneumonia but you are not sure about the exact cause of death.

Rank in order the following actions in response to this situation (1= Most appropriate; 5= Least appropriate):

A. Put pneumonia as the cause of death, having checked that nothing else happened with the ward staff.

B. Look through the notes as thoroughly as possible to establish the exact cause of death.

C. Tell the bereavement office that you will do it later in the week so you can build up a good picture of what happened from all those involved.

D. Contact the junior doctor and registrar on-call over the weekend and establish what happened. Then complete the certificate in a timely manner.

E. Inform the bereavement office that you are not able to complete the certificate as you are not sure of the cause of death.

Question 29

An elderly gentleman is admitted to the ward after collapsing at home earlier this afternoon. He tells you he takes 3 mg warfarin tablets every day at 6pm, and is very concerned about having missed his dose today.

Rank in order the following actions in response to this situation (1= Most appropriate; 5= Least appropriate):

A. Prescribe him 3 mg of warfarin tonight.

B. Reassure him that he will not suffer any consequences by omitting his warfarin dose for just one day.

C. Take a clotting sample and consider prescribing warfarin only if the INR is not high.

D. Start an unfractionated heparin infusion as this can be reversed quickly.

E. Consult your registrar about whether it is sensible to restart the warfarin at this time.

Question 30

You receive a call from microbiology about a wound swab sample sent from one of your patients that has grown herpes simplex virus type 1. This will require treatment with oral acyclovir. You are familiar with the patient, but remember that she was discharged a few days ago.

Rank in order the following actions in response to this situation (1= Most appropriate; 5= Least appropriate):

A.   Call the patient at home and tell her to either visit the GP or the ward to collect a prescription as soon as possible.

B.   Write a letter to the patient.

C.   Write it in the patient's notes and wait until she is seen in the outpatient clinic in two weeks.

D.   Notify the Centre for Disease Control and Prevention (CDC).

E.   Call the patient's GP and ask him to prescribe her oral acyclovir.

Question 31

You are the junior doctor on-call for surgery, and a 15 year old boy comes in febrile with a rigid abdomen and right iliac fossa pain. You suspect a perforated appendix and inform your registrar who tells the patient he will need to have emergency surgery. The patient refuses to consent for surgery even though he appears to fully comprehend the benefits of surgery and the risks of not having it. His parents are a few hours away and unreachable by phone.

Rank in order the following actions in response to this situation (1= Most appropriate; 5= Least appropriate):

A.   Raise this issue with your seniors.

B.   Await his parents' arrival for a decision to be made by them.

C.   The patient has not given valid consent, and since he fully understands the risks vs. benefits do not go ahead with the surgery and discharge the patient.

D.   Attempt to further highlight the urgent need for surgery to the patient, outlining the risks and benefits more comprehensively.

E.   Manage the patient conservatively with intravenous antibiotics, analgesia and fluids.

Question 32

You are the junior doctor doing a surgical attachment. You are asked by the surgical registrar to assess a patient in the emergency department. He is tied up in theatre and has told you not to disturb him as the case in theatre is very complex and may take a further few hours. You go to see the patient and discover he is bleeding profusely from his back passage. You are unsure how to manage the situation.

Rank in order the following actions in response to this situation (1= Most appropriate; 5= Least appropriate):

A.   Assess and manage the patient using A, B, C principles initially.

B.   Call your registrar anyway as you are unsure how to manage the situation.

C.   Ask for help from senior colleagues in the emergency department.

D.   Take a history, perform a full examination, do urgent investigations and ensure blood has been cross-matched.

E.   Go to theatre to try and speak to your registrar directly.

Question 33

You are one of two junior doctors on a busy medical firm. Your colleague has been consistently turning up for work late and appears distracted. You have also been informed by the pharmacist of a few prescribing errors they have made recently, one of which almost resulted in a serious incident but was fortunately discovered by a member of the nursing staff. What should you do?

Rank in order the following actions in response to this situation (1= Most appropriate; 5= Least appropriate):

A.   Speak directly to your educational/clinical supervisor.

B.   Talk to your colleague yourself before involving any seniors, exploring any personal issues they may be dealing with.

C.   Inform your colleague's clinical supervisor that you believe he is struggling and may benefit from some extra guidance.

D.   Fill in a clinical incident form regarding the prescribing error.

E.   Discuss the matter with other doctors on your firm.

Question 34

You are the junior doctor on a busy surgical firm. It is a Friday evening, and several of your patients are quite unwell post-operatively. You are supposed to handover to the junior doctor who will be covering on the weekend, but is unfortunately running late. You need to leave promptly as you have your best friend's engagement party to attend.

Rank in order the following actions in response to this situation (1= Most appropriate; 5= Least appropriate):

A.   Attempt to contact your junior doctor colleague to give a verbal handover over the telephone, listing any important jobs and problems.

B.   Write up a detailed handover sheet outlining all the patients and jobs your colleague will be responsible for, and leave the written handover in the surgical office.

C.   Contact the surgical registrar, and give them a verbal and written handover which they can pass on to your colleague when he or she arrives.

D.   Leave a summary of each patient and the jobs that need doing over the weekend in the notes, and inform your colleague that this is what you have done.

E.   Await the arrival of your colleague to ensure appropriate handover, even though this may mean missing the engagement party of your best friend.

Question 35

The family of one of your patients has been increasingly rude and demanding to you and other staff on the ward. Most recently they have been complaining to you about your consultant, and have informed you that they are going to make a formal complaint.

Rank in order the following actions in response to this situation (1= Most appropriate; 5= Least appropriate):

A. Ignore the family as they are being unreasonable, and continue to maintain the highest standard of care for the patient.

B. Talk to the family about their concerns and their behaviour, exploring their views but also explaining that their behaviour on the ward is inappropriate.

C. Speak to the sister in charge on the ward about how to handle the situation.

D. Discuss with your consultant and team about how best to manage the situation.

E. Inform security about the family.

Question 36

You have been working very closely with a young patient who initially presented after a road traffic accident. His family are extremely grateful to you for your role during his initial recovery and rehabilitation. After his discharge, his family present you with a card and £100 cash as a token of their appreciation. They are very insistent that you accept the gift, and will not take no for an answer!

Rank in order the following actions in response to this situation (1= Most appropriate; 5= Least appropriate):

A. Thank the family and accept the gift explaining that you will likely donate it yourself to charity.

B. Encourage the family to donate the money to the hospital charity or ward instead.

C. Refuse to accept the gift.

D. Accept the money and ask that the family do not tell any of the other staff.

E. Thank the family for their generosity but explain you are unable to accept the gift.

Question 37

You are on a medical firm in a busy teaching hospital. There is extreme pressure on juniors to discharge patients due to a lack of beds in the hospital. Your consultant has instructed you to discharge a patient, but you are concerned that they will be unable to manage at home alone.

Rank in order the following actions in response to this situation (1= Most appropriate; 5= Least appropriate):

A. Discharge the patient anyway despite your concerns.

B. Attempt to get a more thorough history from the patient and any collateral history from neighbours/family.

C. Get a full physiotherapy/occupational therapy/social worker review before discharge.

D. Present your consultant with the case again, emphasizing your concerns.

E. Discuss the situation with the sister in charge on the ward.

Question 38

You accidentally send an email containing confidential patient details including information regarding their diagnosis and prognosis to the wrong person.

Rank in order the following actions in response to this situation (1= Most appropriate; 5= Least appropriate):

A.   Email the person again explaining the nature of your mistake, and request them to delete the first message.

B.   Contact the person by telephone immediately and explain the nature of your mistake, requesting them to delete the email.

C.   Re-send the email to the correct person.

D.   Explain the mistake to one of your seniors.

E.   Ignore your mistake.

Question 39

You have been asked by one of the registrars to obtain an arterial blood sample from a patient as he is very busy. You have only ever done this task under observation, and do not yet feel quite comfortable carrying it out on your own.

Rank in order the following actions in response to this situation (1= Most appropriate; 5= Least appropriate):

A.   Watch your colleague so that the next time you have more of an idea about how to insert one.

B.   Document in the notes the reason for the test.

C.   Contact the on-call doctor to put it in.

D.   Tell the registrar that you do not feel comfortable undertaking this task.

E.   Ask the registrar to have a go herself, if he or she can spare any time.

Question 40

You are a junior doctor working in the emergency department and an elderly gentleman presents with chest pain and is diagnosed with acute coronary syndrome. You explain this to him but he appears quite confused and declines treatment. His wife, who is accompanying him, says he has been a bit confused for the past couple of days.

Rank in order the following actions in response to this situation (1= Most appropriate; 5= Least appropriate):

A.   Request an echocardiogram to confirm the diagnosis first.

B.   Speak to your seniors.

C.   Assess his mental capacity.

D.   Respect his autonomy and do not treat him.

E.   Treat him with the appropriate medical treatment despite his wishes.

Question 41

Your junior doctor colleague who was meant to be on-call has gone home early as they have said they are unwell and you agree to cover for them. After finishing the shift, you head to the gym and are surprised to see your apparently ill colleague there.

Rank in order the following actions in response to this situation (1= Most appropriate; 5= Least appropriate):

A. Turn a blind eye to the situation if he offers to do some of your ward jobs.

B. Tell him a few weeks later about your feelings as you feel awkward bringing it up now.

C. Ask your fellow junior doctor colleagues for advice.

D. Approach your colleague at an appropriate time and discuss with him the incongruity of the reason he gave and the fact that he is in the gym.

E. Discuss the incident with your consultant.

Question 42

You are the junior doctor on-call and your registrar has asked you to insert a nasogastric tube even though you have never performed or observed the procedure. You are aware that such opportunities are hard to come by and this will count as a DOP for your ePortfolio. Your registrar says she will supervise you if you would like her to.

Rank in order the following actions in response to this situation (1= Most appropriate; 5= Least appropriate):

A. Watch your colleague do the procedure and then try and do it at the next given opportunity.

B. Carry out the procedure unsupervised.

C. Ask the registrar to carry it out.

D. Ask the registrar to do the procedure so that you can learn the technique by observing her, but help out as much as possible within your competency.

E. Carry out the procedure under supervision.

Question 43

You are the junior doctor and have been away on annual leave for a week. During this time the senior house officer has failed to keep the blood results folder updated. On the ward round your consultant keeps asking about the trend in blood results and you do not know as no results were written into the folder for one week.

Rank in order the following actions in response to this situation (1= Most appropriate; 5= Least appropriate):

A. Politely inform the consultant that you have been away though you understand the importance of the situation, and say that you will update the bloods folder and will take steps to ensure the folder will always be updated.

B. Tell the consultant that unfortunately you have been away and that this was the senior house officer's mistake.

C. Privately discuss this with the senior house officer later.

D. Apologise to the consultant and update the bloods folder after the ward round.

E. Tell your educational supervisor that your consultant criticised you unfairly.

Question 44

You want to pursue a career in plastic surgery. Unfortunately you do not have a plastic surgery rotation and are struggling to get much exposure to the specialty as an junior doctor. You have tried discussing the situation with senior members of your team, but they do not seem to be providing much useful advice.

Rank in order the following actions in response to this situation (1= Most appropriate; 5= Least appropriate):

A. Make a visit to the hospital's plastic surgery team concerning a taster week/practical exposure.

B. Ask to speak to one of the plastic surgery registrars or consultants to see if there is a project that you could get involved with.

C. Negotiate time off with your team when you are not busy to go to the plastic surgery department.

D. Discuss career progression with your educational supervisor and ask his advice regarding gaining exposure to plastic surgery in this hospital.

E. Look into which exams you must sit to pursue a career in plastic surgery.

Question 45

You are the junior doctor and are about to present at the hospital grand round, which you have spent a long time preparing for. Suddenly your bleep goes off and it is one of the nurses from the ward who informs you that a patient has just fallen out of bed and she is concerned he has suffered a head injury.

Rank in order the following actions in response to this situation (1= Most appropriate; 5= Least appropriate):

A. Contact one of the doctors on your team and ask them to attend to the matter urgently.

B. Attend to the patient and inform the audience that you have an urgent matter to deal with, and that you will present another time.

C. Tell the senior sister that you will attend to the matter once you have finished your presentation.

D. Attend to the matter urgently without informing anyone. Patient safety takes priority over anything else.

E. Ask one of your colleagues to start the presentation whilst you call the senior sister back to find out more information about the matter to see if it can be delayed until after your presentation.

Question 46

A patient is admitted with recurrent pulmonary embolisms. It becomes evident to your team that she is not adhering to her warfarin medication. She says she is getting very forgetful and cannot remember her medicines.

Rank in order the following actions in response to this situation (1= Most appropriate; 5= Least appropriate):

A. Explain that if she does not adhere to treatment then she will die from a pulmonary embolism.

B. Explain the pathogenesis of pulmonary embolism.

C. Discuss with her the importance of taking her medication. Arrange for input from pharmacy to obtain a dosset box for the patient.

D. Give her a leaflet explaining the reasons for taking warfarin.

E. Explain you will refer her to the anticoagulation clinic to get her restarted on warfarin.

PART TWO – Multi-Action Questions

Question 47

An elderly lady from a nursing home is admitted to the hospital with increasing confusion and signs of sepsis. Her daughter is currently abroad but she will be in the hospital to see her mother in two days. Unfortunately there are no other family members available to speak to and the hospital has no past medical records for the patient. The nursing home staff are unclear regarding any past medical history about the patient. Your consultant feels it is imperative that more information about the patient is obtained.

Choose the THREE most appropriate actions to take in this situation:

A. Treat the urinary sepsis with antibiotics then transfer the patient back to the nursing home as soon as possible before more health problems arise in hospital.

B. Try your best to transfer the patient to another hospital so that you do not have to deal with a difficult patient.

C. Wait for the daughter to return from the holiday abroad and when she arrives ask her if she has any other information about the patient.

D. Try to contact the daughter (who is also next of kin) abroad who might have details on the patient's health and can advise you on specific medical needs of the patient.

E. Contact all relevant specialties in the hospital to review the patient so that they can ascertain whether she has any 'general' cardiology, respiratory or neurology problems that they can treat.

F. Liaise with the GP who cares for the nursing home residents. Ask if the GP has any records relating to the patient's past medical condition, drug history and allergy history.

G. Do not treat or prescribe any medication to the patient until her daughter is present as you are not sure what medications she is on or any of her allergies and you do not want to do anything until all information is at hand.

H. Obtain a full septic screen including a microbiology, sensitivity and culture testing of her urine and start her on empirical antibiotics in the meantime.

Question 48

A 56 year old gentleman with decompensated alcoholic liver disease presents with gross ascites. You are the junior doctor on a gastroenterology firm and performed an ascitic tap supervised by your senior house officer earlier on in the afternoon. The results of the tap will not be back until well after working hours and you want the on-call junior doctor to help you check these results. You try calling the on-call junior doctor at 5pm but find that he is not answering his bleep.

Choose the THREE most appropriate actions to take in this situation:

A. Leave a note for the junior doctor on the ward in the 'job book'. When he does his rounds of the wards in the night he will see the note and act upon the jobs.

B. Bleep the on-call senior house officer, apologise for disturbing them but ask them to pass the message to the junior doctor or help to chase the results up themselves.

C. Advise the on-call senior house officer to prescribe intravenous antibiotics if the neutrophil count is above 250.

D. Try calling the on-call junior doctor on his mobile phone.

E. Provide clear documentation in the notes regarding the plan of the patient, what actions need to be taken should the results be abnormal and the details of the doctor(s) you have contacted who can be reached by nursing staff if these actions are not performed.

F. Chase the results up yourself tomorrow instead as you doubt there will be any harm from one more extra day of delay.

G. Leave the hospital and try bleeping the on-call junior doctor from home later on in the evening when you hope he will be less busy.

H. Make a complaint to the registrar on-call to tell him that his junior doctor is not answering his bleep and that it is compromising patient care.

Question 49

You are a junior doctor working on a neurology firm. Your team review a 6 year old girl, Sara, who has been having multiple generalised seizures. After full investigations ruling out any organic cause for the seizures, your consultant decides that it would be in the patient's best interest to start anti-epileptic medication. The patient's parents are very anxious and are aware from reading the internet of all the side effects these drugs could be responsible for. They would rather the team just monitor their child and put off commencing her on medication for as long as possible.

Choose the THREE most appropriate actions to take in this situation:

A. Explain to Sara's parents that you are obliged to commence her on anti-epileptic medication regardless of their wishes.

B. Explore why Sara's parents are anxious about her being commenced on medication, addressing their ideas, preconceptions and beliefs about anti-epileptic drugs.

C. Contact social services as you believe these parents are not looking out for their child's best interests.

D. Assess whether there is a risk of serious harm to Sara if she were not to have anti-epileptic medication commenced and try to explain this situation to the parents.

E. Inform Sara's parents about the benefits of anti-epileptic medication as well as the complications in non-jargon manner in order to persuade them that the benefits outweigh the risks.

F. Seek a court order.

G. Contact the Child Protection lead in the hospital.

H. Defer the consultation and tell the parents that they should speak to their GP who you will ask to describe in more detail the benefits of anti-epileptic medication.

Question 50

Your team have been short-staffed due to illness over the winter months and you notice your registrar working overtime to help complete the ward jobs for all the patients. Over recent days he has become more overworked to the extent that he is starting to make errors. This seems strange considering that he is normally very efficient at managing patients.

Choose the THREE most appropriate actions to take in this situation:

A. Inform your consultant that the registrar may be struggling with the workload on his own and ask whether there is any way more staff could be appointed to cover the recent staff illnesses.

B. Approach the registrar when appropriate and discuss what you have noticed in a non-threatening and non-accusative manner.

C. Accept that this is just a brief hectic time for the registrar and things will get better soon.

D. Report the registrar to the GMC as he has neglected some patients by not asking for certain investigations and misdiagnosing a few.

E. See how you could ease the workload of the registrar and help him out where possible.

F. Tell the registrar that he is too incompetent to deal with any patients and should go home.

G. Suggest that a new more competent registrar be appointed instead who would be less prone to making so many mistakes.

H. Tell the registrar that he should seek help from his GP for work-related stress.

Question 51

You are a junior doctor working in a GP surgery. A 14 year old girl attends your clinic asking for the morning-after pill. She has had unprotected sex with her boyfriend who is in her class at school and the same age. She is very concerned that you will discuss the situation with her mother who is a nurse at the same GP practice.

Choose the THREE most appropriate actions to take in this situation:

A.   Reassure the patient that all patient information is confidential and that this will not be mentioned to her mother.

B.   Explain to the patient that you will not tell her mother but that the patient must get parental consent for any underage contraception that is prescribed.

C.   Report the matter as underage sex is an offence.

D.   Prescribe the patient the morning-after pill and offer the patient advice on long-term contraception and safe sex.

E.   Talk to her mother as her daughter is underage and therefore she has a right to know.

F.   Inform the patient that she should try to find another GP to ensure her mother does not find out.

G.   Discuss the patient details with the patient's mother after the consultation. Tell her to have a mother-daughter conversation when she gets home as her daughter will require parental support at this time.

H.   Offer to perform a full sexual health screen for the patient if she wishes and explain the risks of unprotected sex.

Question 52

You are a junior doctor working on a general medical firm. As you review the notes for your patients in preparation for the morning ward round, you notice a completely illegible entry in one of the medical notes from the night before. It is not signed by anyone but there is a contact bleep number next to the entry. You recognise the writing and remember that it belongs to the doctor on-call from the night before.

Choose the THREE most appropriate actions to take in this situation:

A.   Add the doctor's name to the entry so future clinicians can know who wrote the illegible entry.

B.   Tear out the page with the illegible entry written on it and rewrite the events from the night before in your own words.

C.   Bleep the number and ask the doctor what the entry is supposed to have said and ask them for an update on the patient status from the night before.

D.   Ask the doctor to return to the ward to write up the entry again if they are still in the hospital.

E.   Leave a very legible note in the patient file next to the entry asking the doctor to please rewrite their entry if they return to see the same patient again.

F.   Do your best to decipher it and use this example as a lesson to yourself to remember to make your own entries clearer.

G.   Ask the nurse to rewrite the entry in the notes as you don't feel it is your job to rewrite work that has already been done.

H.   After discussion with the patient and nursing staff, try your best to decipher the events from the night before and write what you understand has happened next to the last illegible entry, giving a summary of the latest patient status.

Question 53

You are a junior doctor in a GP surgery assessing a patient when a middle-aged gentleman storms into your room with a prescription belonging to his 15 year old daughter for oral contraception. He demands to know why you have given her this without consulting him and who she is sleeping with. He is rather rude and unpleasant towards you.

Choose the THREE most appropriate actions to take in this situation:

A. Explain that you assessed his daughter and thought she was competent to make the decision regarding oral contraception. Tell him that parental consent is not required to prescribe contraception in such circumstances.

B. Excuse yourself from the consultation and take the angry father to a private room. Call for senior support.

C. Ask him to make an appointment and go away.

D. Ask the angry father to wait his turn outside until you have finished with the current patient.

E. Ask the current patient you are seeing to wait outside the room so you can talk to the angry father in private.

F. Ask him to discuss the matter with his daughter and encourage him to be supportive and understanding about the situation.

G. Tell him you refuse to talk to him because of the manner in which he has approached you.

H. Call the police or on-site security to escort the father off the premises.

Question 54

You are a junior doctor working in the emergency department. A young female patient presents after having collapsed at home. She is 32 weeks pregnant and on vaginal examination you notice a large amount of clotted blood in her underwear with some small solid lumps of soft tissue. You are concerned that the patient is having a miscarriage. She keeps asking you, "Is my baby OK?"

Choose the THREE most appropriate actions to take in this situation:

A. Apologise to the patient for your uncertainty but explain that the most accurate way to tell is to refer her for an ultrasound scan.

B. Shrug your shoulders and say "maybe".

C. Tell the patient that everything is fine and that there is nothing to worry about.

D. Explain to the patient you will ask an obstetrician to review her and perform a full examination. Suggest that they may be better experienced to deal with her questions.

E. Reassure the patient that you are going to try your best to expedite all referrals and investigations.

F. Tell the patient that you suspect she is having a miscarriage and that she should not be too surprised if your senior comes to speak to her about this in more detail later.

G. Ask the patient if she has ever had a miscarriage before and if she recognises this feeling.

H. Tell the patient to be quiet as you cannot concentrate and examine her properly at the same time if she keeps talking to you.

Question 55

It is 2am on your first night shift working in general medicine. You accidentally prick yourself with a venflon needle whilst trying to cannulate a patient and sustain a needlestick injury. You are not part of the general medical team directly involved in the care of this patient and so are not familiar with the patient's past medical history. You are worried that you may be at risk of contracting a blood-borne disease.

Choose the THREE most appropriate actions to take in this situation: (not in order)

A.   Contact occupational health immediately even though it is out of hours.

B.   Go to the emergency department immediately to have your blood taken and to possibly obtain a dose of post-exposure prophylactic medication.

C.   Read the notes of the patient to find any relevant medical history of blood-borne disease.

D.   Call the haematology laboratory to ask them to test any sample they have of the patient's blood for HIV, hepatitis and any other blood-borne disease.

E.   Explain what has happened to the patient and take a sample of blood with their consent to send off testing for HIV and any other blood-borne diseases.

F.   Wait until the day team arrive on the ward and ask them for more information about the patient.

G.   Contact occupational health in the morning and inform them of the situation. Take down the patient details and hospital number in case they need to investigate the situation further.

H.   Contact your GP to get a hepatitis B vaccine booster.

Question 56

One of your patients on the hepatobiliary surgical ward is a 47 year old woman who has undergone a liver transplant three days ago. She has just returned to the ward from the ITU, and is insisting that she be discharged today as she has "had enough of being in hospital". You have explained to her that she would be doing this against medical advice but she is determined to leave.

Choose the THREE most appropriate actions to take in this situation:

A.   Ask the patient sign a self-discharge form and let them leave.

B.   Tell the patient that if they leave and get worse then they will lose their hospital bed and may not be admitted again.

C.   Call hospital security to try to prevent the patient from absconding.

D.   Explore the patient's reasons for wanting to be discharged and see if there is anything you can do to persuade her to stay.

E.   Give the patient a strong sedative to calm them down.

F.   Assess the patient's mental capacity and risks of leaving against medical advice. If she still insists then let her leave.

G.   Call the patient's next of kin and encourage them to come to hospital to try and calm her down.

H.   Call the consultant and/or registrar from your team and inform them of the situation.

Question 57

There is an outbreak of diarrhoea on your general medical ward with many patients suffering severe dehydration and weakness as a result. Some members of staff are also feeling ill and have not come into work during this time meaning the ward is very short-staffed. You are keen to control the outbreak and prevent spread of the virus in the hospital as well as not getting ill yourself.

Choose the THREE most appropriate actions to take in this situation:

A.   Try to determine the virus/bacteria causing all the diarrhoea and send all stool samples from the patients for microscopy, culture and sensitivity tests.

B.   Use extra hygiene precautions such as changing gloves and aprons between seeing each patient and regularly washing your hands with soap and water.

C.   Use alcohol gel between seeing each patient.

D.   Prescribe an anti-diarrhoeal medication such as loperamide for all the patients affected.

E.   Contact infection control for advice.

F.   Prescribe general multivitamin supplementation tablets for the patients affected.

G.   Blindly treat all patients with a broad spectrum antibiotic that will surely kill off the most common bacteria that may be the source of infection.

H.   Consider an alternative source of infection.

Question 58

You are a junior doctor working in a sexual health clinic when a woman storms into your office. She begins shouting loudly and saying that she found a clinic appointment letter belonging to her husband signed by yourself. She demands to know what he has been up to behind her back and if he has been diagnosed with any infections. She says she has a right to know if she is at risk of catching anything off him. You remember that the husband had undergone a full sexual health checkup but the results of these are not currently back yet.

Choose the THREE most appropriate actions to take in this situation:

A.   Explain to the woman that you are unable to divulge any medical information regarding her husband due to patient confidentiality but would be happy to offer her a full sexual health checkup to determine if she has any sexual infections.

B.   Agree with the patient and tell her you will go and find the husband's notes to see if she is at risk of catching any infections from him.

C.   Suggest to the woman that her husband may have an infection and ask her if she would like to start a course of prophylactic antibiotics 'just in case'.

D.   Call up the husband and tell him that his wife is in the clinic asking about his recent consultation and sexual health checkup results.

E.   Try to calm the woman down and take her to a private consultation room.

F.   Offer the woman a free pack of condoms to take home and suggest that until she resolves this issue with her husband they should practise 'safe' sex.

G.   Encourage the patient to discuss the matter with her husband at home. Suggest he may be embarrassed and she might want to return with him to see a counsellor or sexual health adviser in the clinic.

H.   Suggest to the woman that if her husband is going to a sexual health clinic behind her back then he may be having an affair and she should consider leaving him.

Question 59

You are a junior doctor with a keen interest in general surgery. You have enrolled to sit Part A of the MRCS examinations in the next month but your workload in the hospital is making it very difficult for you to revise efficiently. You have requested to take some study leave for revision but due to poor staffing on your firm, this has been rejected. You are keen to make a good impression on your current job but also dread the thought of failing your examinations.

Choose the THREE most appropriate actions to take in this situation:

A.   Ask for a refund for the money you spent on the exam application.

B.   Try to balance your educational needs with service provision as much as possible in your daily routine by asking for teaching from your senior house officer and registrar.

C.   Call in sick during the week leading up to the examination so you don't have to attend work and can revise at home.

D.   Postpone sitting the examination instead and cancel your application.

E.   Instead of requesting for more study leave, try to leave work an hour early each day so you can revise at home.

F.   Use daily work experiences such as examining patients on-call and reading up about the diseases your patients are suffering from as opportunistic learning that can benefit you in the exams.

G.   Tell your consultant that you have an exam and this is your main priority at this time. Demand that you be given the time off.

H.   Speak to your team and try to negotiate an arrangement that benefits you but does not compromise the team.

Question 60

You are the junior doctor working on a general medical firm. Upon reviewing the blood results for all your patients at the end of the day you notice that one patient's inflammatory markers have risen dramatically. You distinctly remember that she was clinically stable on the morning ward round but had been treated for C. Difficile during this admission. You worry that a recurrence of the C. Difficile is a possibility. Your senior house officer and registrar have both gone home for the day.

Choose the THREE most appropriate actions to take in this situation:

A.   Bring the blood result findings to the immediate attention of your registrar at the ward round the next morning.

B.   Review the patient as soon as you can and obtain a full 'septic screen' including a urine sample and blood cultures.

C.   Call your registrar on their mobile phone for advice.

D.   Contact the on-call registrar and ask for their opinion.

E.   Ignore the blood result findings, dismissing them as spurious.

F.   Call the nurses on the ward and ask about the patient's observations.

G.   Ignore the findings as you know the patient has been fully treated in the past and they can be reviewed on ward round the next day.

H.   Handover to the on-call house officer to review the patient as it is now beyond your contracted hours.

Question 61

As the junior doctor on-call you are asked by the nurses to review a patient who is spiking temperatures. When reviewing the patient's notes and drug chart you find it quite difficult to read the drug names, doses and patient history as they are only just about legible. The nurse agrees with you on this observation.

Choose the THREE most appropriate actions to take in this situation:

A. Continue to review the patient with the little information you can gleam from the notes.

B. Write a note to the team looking after the patient informing them to rewrite the drug chart in a more legible manner.

C. Rewrite the drug chart yourself from what you can read and leave out any medications which you cannot decipher.

D. Document in the notes your findings from the review and also mention the illegibility of the drug chart.

E. Inform the nursing staff that they should raise this concern with the admitting team the following morning.

F. Refuse to rewrite the drug chart as you are not a member of the team that is looking after this patient and consequently are unfamiliar with the medications that he is on.

G. Discuss the situation with the on-call registrar.

H. Help the admitting team by rewriting the drug chart with assistance from the nursing staff, patient and admission documentation in the patient's notes.

Question 62

You are asked to see a 14 year old boy in the emergency department who has been admitted with an acute exacerbation of his asthma. After reading the patient notes you find that this is the third admission for the same problem in the last month. On closer questioning the patient tells you he has not been using his asthma medication as he is embarrassed and doesn't want his friends to know that he has a 'disease'. He fully understands the consequences of not taking his inhalers regularly.

Choose the THREE most appropriate actions to take in this situation:

A. Speak to his mother about encouraging her son to take his medication.

B. Ask his GP to review the patient due to the time pressures in the emergency department.

C. Explore his fears and understanding of asthma and taking his inhalers.

D. Firmly discuss with him why he needs to take the inhalers.

E. Recommend the patient books an appointment with his asthma specialist nurse to discuss methods of controlling his asthma better and prevention of such frequent admissions.

F. Attempt to scare the patient in order to help him understand the potential severity of not taking his inhalers.

G. Check his symptoms have resolved before discharge.

H. There is nothing further you can do so accept that this patient will always be a 'heart sink' and try to ensure he is treated to the best of your ability on this admission.

Question 63

You are one of two junior doctors working on a general surgical firm. You notice your junior doctor peer has labeled a 'group and save/cross-match' request with one patient's details but the bottle with the blood is labeled with a different patient's name. She asks you to drop off the blood and the request form into the haematology laboratory as soon as possible as the patient is booked for theatre in the morning.

Choose the THREE most appropriate actions to take in this situation:

A.   Fill in a clinical incident form.

B.   Rectify the mistake by either rewriting an appropriate request form or repeating the blood sample from the correct patient, depending on who is supposed to have the operation the next day.

C.   Quietly write out a different request form to match the details written on the blood bottle without telling your colleague. You don't want to embarrass them and they look very busy.

D.   Tell the patient that there has been a mistake and that they will need their operation cancelled tomorrow.

E.   Ignore the situation as it does not directly concern you and just drop off the blood sample you have been asked to do.

F.   Raise the mistake with your colleague and ask them to clarify which patient is supposed to have a 'group and save/cross-match' sample for the operation tomorrow.

G.   Discard the erroneously labeled sample or request form.

H.   Speak to your colleague's clinical supervisor and explain that you have seen them make a mistake that could compromise patient safety.

Question 64

You are one of the surgical junior doctors working in a busy district general hospital. You are a budding surgeon but find that you rarely get the opportunity to go into theatre to assist in elective lists. Due to the high turnover of patients, your daily duties primarily include checking your patient's blood results, completing discharge summaries, phlebotomy and reviewing any critically ill patients. Your team consists of yourself, a senior house officer, a registrar and your consultant.

Choose the THREE most appropriate actions to take in this situation:

A.   Accept that the duty of a junior doctor is first and foremost to cover the ward jobs and you are unlikely to get time to go into theatre.

B.   Raise the issue with your senior house officer and ask him to swap sessions with you so that he does ward cover occasionally while you go into theatre.

C.   Discuss the situation with your registrar to see if there is an obvious solution whereby everyone on the team can be happy with their duties whilst learning new skills.

D.   Ask your fellow junior doctor colleagues who are less busy to cover your duties while you spend an hour or so in theatre whenever the opportunity arises.

E.   Come in early to work each day so you can finish your jobs quickly and make time to get into the operating theatre to assist.

F.   Mention your interest in a future in surgery to your consultant to see if there are opportunities for you to get involved in theatre or in research and audit projects.

G.   Leave the ward jobs unattended in order to assist in theatre. Your training is more important and you can always ask the ward nurse to ask the on-call to cover any emergency issues.

H.   Request that the rota coordinator finds a locum to cover your shifts in order to free up your own time.

Question 65

You are the junior doctor on the endocrinology firm. On a Friday ward round you see a patient that is under joint care with the cardiology team. Your consultant deems the patient to be medically fit for discharge and requests that you liaise with cardiology to arrange for this to happen. Unfortunately the cardiology team take until the end of the day to review the patient and only tell you at 5pm that the patient is fit for discharge from a cardiology point of view. As it is so late in the afternoon, the hospital pharmacy is closed and will not be able to deal with the patient's discharge prescription until the next morning. The patient is clearly upset that he will not be going home today and asks you if there is any way you might be able to let him leave the ward tonight instead.

Choose the THREE most appropriate actions to take in this situation:

A. Bleep the cardiology registrar and explain to him that this is not appropriate patient care.

B. Apologise to the patient but tell him that this is not possible as he cannot leave without his new prescription of medications.

C. Write the patient's discharge drug prescription so that the medications can be prepared first thing the next morning to prevent even further delay the following day.

D. Talk to the junior doctor on the cardiology firm and ask him to relay to his team how upset the patient is because of his team's late actions.

E. Inform the nurses and request that they contact the cardiology team frequently during the day to prompt them, should this situation unfold again.

F. Do nothing. Sometimes these things happen as the hospital is a busy place.

G. Discuss the matter with your consultant. Ask if it might be possible for the patient to still go home this evening but to return the next day to pick up their prescriptions.

H. Explain the situation to the patient and encourage them to write a letter of complaint against the cardiology team so future incidents do not occur.

Question 66

You are part of a medical team that includes two senior house officers and a consultant. During one day you are constantly getting bleeped about wrongly written drug charts with missing signatures and wrong doses. You go to investigate these errors and find out that all of these mistakes have been made by one of your senior house officers. The nurse highlights to you that this is not the first time your colleague has made errors and that they are in fact a frequent occurrence.

Choose the THREE most appropriate actions to take in this situation:

A. Go to all the wards where the errors have occurred and correct the senior house officer's mistakes. Apologise to the staff nurse and thank them for bringing it to your attention.

B. Discuss the event with the senior house officer in question, pointing out what he should do in the future when filling in drug charts.

C. Ask your senior house officer to go and correct all the drug charts where the errors have been made as he was the one who made them and won't learn unless he corrects them personally.

D. Report the senior house officer in question to the hospital lead clinical director.

E. Ask the nurse to bleep the senior house officer in question in future to correct his/her own mistakes instead of bothering you.

F. Tell your senior house officer that they should go home and take the day off as they are clearly tired and are making careless mistakes.

G. Encourage your senior house officer to liaise with your registrar or consultant if there are aspects of clinical care he is not completely comfortable or familiar with. Offer to speak to the seniors yourself if he does not try to improve his actions.

H. Fill in clinical incident forms for each mistake that the senior house officer has made.

Question 67

Your team has been treating a gentleman who initially presented with mild abdominal pain but was later found to be suffering with renal cell cancer and multiple widespread metastases. The hospital oncologist deems the patient too unsuitable for chemotherapy or radiotherapy and suggests that the palliative care team should be involved. However, the patient's wife is a nurse at a specialist oncology centre and advises her husband to enter a clinical trial that is investigating a new treatment for his cancer. The patient has asked whether it would be possible for you to refer him.

Choose the THREE most appropriate actions to take in this situation:

A.   Advise the patient that the trial may not be suitable for him and refuse to make the referral.

B.   Speak to the oncologist about the patient's request and ask if they can make the referral if they think it is appropriate.

C.   Speak to the oncology centre about the details of the trial and ask them to send you some paperwork about it so you can discuss it with the oncology team.

D.   Discuss with the patient why he wants to enter the trial and explain that there is very little hope for any real cure for his condition. Try to give the patient realistic expectations of his outcome so that he doesn't get his hopes up about being cured.

E.   Advise him that the clinical trial may not be safe and may even make his condition worse. Deter the patient from entering the trial telling him that the results of these 'experimental' treatments are very unpredictable.

F.   Speak to the wife and try to explain to her again that the oncologist has already reviewed the patient and explain to her clearly that her husband is for palliation only.

G.   Transfer the patient immediately as he has a right to choose his treatment and if this is what he wants then you should not stand in his way. After all, his metastases are widespread and any delay may affect his lifespan.

H.   Tell the patient that if he wants to enter the trial he should contact the specialist hospital and doctors responsible for the trial directly. They should assess whether they would be happy to take him on board or not.

Question 68

A young man is admitted to the emergency department with facial injuries after an altercation at the local pub. Once in the hospital you notice him raising his voice to the nursing staff and verbally abusing them in front of the other patients. As one nurse tries to take his blood pressure he punches her and she falls to the floor. The patient is demanding to be seen by a doctor straightaway and starts to vent his anger by throwing hospital equipment around. He is visibly confused and smells of alcohol. All the other senior emergency department doctors are attending a major trauma call and cannot help you.

Choose the THREE most appropriate actions to take in this situation:

A.   Call hospital security straightaway to ensure the patient can be guarded against being more violent to other members of staff, other patients and yourself.

B.   Call the police and ask them to charge the patient with the assault of a member of staff.

C.   Attempt to restrain the patient yourself whilst trying to talk him into calming down.

D.   Try to calm down the patient by talking to him and explaining that you are here to help him sort out his injuries, but maintain your distance the whole time.

E.   Call a colleague away from the trauma call to help you restrain the patient. You cannot manage the situation single-handedly.

F.   Attend to the nurse and assess any possible injuries.

G.   Politely ask the patient to leave the hospital and explain that neither the staff nor you are required to treat abusive and rude patients.

H.   Attempt to sedate the patient with a tranquiliser whilst healthcare assistants and nurses hold him down for you to do this.

Question 69

You are the junior doctor on a general medical firm. Your sister is unwell with a urinary tract infection and she has asked you to prescribe a course of antibiotics for her so she can carry on with her work. She is not registered with a GP and is flying abroad on an important business trip tomorrow. She tells you that she is desperate and wouldn't ask you unless she was in such a state.

Choose the THREE most appropriate actions to take in this situation:

A.   Tell your sister to visit her nearest emergency department or walk-in clinic as you do not need an appointment for this and treatment can be provided.

B.   Ask one of your colleagues who works in the emergency department to write your sister a prescription for Trimethoprim without seeing her.

C.   Prescribe the medication on a private outpatient prescription for your sister.

D.   Explain the situation to the ward pharmacist and ask for a 3 day course of Trimethoprim to take home to your sister.

E.   Apologise to your sister explaining that the GMC does not encourage you to provide prescription medications to friends or family.

F.   Encourage your sister to register with a GP urgently and get the prescription from him/her.

G.   Discuss the situation with your consultant.

H.   Reassure your sister that the infection will resolve without taking antibiotics by drinking plenty of fluid alone.

Question 70

It is your first on-call shift as a junior doctor working in orthopaedics. The only members of the on-call team are you, a senior house officer and the registrar. Due to a recent trauma call, the registrar and senior house officer have had to rush to the emergency department and then onto theatre. Before this they tell you to hold their bleeps as they will not be contactable for at least two hours and ask you to attend to any referrals that may arise. Within 5 minutes you get a bleep from a local GP asking you to admit a 10 year old boy who he suspects may have septic arthritis.

Choose the THREE most appropriate actions to take in this situation:

A.   Take as much of a history over the phone as possible regarding the patient concerned. Explain your situation and tell the GP you will speak to your registrar in theatre, and will ring him back with the registrar's advice.

B.   Try and advise the GP as much as you can, based on your experience of similar cases you have seen whilst on this orthopaedic firm.

C.   Accept the referral and ask the registrar to review the patient as soon as he finishes in theatre. In the meantime, attend to the patient on arrival and ensure that he is stable.

D.   Ask the GP to contact another registrar for advice as he is in theatre. If he is having problems finding someone else he can try to call back later when your registrar is out of theatre.

E.   Ask the GP to ring back later when your registrar may be finished in theatre. If he needs an immediate opinion he can contact the orthopaedic consultant on-call.

F.   Advise the GP to book the patient to be seen in the next available urgent outpatient orthopaedic clinic.

G.   Ask the GP to contact the on-call paediatric registrar.

H.   Advise the GP to give the patient a course of antibiotics and arrange an outpatient X-ray of the joint in question.

Answers to Examination 4

PART ONE – Answers to the Ranking Questions

Answer Question 1

EDABC

It is imperative that the on-call team is fully aware of the patient's details, current situation, location and medical background. As the person handing over it is crucial that all this information is correctly and accurately given to the doctor taking over the patient's care. Careful documentation also ensures that other healthcare professionals are able to interpret any extra details that may have been lost in transition. The patient should be kept involved in their management and advised about the treatment he has received and future care that he may need.

Answer Question 2

ACBED

Student feedback is vital in improving undergraduate teaching. A simple conversation with the consultant or undergraduate teaching coordinator might help solve the issue and a teaching programme set up by junior doctors would not only help undergraduate students but would also improve the teaching skills of the Foundation doctors. If these strategies fail then the medical school should be informed. The worst solution is to do nothing about the situation.

Answer Question 3

DEABC

It is important to be honest with your consultant about your arrangements for the evening. Notifying your seniors in advance allows them to ask another colleague to do the presentation who may be less busy. It would be unwise to prepare the presentation after returning from the birthday party, especially if you do not know what time it may be. You might be exhausted and compromise the quality of the presentation you prepare. In addition, returning to work the next day after having little sleep could make you prone to clinical errors when seeing patients.

Answer Question 4

EBCDA

All five choices are valid and should be carried out. Both patients should be informed about the mistake and assessed for any adverse effects, especially evidence of allergy and anaphylaxis. Your team must be informed so that your senior colleagues can advise you about appropriate further actions that need to be taken. The decisions concerning giving/not giving the laxative should not be made by you alone as a junior doctor. It is imperative that an incident form is completed so that a record of the incident is in place for legal and medical reasons. Thorough documentation is strongly recommended.

Answer Question 5

ACBDE

In such a situation it would be best to gather more information over the phone about the patient. Patients are often drowsy after general anaesthetic but the symptoms could herald something more serious, and so more information is crucial. As you have a major presentation to give, it would be reasonable to delegate the task of assessing the patient to a competent colleague. By doing this you ensure that the patient is cared for and the results of your audit are relayed to the department. It may be difficult for a colleague to deliver a presentation they are unfamiliar with for you. Ignoring the patient is unprofessional and puts the patient at risk.

Answer Question 6

BCAED

The GMC guidelines clearly state that it is "not acceptable to opt out of treating a particular patient or group of patients because of your personal beliefs or views about them." However, it does acknowledge that if a doctor has an objection to a procedure they can advise the patient to see another doctor or ensure that another doctor takes over their care without delay. Therefore in this case, if there is no other doctor to attend to this patient, you are obliged to assist in theatre as patient care should not be compromised. Option D is the most inappropriate action as it entails you being dishonest with the consultant.

Answer Question 7

BEDCA

Drinking alcohol impairs judgement, and the doctor should not continue to work until the effects of the alcohol wear off. Patient safety may be compromised if they are not attended to by a competent doctor, so cover must be arranged. Not realising that this is unacceptable behaviour in the first case is worrying, and senior team members should be informed as they may want to take further action. Informing the staff is not likely to be very helpful unless the colleague ignores you and you cannot find anyone to support you. The doctor is not a danger in the sense that he is violent and hospital security is unlikely to be necessary.

Answer Question 8

ABCED

Your first priority is to remove the list, minimising public access to confidential patient information. You should alert your colleagues on the cardiology team to their mistake, ensuring that all members of the team are aware of the incident. To improve practice as a whole, one should seek to advise and educate other staff within the hospital and this can take place at handover or at grand rounds. Signs could then be put in place to minimise future occurrences and the anonymisation of patient details should be encouraged.

Answer Question 9

DCAEB

Most hospitals have a readily available translator service and the best option would be D, to organise a meeting with a translator without the patient's family being around. It is best to assume that the patient does not want their confidentiality breached unless they tell you, even to their own family. Past medical history from the GP may be useful if communication from the patient is difficult. A member of staff could act as a translator if the patient agrees and they know not to disclose this information. Speaking to the patient yourself may be difficult but should always be attempted to ascertain their level of understanding. Using his sister as a translator may not be ideal as there may be aspects of his health that he does not wish her to know about.

Answer Question 10

CBADE

Exploring the patient's fears and understanding provides the key as to her uncertainty and it may lie in an incomplete understanding of the diagnosis, prognosis and options. Repeating her treatment options slowly and clearly may help her to make a decision. It is unlikely that your opinion would be significantly different from your consultant's. Giving your opinion is not necessarily wrong if the patient has specifically asked for it and is unsure about how to proceed. It is important to weigh-up their understanding before saying something that may influence their decisions. If you yourself are unsure then explaining that is perfectly reasonable.

Answer Question 11

DECBA

In this scenario the best way to deal with upset, emotional parents would be to apologise and explain how you are currently going to manage their son. You have not admitted responsibility by apologising, and a simple apology may go a long way. If this fails, try to calm them down. Contacting a senior should be done but not before you have taken initial measures to relax the situation yourself. Finding security officials may inflame the situation, and finding the doctor who made the decision yesterday is not likely to be helpful.

Answer Question 12

CBADE

This is a common scenario, and if you receive a bleep about an acutely unwell patient you need to ensure that they are assessed either by a colleague or yourself. The registrar may well be carrying out other duties, and it is impractical to expect them to assess such patients without ensuring that basic assessment and management is first carried out. Giving ACS medications without assessing the patient is dangerous.

Answer Question 13

EACBD

Although this may seem like the ideal scenario to some, your Foundation years are very important for training and getting suitable experience. Helping other colleagues will mean you do not lose practical skills yourself and still gain valuable experience. If you are lucky enough to still have free time, you can use it to complete your required competencies, get theatre experience etc. Some jobs are less busy than others, but if you feel that you cannot find enough activities to engage yourself it would be prudent to discuss the situation with your clinical supervisor or Foundation Programme director. Enjoying your free time, whilst tempting, would not be beneficial for your future.

Answer Question 14

CDBEA

Completing your ePortfolio is an important part of your professional development and should be done properly and completely. Discussing the situation with your registrar, or finding an alternative senior, are the most appropriate options. If you fail to meet the criteria within the allocated time, speaking to your Foundation supervisor is always an option. Completing the assessment incorrectly should not be done as it puts patients at risk by potentially advertising competencies that you do not have.

Answer Question 15

BDACE

Other healthcare workers may be able to provide teaching in the meantime. If this is not possible, helping with your jobs may be a valuable learning experience for them. Rearranging teaching with the students for later in the day/week may be an easier solution than discussing with your consultant. Cancelling the teaching entirely is the least suitable option as not only do the students lose out but teaching is an important skill and opportunity for junior doctors.

Answer Question 16

DECBA

The best solution would be to attempt to complete the audit, but if this was not possible it would be advisable to speak to your supervisor about getting an extension in order to complete the audit properly. It may not be entirely necessary to include all 100 patients for your audit to have good results. It is never appropriate to duplicate or to falsify data.

Answer Question 17

ABECD

Clarifying with your registrar exactly what he means is the best start in this situation. Obviously you should clerk the patient in if this has not already been done. Other junior doctors, particularly those who have already worked on renal jobs, may give you valuable advice. Speaking to radiology may be necessary, but this depends entirely on your registrar's plans. Calling the consultant on-call is only necessary if the other steps have been taken and no solution has been found.

Answer Question 18

CBDAE

It would be polite and helpful of you to allow your colleague to get the experience that would help them progress in their career. As long as you have enough support and they are contactable, you should allow them to take the opportunities that arise.

Answer Question 19

BADEC

As soon as you suspect a transmissible disease you must isolate the patient and inform your consultant. You must ensure your own safety as well as that of colleagues and other patients. Hospital protocols vary depending on location and once the consultant has deemed it necessary you should involve the communicable disease team. When to remove the patient from isolation depends on local policies but you should never wait for confirmatory investigations before isolating a patient.

Answer Question 20

ECBDA

Although you have no direct responsibility for this patient, failure to act could cause the patient harm. If you leave it for the morning then the dose could be given on the morning medication round so you should ensure that doesn't happen.

Answer Question 21

DCAEB

If you see any collapsed patient in distress you should immediately approach the patient and begin assessment. It is likely you will be tired, so ask a nurse to contact the appropriate medical team whilst you tend to the patient. In this scenario it is acceptable to stay after your shift has finished until another doctor arrives. If you need to handover then do so in a way that will not affect medical care. Never lift a patient suspected of a traumatic injury.

Answer Question 22

ABECD

If you believe a medication to be dangerous for a patient you must act on it immediately to avoid it being given by mistake. It should not simply be crossed off and left, as the patient will need a replacement antibiotic. The ward round is the best time for these decisions to be made as they may be forgotten later.

Answer Question 23

ADBCE

This is a situation that you would not be expected to handle alone as a junior, and it would be prudent to seek advice from your seniors at the earliest possible opportunity. Many hospitals have a policy for these situations. Explaining the severity of the situation to the parents and the urgency of the transfusion may mean they change their mind regarding the blood transfusion, and that should be done by a senior doctor if possible. The scenario states that the child "requires" the blood transfusion. If the parents do not consent and there is time the hospital may attempt to get a court to overrule the parents' decision. If there is not time for this the consultant may decide to give the blood to save the child's life.

Answer Question 24

ADCBE

Facilitating discharge in amputee patients is carried out by all members of the multidisciplinary team. It is important to respect and recognise that all members have important and valid opinions. Questioning the physiotherapist and asking her to explain her view is important as she may raise significant issues. After this, you can give your opinions and those of the medical team, whilst asking for input from other members of the MDT. You should not discharge the patient as this can be unsafe if the correct physiotherapy and occupational therapy measures have not been taken.

Answer Question 25

ACBDE

If you have a good working relationship with your colleague, speaking to him directly is the simplest option. Hopefully you will be able to reach a mutually convenient agreement. If not, discussion with your registrar or your consultant will be necessary. Explain your feelings and viewpoint. It could just be a simple misunderstanding. Even though you require a sign-off from your consultant, this does not excuse their behaviour and you will get support from the Foundation school in regard to matters like these. If after making them aware you feel this favouritism continues, making a complaint may be necessary.

Answer Question 26

BADCE

It is important you have functioning coping strategies in place to help you relax and deal with the pressures of being a Foundation doctor. While having the odd glass of wine is harmless, it may be easy for this to become habitual. A simple technique would be to find alternative relaxation, and monitoring your alcohol intake to ensure it does not become excessive. Attempting to cut back if you feel you are drinking above what is recommended is sensible. Binge drinking instead is not an advisable way of managing the situation.

Answer Question 27

CDABE

Patient safety is paramount. You should discuss the patient with the nurse to see if she has seen something you have missed. If there has been a disagreement about patient care you should always review the case to see if you are the one at fault. It would also be appropriate to obtain another opinion, preferably from someone senior. Maintaining working relationships is also very important and you should always try to talk to the colleague first before discussing them with their line manager.

Answer Question 28

DBECA

You must take appropriate steps to ensure that any official document you write is not incorrect or misleading. In this scenario this may involve speaking to all those looking after the patient or reading through the clinical notes. If you agree to complete a document you must do so without delay. Note that there may be other doctors who may be more familiar with the patient than you who are available, but this is not listed in the possible answers.

Answer Question 29

ECDBA

Although prescribing warfarin is simple, we do not know enough about the scenario to know whether it is sensible to restart warfarin. For example, did the patient hit their head in the fall? The most sensible thing would be to get a complete history and examination and then discuss with your registrar the working diagnosis. The reason the patient is on warfarin also needs to be determined, as this will also help decide how urgently the warfarin needs to be started. A clotting sample to determine the INR is important, as if the patient was overly anticoagulated it could have caused a bleed and be the reason for his collapse. If he needs to be anticoagulated (e.g. has a metallic heart valve) it is important to start an unfractionated heparin infusion as the effects of this can be reversed quickly. The patient will obviously need reassurance, but you need to know the reason he takes his warfarin before you can do this. You should not blindly prescribe the warfarin without checking all of the above.

Answer Question 30

AEBCD

Even though the patient is no longer an inpatient it is still your duty to follow-up this information as it has been passed on to you. The most sensible thing to do would be to attempt to contact the patient directly so she can get appropriate treatment. You should additionally contact the GP, and indeed if you are unable to contact the patient the GP may be able to follow this up. You could also write a letter to the patient if you are unable to speak to her via the telephone, but this may be several days in arriving. Writing in the notes is essential, but it should not be left until her clinic appointment for her to be offered treatment. Herpes simplex is not a notifiable disease and the CDC does not need to be involved.

Answer Question 31

ADEBC

This is not a situation you would be expected to manage as a junior doctor. Under 18s are allowed to consent for treatment if they are deemed to have Gillick (or Fraser) competence. However, they are not legally allowed to refuse treatment. In practical terms, however, it is almost impossible to bring a patient to theatre against their wishes, and so it is necessary to try and urge them to reconsider. Ensuring the patient has fully understood all the implications is important when gaining consent, although care must be taken not to coerce him into making a decision. Conservative management such as antibiotics should be started in the interim. Waiting for his parents is sensible as they may be able to discuss with him the need for surgery.

Answer Question 32

ADCEB

Correct emergency management is the most important option here. Taking a history, examining the patient, drawing bloods including a cross-match are very important in fully assessing the patient, but should only occur after an 'ABC' approach in this emergency situation. Senior colleagues in the emergency department may be more readily accessible than your registrar in this instance, but your registrar should also be contacted as he does need to know about this case. Often it is best to change into scrubs to talk to the registrar if he or she is operating, rather than calling them up on the phone.

Answer Question 33

BCEAD

Talking to your colleague may be a simple and therapeutic solution in discovering the root cause of their behaviour. Informing their clinical supervisor can also provide support for your colleague. Other doctors on your firm may be able to offer support and advice. Your educational/clinical supervisor may also provide support and advice. A clinical incident form may indeed need to be filled out regarding the prescribing error, but as this does not appear to be an event you were directly involved in this is the least appropriate option here.

Answer Question 34

ECBAD

In this situation ensuring an appropriate handover for the weekend is important for patient safety. Additionally it may be necessary to ensure that somebody actually arrives and the covering doctor has not simply forgotten! Leaving a verbal and written handover with the surgical registrar may be an alternative option, but is not as good as handing over personally as the registrar may be called to theatre and be unable to handover to the doctor when they arrive. Leaving a summary in the notes is probably the least safe option as it will rely on your colleague going through all the notes and will not allow for prioritisation.

Answer Question 35

DCBEA

Discussing with your consultant and team should be done initially as they will be better placed to give advice regarding managing this family, and since the nature of the complaint directly involves them this is the most appropriate course of action. The sister in charge will also be able to advise accordingly. Talking to the family is necessary, but it would be best to discuss this with your seniors first as they may want to be present. Calling security should be done immediately if there is any violent behaviour, aggression or threats. Ignoring the situation is not an option as it may easily escalate.

Answer Question 36

EBCAD

Accepting monetary gifts from patients and relatives is against GMC guidelines, and this should be explained to the family whilst thanking them for the offer. The family may accept the compromise of donating to a charity. You should not take the money with the intention of donating yourself, however, as this is still not allowed. Obviously you should not take the money and keep it a secret either.

Answer Question 37

BDECA

A more thorough history may help confirm your worries. If you still have concerns it is important to inform the consultant in the first instance, they are likely to be receptive to your input. The ward sister is experienced in making these decisions and is in a good place to arrange for an urgent social review.

Answer Question 38

BADCE

You should try and rectify the situation as soon as possible, and if this can be done by phone, that would be preferable to email. Discussing the situation with a senior after steps have been taken to try and resolve the situation is appropriate to see whether there is anything further that needs to be done. Obviously you should also resend the email taking care that it is to the correct person this time. Ignoring the mistake is not an option.

Answer Question 39

DEACB

You should never attempt a procedure that they you not feel comfortable performing. Patient safety is most important and therefore if there is any doubt about the competency of your ability you should gain more experience before attempting it. The on-call doctor may have other responsibilities but could be contacted as a last resort. Documenting the reason for the test should be done but does not solve the problem.

Answer Question 40

CBEDA

Although he may appear confused this should be confirmed by assessing his mental capacity formally. If he does not have capacity, which is probably the case here, you should then discuss the case with your senior colleagues. Without capacity you can treat him in his best interests even if he does not agree. An echocardiogram is unhelpful in this case as you have been told that he has already been diagnosed, and this is unlikely to change his acute management.

Answer Question 41

DCEBA

You should allow your colleague to explain themselves but it does look like they were taking time off work for their own leisure activities. Speaking to others gives you the opportunity to find out if someone else has a useful suggestion about how to approach this problem. The issue affects everyone on the rota so it makes sense to discuss it together. However, if you feel unable to tackle the situation yourself your consultant may be needed to arbitrate. Option B does not address the situation in a timely manner and A is unethical – he may be causing other members of the team to have to work harder without knowing about his behaviour.

Answer Question 42

DACEB

It is dangerous to carry out procedures without having ever seen the procedure being done. You should watch the procedure in order to understand the technique before attempting to carry it out yourself. It would be best to first assist in the procedure whilst watching your registrar carry it out.

Answer Question 43

ADCBE

Although it is clear that you were not at fault in this scenario, you must remember that this mistake can affect patient care. For this reason, even though you were not the guilty party, you must make also every effort to ensure that this does not happen again. Both the senior house officer and the consultant should discuss the events and the necessary actions that need to be taken to ensure no recurrence. If you feel that you are being bullied you must inform your educational supervisor, although there is no evidence of this in the scenario described.

Answer Question 44

DABCE

It would also be wise to discuss your aims with your educational supervisor who may be able to assist you in fulfilling your aspirations. Most departments are happy to provide advice and opportunities to people who take a special interest in their field. It would be advisable to find a mentor, someone who can guide you through applications and career progression. If you can negotiate time off with your team then you can gain experience within your chosen specialty. Sitting exams is important, but gaining exposure to the specialty first is more important.

Answer Question 45

ABDEC

You must ensure that the patient is properly assessed but this can be delegated to a colleague which is preferable in this situation. The patient must be assessed urgently and this cannot be delayed if there is a suspicion of a head injury.

Answer Question 46

CEDBA

The primary problem seems to be her forgetfulness, and so a dosset box will likely be very helpful. She may also not understand the importance of the tablet, although this should be discussed without scaring her. Referral to anticoagulation clinic is necessary. A leaflet may help her understand the medication although this does not seem to be the primary reason for her lack of compliance.

PART TWO – Answers to the Multi-Action Questions

Answer Question 47

DFH

"Good doctors make patients their first concern" according to the GMC *Good Medical Practice* guidelines. You should seek to treat the patient and properly assess them for their presenting complaint without delaying any urgent treatment (unlike options C or G). Trying to rid yourself of a difficult patient does not place the patient's best interests as a top priority and is considered bad medical practice (options A and B).

In this scenario a proper work-up including a full septic screen with antibiotic therapy (option H) should be first instigated. If the patient or her carers are not certain of their past medical history, then the GP practice with whom the patient is registered with (option F) is a good source of information. Contacting the patient's next of kin can also shed some light on the patient's general condition and regular medications (option D). Contacting all specialties in the hospital to review a patient without any specific issues is a waste of the hospital resources and clinicians' time (option E).

Answer Question 48

BCE

This scenario is centred on communication skills and problem solving. It is important to ensure that jobs which need to be acted upon during the night shift are clearly and appropriately handed over to a doctor who is capable of carrying out these tasks. If the most junior Foundation doctor cannot be contacted, then the next port of call would be the senior house officer (option B). Tasks to be carried out should be clearly documented (option E) and also clearly relayed to the doctor carrying out the task, including what actions to take (option C). Although you may want to try calling the junior doctor on their mobile phone if they are not answering their bleep (option D), this may not be the most appropriate action as the reason they are not answering their bleep could be that they are too busy and will therefore not answer their phone either. Equally, if they are on duty in hospital, it may be unprofessional for the doctor to answer their personal mobile phone in front of patients or on the ward.

As the results may not be back for hours it is unreasonable for you to remain in hospital until they are ready or to leave the task to the next day if urgent action should be taken overnight (option F). Leaving a note on the ward book is not an assured method for handing over jobs as sometimes these may not be read by the doctor on-call or they may not recognise the importance of such tasks (option A).

Answer Question 49

BDE

In this situation there is a balance that needs to be met between the patient causing more injury to themselves from further seizure episodes and the risk of side effects from the medication. The medical decision made by the consultant is that the risk of side effects from anti-epileptic medication is much less and starting this drug would be in the patient's best interest. This may be something that the parents do not quite understand and it is important to understand what their concerns and fears are regarding the medication (options B, D and E).

The discussion with the parents should not be a way of forcing them to comply with your instructions and it would be premature at this stage to start contacting external organisations to become involved. Asking the parents to discuss the matter with their GP when they are in hospital under the care of a neurology specialist (option H) is not appropriate as the GP will certainly know less about this topic than the consultant or your seniors. If you feel that they are asking questions that you cannot deal with, it is better to refer them to your seniors than to ask them to speak to their GP.

Answer Question 50

BEA

According to the GMC *Good Medical Practice* guidelines, "You must protect patients from risk of harm posed by another colleague's conduct, performance or health. If you have concerns that a colleague may not be fit to practise, you must take appropriate steps without delay, so that the concerns are investigated and patients protected where necessary."

Speaking to the registrar himself would be the best initial option (option B). Perhaps there might be something else causing his mistakes other than the workload itself. During the conversation, it may be prudent to see whether there is any way in which you can help support your colleague (option E) and if you find that the situation needs to be escalated to a senior colleague, the consultant would be the next port of call (option A).

Should further action be taken, the consultant may be the best person to determine whether the registrar should be sent home for the day or whether the hospital managers or GMC need to be alerted. In this particular situation, and such measures would be excessive.

Answer Question 51

ADH

In this scenario, the patient appears to be able to engage in decision-making and is competent. Therefore after careful counselling on the risks of the morning-after pill and instructions on taking the medicine, if the patient still wishes to go ahead it would be appropriate to prescribe the morning-after pill (option D). It is also the duty of a good doctor to promote public health and education and therefore advice on safe sex (option H) should be given.

The issue of confidentiality is also highlighted here. In accordance with the GMC guidance on confidentiality "you should establish with the patient what information they want you to share, who with, and in what circumstances." This complements the guidance published on treating young persons aged 0–18 years old with relation to confidentiality, which states that "if children and young people are able to take part in decision-making, you should explain why you need to share information, and ask for their consent."

In this situation there is no requirement for yourself to explain the situation to the mother and therefore if the patient is not happy for this information to be given, you should not disclose the matter to anyone else.

Answer Question 52

CDH

Patient records must be accurate and legible. They must contain all details of findings, impressions and the plan for the patient. Being unable to read this means a patient may not receive the appropriate treatment and therefore you should contact the doctor who you believe wrote the entry to determine if there is anything you need to immediately act on as well as asking him to return to rewrite out the notes (options C and D). If it is not feasible for the doctor to return to record the entry in the notes or to contact the person responsible, you should do your best to understand the clinical situation that has occurred by talking to other staff members present at the time and rewrite a legible entry with the most current up-to-date patient status (option H). Always document if you cannot read an entry in case you are accused of not adhering to the instructions given.

Entries written in patient notes are regarded as legal documentation of events and should not be torn out and thrown away (option B). Writing a message to the offending doctor in the patient notes is not appropriate as they may not return to see the patient or look at the entry in the notes again (option E).

Answer Question 53

ABF

In this scenario you are being tested on your ability to deal with a difficult relative and also your knowledge of patient confidentiality. As discussed in a previous scenario, if a patient is deemed to be competent and requires that personal information not be disclosed to other relatives or friends, then given there is no other legal requirement on your part to disclose this information, the patient's medical records should remain private.

When dealing with an angry individual, you should do your best to remain calm and try to fully explain the situation as well as understand why the person in question is so angry (option A). You are not permitted to disclose patient details and if the patient would like their relative to be informed then they should either directly provide you with consent or discuss the matter themselves (option F). It is important that you do not allow the angry relative to ruin your consultation with your current client and that they do not feel ignored. The best way of doing this is to deal with the angry relative in a private room (option B) whilst allowing the current patient to stay in the consultation room rather than telling them to leave.

If you feel that your safety may be in danger or that the angry relative is rather aggressive towards you, ensure that you alert someone else in the practice and get senior help. It may be a little premature in this case to call the police immediately (option H).

Answer Question 54

ADE

Although the most likely situation in this clinical scenario is that the patient is having a miscarriage, you cannot be completely certain without further investigations such as an ultrasound scan (option A). To help relieve the patient's anxieties you can try to expedite any specialist referral and reviews (options D and E).

It is important to be honest with the patient and to act with integrity. If you are asked specifically whether a miscarriage is a possibility you should not lie and falsely reassure the patient (option C), neither should you jump to conclusions before a full assessment by a specialist has been performed.

Answer Question 55

BCG

Many hospitals have policies and guidelines on what you should do in this specific circumstance. If the incident occurs during working hours, you should contact the occupational health department for further information. If this occurs outside working hours, you should attend the Accident and Emergency department where you may be able to receive a hepatitis B booster vaccination or post-exposure prophylaxis if necessary (option B).

Trying to ascertain the patient's previous clinical history can be useful in determining the sort of post-exposure medication and testing you should have (option C). It is not appropriate for you to ask for testing of the patient's blood without their consent (option D) or to take the patient's blood yourself (option E). Ideally somebody else should take blood from the patient if their viral status is unknown. Contacting the occupational health department as soon as possible the next working day will ensure that the incident is documented and they can arrange for any further testing and counselling for yourself and the patient should more testing be required (option G).

Answer Question 56

DFH

This situation needs to be handled carefully, as self-discharging so soon after a liver transplant could have disastrous consequences. There needs to be a balance in this scenario between putting patient care as your first concern and the patient's right to autonomy if they have capacity to decide on their own treatment.

In the first instance you should try to explore why the patient is contemplating the decision and if there is a simple way of resolving any specific issues they are unhappy with in the hospital (option D). You must also enlist the support of your senior colleagues (option H) as the patient is at risk of death and post-operative complications should they disregard medical advice at this stage.

If the patient cannot be persuaded and they do have mental capacity to make their own decisions, you cannot detain them against their will (option F). It is important to document all discussion and ask the patient to sign a self-discharge form to prove that they have understood the consequences of leaving hospital. It is not appropriate to threaten the patient with poor medical treatment should they change their mind and wish to return (option B), nor is it good practice to sedate a competent non-compliant patient (option E).

Answer Question 57

ABE

Infection control in the hospital is the duty of all healthcare professionals, not just the infection control nurses, although they will be one of the experts to advise on specific measures to take (option E). A diarrhoea outbreak can have severe consequences for patients and staff and should try to be isolated as soon as possible. Urgent stool cultures must be sent (option A) and clearly labeled so that staff in the microbiology laboratory will take care with the potentially infectious samples. Extra hygiene precautions should also be used (option B) such as hand washing, gloving and gowning as well as reducing the number of visitors to the ward.

The use of alcohol gel only (option C), although necessary on general wards, will not eradicate certain infections such as C. Difficle and hands must be washed with soap and water. Blindly treating patients with a broad spectrum antibiotic is not advised as this may be the reason for the initial outbreak in the first place. Specific targeting therapy should be sought (option G) and anti-diarrheal medication may prolong the outbreak and should be avoided (option D). Ensuring the patients are well nourished with multivitamins (option F) and considering other causes for infection (option H) are reasonable steps to take, but not the most appropriate immediate actions.

Answer Question 58

AEG

In this scenario you should maintain a calm and non-threatening composure whilst ensuring that you do not breach patient confidentiality. You should be honest and open to the woman and explain that you cannot divulge this private information (option A), but offer her the option to protect her own health by being screened for any infections. Ensuring the woman is spoken to in a private and quiet room will help to calm the situation whilst ensuring other patients are not put in an uneasy atmosphere (option E).

If the patient in question would like to discuss and disclose personal information with the woman, then it should be their choice and the woman should be encouraged to speak to her partner regarding the matter (option G). Sexual health advisors within sexual health clinics can usually help to arrange appointments for relationship counselling and explanation of test results should the couples wish to do this.

You should not encourage the woman to leave her partner (option H), nor should you divulge private details of any patients (option B). Although it is good advice to offer the patient condoms and to practise safe sex, this is not the most appropriate action in the current scenario (option F).

Answer Question 59

BFH

Unfortunately, sitting exams and working at the same time goes part and parcel with the job and as a junior doctor your task is to prioritise your workload and work as efficiently as possible (options B and F). If you find that this is all too much to handle then you can try to arrange a different method of obtaining study leave in terms of having occasional 'half study days' off or asking whether a senior or junior colleague can cover some of your tasks so you can at least leave on time daily to study at home (option H).

It may be possible to get a refund and pull out of the examination altogether if the workload is too high, however, the sittings do not happen that often and it may be the only chance you get before applying for your training jobs. In any case, revising for the examinations, whether you pass them or not, can only help improve your knowledge of patient care and benefit your team.

It is wrong to demand time off from your consultant if you have clinical duties to attend to (option G) and you would be committing fraud should you call into work sick when you are actually fit and well (option C).

Answer Question 60

BDF

Despite the patient appearing stable and well during the morning ward round, it seems that the patient's clinical situation has changed during the day. Although the patient has been treated for their infection in the past, recurrence is still a possibility.

As the doctor most familiar with the patient's history it is your duty to deal with the abnormal findings as soon as possible to prevent further deterioration of the clinical situation. To this end you should fully assess the patient (options B and F) and ask for senior advice before changing any management plans (option D). The key point here is to review the patient first before speaking to the registrar on-call as members of your own team have left hospital and the senior who will be advising you may never have met the patient before.

Answer Question 61

ADH

An illegible drug chart is an issue for patient safety. Medication which is written wrongly or illegibly can lead to the incorrect administration of drugs. As you have been called to review the patient it is important you do this as a priority rather than leave a sick patient (option A) and after doing so, you must document your findings clearly within the notes (option D). You should attend to the drug chart which needs to be altered to prevent the possibility of future prescribing errors arising (option H).

Although there are many appropriate actions listed, the most immediate ones are to assess the patient and review their notes and drug chart. After this initial assessment, you may wish to discuss the matter with your seniors (option G) or the patient's medical team (option B).

Answer Question 62

CEG

Although you may be limited by time pressures in the Accident and Emergency department, it is important to explore why this patient is not taking his inhalers (option C). Empowering the patient to take charge of their own health may prevent reattendance and further serious consequences. It may be worth discussing the matter with the respiratory nurse specialist to consider methods of optimizing their asthma control (option E) and allowing the patient to understand the importance of their health. Asking the patient to see their GP may also be an alternative option. However, the GP may be under similar time pressures in their general clinic. Threatening or intimidating language is not appropriate (option F) and neither is 'giving up' on a patient (option H).

You should not consider discharging any patient until you believe you have treated their admitting medical problems to your best ability and this situation is no different (option G).

Answer Question 63

BFG

This scenario relates to patient safety. Although the situation has been recognised by yourself, there is the potential that this mistake could result in an incorrect blood transfusion with disastrous consequences.

You should take steps to rectify the situation (option B) and this should be relayed to the doctor who made the mistake so they can learn from the situation and prevent future issues from happening (option F). The erroneously labeled blood and request form should be discarded to avoid confusion and should not be re-labeled with correct details as this is confusing for the laboratory technicians and could cause further problems (option G).

It is negligent to ignore the situation (option E) and if the solution is rectified immediately there is no reason for the patient's operation to be cancelled (option D).

Answer Question 64

CDF

In accordance with the *New Doctor* publication, "systems should be in place to ensure appropriate support for the academic and welfare needs of Foundation doctors" and "Foundation doctors must have a summary of agreed educational objectives and assessments for each placement and must review the summary with their educational supervisor during the placement."

If you are particularly interested in learning a new skill such as suturing in theatre or gaining experience of scrubbing up for an operation and assisting, you should raise your interest with your consultant or educational supervisor to discuss ways in which your educational needs may be met (option F). Your senior colleagues may also be able to advise you in this respect having gone through a similar process themselves (option C).

It may not be appropriate to ask your senior house officer, who may be in specialty surgical training themselves, to sacrifice their own educational needs for yours to be met (option B) and leaving jobs on the ward unfinished (option G) is clinically negligent. However, if you have other junior colleagues who are happy and willing to cover for you during the occasional hour or so you have in theatre, this may be a viable alternative (option D).

Answer Question 65

CEG

It is your duty as a doctor to put patient care first as your priority. Although the patient may ask to leave, you should check with your consultant whether this is still appropriate given that the discharge medications will not be ready until the next morning (option G). In certain situations, patients may be entitled to 'night leave' where they can go home for the evening but return the next morning for medications. If this is not a possibility, then you should try your best to make sure the same situation does not occur again by informing the nursing staff of the situation (option E) and trying your best to ensure the patient can leave as early as possible the next morning (option C).

You may wish to express your disappointment with the other medical teams (options A and D), but this will not directly benefit your patient at the present time and may cause friction with other colleagues. You may wish to apologise to the patient, however, encouraging a 'blame culture' by asking them to write letters of complaint will not help matters (option H).

Answer Question 66

ABG

This clinical scenario is testing your ability to recognise when patient safety is at risk and how to deal with an 'unsafe' colleague. According to the GMC *Duties of a Doctor*, "You must protect patients from risk of harm posed by another colleague's conduct, performance or health" whilst maintaining patient concern and safety as your top priority.

In the first instance you should correct any of the errors that have been made to the best of your ability so no undue harm will reach any patients (option A). You should also take steps to point out such mistakes to your senior house officer (option B). It may be that he/she did not realise that they had made a mistake and now it has been pointed out, they will stop recurring. If, however, you find that this is not the case and they do have obvious gaps and inadequacies in their clinical care, you should encourage your colleague to seek help either by speaking to the consultant in charge or offering to do this yourself if they do not want to (option G).

Asking your senior house officer to go back and correct their own mistakes (option C) may help them learn what they did wrong but there is no guarantee that they will correct the mistakes appropriately if they really do not understand what the error was in the first place. In addition, completely ignoring the situation by asking the nurses to go away (option E) is negligent. You are not in the position to dismiss your senior house officer from work (option F) and before speaking to the clinical director (option D), you should escalate the matter within your own team to your consultant.

Answer Question 67

BCD

This question deals with empathy and sensitivity, in particular responding to the needs and concerns of the patient. In the first instance you should discuss the matter with the patient and his wife to determine what their views, hopes and expectations are regarding his current situation and outcome of treatment from the trial. It may be that his expectations are unrealistic, in which case you should seek to fully inform him of the actual potential risks and benefits (option D).

As a junior doctor, it is unwise for you to make the letter of referral to the oncology centre without first finding out a little more yourself about the trial in question (option C) and informing the patient's oncologist (option B). He may be able to advise you and perhaps even make the referral himself. Speaking to the oncology centre themselves is crucial as there may be details the patient and his wife have overlooked which make the patient ineligible to enter the trial.

Answer Question 68

ADF

Violence against health professionals (and patients) is not acceptable and some trusts have policies in place to withhold treatment from violent individuals. Situations where it may not be appropriate to withhold treatment from violent behavior include those where the aggression is secondary to illness, drugs/alcohol (as in this case), mental illness or patients who require emergency treatment.

Where medical treatment is still indicated for a violent patient the following actions should be taken:

- contacting the hospital security to accompany the patient (option A)
- ensuring that no clinician or healthcare professional be left alone with the violent patient during assessment or treatment
- enlisting help from another healthcare professional who the patient was not violent towards
- completion of a clinical incident form with all relevant details of the circumstances in which the violent action has occurred.

In this scenario you must also attend to the medical needs of the abused nurse (option F) and try your best to reason with the patient so that their medical treatment can be commenced (option D) without escalating the situation.

Although the situation is a sensitive and difficult one, it is not a medical emergency and it would be inappropriate for you to call a colleague away from a trauma call where they are needed if other members of staff can help you instead (option E). You should not attempt to restrain the patient yourself (option C) but if the hospital security and other members of staff are unable to handle the situation, it may be necessary at a later point to contact the police (option B).

Answer Question 69

AEF

According to the GMC *Good Medical Practice* guidelines, "Wherever possible, you should avoid providing medical care to anyone with whom you have a close personal relationship."

You should therefore refrain from providing a prescription for your sister in this situation and advise that she go to the nearest walk-in centre (option A) as you do not need to have an appointment for this or you could encourage her to seek advice from and register with a GP (option F).

There is little that will be gained from discussing the situation with your consultant (option G) who will suggest very similar advice to the above and it would be wrong to tell your sister to ignore her infection (option H) as it may worsen.

Answer Question 70

ABC

This case involves a potentially unwell patient who may need to be seen immediately. It is not appropriate to turn the patient away (options G and H). The most appropriate step in this circumstance is to ensure that the patient is assessed in a timely manner and that their safety is not compromised.

You should take as much of the history over the telephone regarding the patient concerned as possible (option A) and advise the GP to the best of your ability whilst bearing in mind your clinical limitations (option B). Once you have spoken to the GP you should inform your registrar in theatre of the patient and seek advice on what to do once they reach the hospital (option C).

You may wish to refer the patient to another clinical team where their registrar is less busy than yours (as in option G), however, you must bear in mind that given the clinical complaint, another specialty may not have the expertise to deal with this problem and may therefore only delay effective patient treatment.

Examination 5

PART ONE – Ranking Questions

Question 1

An elderly man with advanced glaucoma has just failed his visual field test and you have to inform him to stop driving. His job depends on driving to different locations and you know that this news will clearly upset him but you are not exactly sure how he will react or how to break it to him.

Rank in order the following actions in response to this situation (1= Most appropriate; 5= Least appropriate):

A.   Start by explaining the test done and what it showed followed by its implications in a 'matter of fact' way.

B.   Tell him that if his glaucoma is not controlled then he will need surgery.

C.   Ask him about his needs for driving, any alternatives and the support available at home.

D.   Tell him that due to his glaucoma he must stop working altogether.

E.   Tell him that an ophthalmologist will see him to discuss his options.

Question 2

Since having medical students on your hospital attachment you have noticed that you are out of practice in reading ECGs (as your registrar and senior house officer always make the decisions about these). You have recently shied away from reading a few ECGs of your own patients whilst the students are continually presenting them to your consultant. It has become so bad that you have even forgotten the basics of ECG interpretation.

Rank in order the following actions in response to this situation (1= Most appropriate; 5= Least appropriate):

A.   Arrange to attend a teaching session/lecture on interpreting ECGs.

B.   Do nothing and hope that you will get more opportunities to read ECGs again.

C.   Encourage the medical students to divide and share out the ECGs of the patients on the ward so everyone has the chance to present the findings to the senior members of the team.

D.   Tell your team about the situation and hopefully come up with a solution with the medical students for you to initially interpret the ECGs.

E.   Tell the students that you (and not them) should present the ECGs to your consultant.

Question 3

Your consultant is carrying out a complicated operation in a few days. The patient has a malignant phaechromocytoma. In addition, the patient has multiple morbidities including increasing shortness of breath (which is new), hypertension and arthritis. The patient is being brought in a few days before to start his alpha blockade medication. What is the best way to manage the jobs for this patient?

Rank in order the following actions in response to this situation (1= Most appropriate; 5= Least appropriate):

A.   Book an urgent ECHO due to the patient's newly found shortness of breath and hypertension.

B.   Carry out an inpatient X-ray of the patient's cervical spine to exclude any pathology that may cause a problem, whilst intubating the patient.

C.   Ensure that a high dependency unit bed has been booked for the day of the operation.

D.   See if the endocrine specialist is available after the operation about discontinuing or continuing the alpha blockade the patient is already on.

E.   Take a set of bloods when the patient comes in and obtain a cross-match and group and save.

Question 4

You are reviewing the notes of a breast cancer patient for tomorrow's MDT (multidisciplinary team) meeting. You notice that your consultant has prescribed a higher dose of methotrexate than that stated by the oncologist in the notes. The patient seems to have been kept on this dose for a long time. Although the patient is improving with the dose, you are aware that a high dose can lead to side effects and you are uncertain if it is safe for this to continue or not.

Rank in order the following actions in response to this situation (1= Most appropriate; 5= Least appropriate):

A.   Look up the dose of methotrexate in cancer patients in the BNF before you take any further action.

B.   Rewrite the patient's drug chart with the dose of methotrexate as suggested by the oncologist.

C.   Leave the dose unchanged as you can discuss this in tomorrow morning's MDT where your consultant and the oncologist will both be present.

D.   Discuss with the patient their usual dose of methotrexate and whether they have had any side effects.

E.   Ring your own consultant as soon as possible to discuss the correct dose of methotrexate.

Question 5

You are bleeped to attend a crash call in the emergency department. You search through the notes while the patient is receiving cardiopulmonary resuscitation, and do not find a 'do not resuscitate' (DNR) form. Despite the effort, the patient passes away. Whilst attending to another patient later on, you notice the DNR form for the deceased patient in their notes, which had evidently been misplaced. The family arrives expressing their frustration that their relative had passed away in pain.

Rank in order the following actions in response to this situation (1= Most appropriate; 5= Least appropriate):

A. Find the person who misplaced the DNR form and report them to your consultant.

B. Wait for your consultant to speak to the relatives.

C. Complete an incident form and discuss this with your consultant.

D. Let your clinical team know that you have found the DNR form.

E. You speak to the relatives yourself and apologise for the situation.

Question 6

A 20 year old man with a tibial fracture is anaesthetised and on the operating table. You are the junior doctor and are assisting your consultant and registrar in the operation – the patient has an irreparable arterial injury. Both you and your team agree that the patient needs an amputation. The anaesthetist goes to check the consent form but cannot find it in the notes. There was no WHO checklist performed at the beginning of the operation as everyone was in a rush and forgot. You know that a different registrar who is not in theatre consented the patient, but you do not know what was written on the consent form.

Rank in order the following actions in response to this situation (1= Most appropriate; 5= Least appropriate):

A. Ask the medico-legal advisor to discuss the case with the team as soon as possible.

B. Obtain a second opinion from another consultant in the same department as to whether amputation is essential.

C. Contact the doctor who consented the patient and ask where they last had the form.

D. Decide with the team what is in the best interests of the patient taking into account all the factors needed to make a decision.

E. Try and find anything in the notes showing that amputation may have been explained to the patient in context of the surgery.

Question 7

You are a junior doctor on a late shift. On more than one day, you have noticed a nurse putting equipment into her bag. After one such occasion an email is sent out concerning missing equipment on the same ward she was working on.

Rank in order the following actions in response to this situation (1= Most appropriate; 5= Least appropriate):

A. Wait till she steals something of considerable value before you report her.

B. Speak to her directly and ask her to explain herself.

C. Report the incident to the senior nurse on the ward.

D. Ask other colleagues on the ward if they have noticed anything.

E. Do not do anything as you may be interpreting her actions wrongly.

Question 8

Your registrar wants you to request a swallow for a patient who is one week post-surgery. The patient is vomiting and has considerable abdominal pain. When requesting the exam, the consultant radiologist asks what type of swallow study is needed and the exact surgery that was performed. You do not know either of these things but do not want any delay in the examination as your registrar was adamant that the scan needs to be done.

Rank in order the following actions in response to this situation (1= Most appropriate; 5= Least appropriate):

A.   Tell the radiologist whatever you feel the answer might be without clarifying it.

B.   Tell the radiologist that if needed you can bring him the patient's notes to have a read through.

C.   Tell the radiologist to do whatever swallow and scan he feels is necessary.

D.   Try and find out the relevant information as soon as possible, even if it means delaying the investigation.

E.   Tell the radiologist to speak to your registrar as you are unaware of all the details.

Question 9

You are a junior doctor doing your GP rotation. Your next patient is a 19 year old Muslim girl, who has just recently come to the country and cannot speak any English. She is with her mother and father, who are requesting an urgent termination of pregnancy on her behalf. Your senior has gone on his break. You are keen to take an accurate history from the patient herself.

Rank in order the following actions in response to this situation (1= Most appropriate; 5= Least appropriate):

A.   Politely ask the parents to leave the consultation room and see if you can obtain an interpreter to discuss this matter with the patient.

B.   Ask the patient's parents to interpret for her.

C.   Obtain an interpreter to discuss this matter with the patient and her parents.

D.   Attempt to communicate with her using non-verbal methods.

E.   Refuse to see her as she is with her parents. Ask her to return by herself for another appointment.

Question 10

You are a Foundation doctor in the emergency department. One of your patients recurrently presents with "funny turns", and he is deeply concerned that he may have epilepsy. He has had numerous investigations for these episodes, and the cause is suspected to be non-organic. The patient insists that one of the neurology doctors come and review him, even though you are confident that this is not required.

Rank in order the following actions in response to this situation (1= Most appropriate; 5= Least appropriate):

A. Refer the patient to the on-call medical team as a neurological referral, even though all investigations have excluded an organic neurological cause.

B. Reassure the patient that all the investigations have excluded an organic neurological cause, and it is unlikely that he has epilepsy.

C. Contact your registrar to come and reassure the patient that there is no neurological cause of these episodes.

D. Explain to the patient that it may be more appropriate for him to be seen as an outpatient and suggest that his GP refer him to the neurologist as an outpatient.

E. Ask the on-call psychiatrist to come and see the patient.

Question 11

A young lady presents with a vast array of medical problems and was brought in by her neighbour. She seems perfectly competent but can only speak minimal English. She has a raised troponin, ST elevation on her ECG and is holding her chest. A search of her notes on the computer brings up an outdated medical history. You need to obtain a history for the purpose of deciding her acute management. Considering that you have no time to find an official interpreter, how would you go about getting a history?

Rank in order the following actions in response to this situation (1= Most appropriate; 5= Least appropriate):

A. Do not try to get a history as it is a waste of time, a myocardial infarction can be fully managed without any history.

B. Treat the patient based on the test results rather than the clinical history and review this later on.

C. Try and get a member of staff to act as an interpreter for now until an official one can be arranged or an English-speaking relative is available.

D. Speak to the neighbour to obtain as much history as possible.

E. Speak to the patient's GP and try to get some indication of her past medical history and possible reason why she has come in.

Question 12

A patient who has been admitted with your team presents with a history that could well be a pulmonary embolism. A CT pulmonary angiogram has been scheduled for later today. He is expressing a desire to leave the hospital and return home. It appears to you as though he does not understand the gravity of the situation and the possible dangers of having a pulmonary embolism. He is becoming irate and rude to nursing staff on the ward.

Rank in order the following actions in response to this situation (1= Most appropriate; 5= Least appropriate):

A. Allow him to leave as he is has mental capacity, but ensure he signs a self-discharge form.

B. Go to the ward to see him and take him to a side room and calm him down.

C. Explain to him that a pulmonary embolism is lethal.

D. Should he self-discharge, contact his GP.

E. Encourage him to wait at least for the CT scan.

Question 13

You are a junior doctor on a respiratory rotation in a teaching hospital. One of the medical students asks you if they can take an arterial blood gas (ABG) from a patient. They have never watched or performed one before. They have only learnt the theory behind the procedure in lectures.

Rank in order the following actions in response to this situation (1= Most appropriate; 5= Least appropriate):

A. Do the procedure yourself while they watch and explain to them what you are doing.

B. Ask them to do the ABG anyway under your supervision.

C. Explain the procedure to them at a convenient time and then ask them to get some practise on mannequin arms first.

D. Ask them to do the ABG unsupervised.

E. Explain the procedure to them at a convenient time.

Question 14

You are a busy surgical junior doctor at a district general hospital. You have several new admissions every day and a heavy workload. You are concerned as you have missed a few teaching sessions and have not attended any grand rounds as you have been so busy doing ward jobs.

Rank in order the following actions in response to this situation (1= Most appropriate; 5= Least appropriate):

A. Start to attend your teaching sessions and do not tell anyone about the pressure of your workload.

B. Inform your consultant that you have missed teaching sessions due to such a heavy workload and this may affect your sign-off for the year.

C. Try to get your team to cover your jobs while you are in teaching.

D. Continue to ignore your teaching sessions as ward duties take priority over your learning at all times.

E. Tell your team that you cannot cope with the current workload and ask for more time off.

Question 15

You are halfway through your first Foundation Programme year. You have experienced a variety of surgical and general medical hospital rotations. Despite feeling more confident in the management of patients you have not been able to get the range of DOPS (directly observed procedures) that you would have liked. You are looking to apply for a surgical job in the future and are aware that a lack of surgical DOPS may hinder your application. You are due to start a new surgical rotation soon.

Rank in order the following actions in response to this situation (1= Most appropriate; 5= Least appropriate):

A.   Attempt to do some surgical DOPS in your current on-call shifts where emergency and acutely unwell patients are referred to you.

B.   Accept that in some hospital rotations it will be difficult to do any DOPS so you stop worrying about it any further.

C.   Ask the senior members of your team and other teams on the ward to call you when 'DOPS worthy' procedures arise.

D.   Try and arrange some surgical DOPS when feasible in your next surgical rotation.

E.   Do other assessments if you cannot find any DOPS procedures to do.

Question 16

You have just clerked a medical patient when on-call. You think that this would be a good case-based discussion for you to include in your ePortfolio. You want to discuss it with the medical registrar although it is clear that she is busy reviewing other patients.

Rank in order the following actions in response to this situation (1= Most appropriate; 5= Least appropriate):

A.   Take down details of the case (being sure to exclude traceable details).

B.   Arrange a time to meet the registrar at a later date to go through the case-based discussion.

C.   Send off the ticket request to the registrar on the ePortfolio system.

D.   Do some background reading regarding the differential diagnosis of this particular case before to discussing it.

E.   Ask for feedback from the registrar on how you can improve.

Question 17

While working in your surgical firm as a junior doctor, you notice that compliance with hand washing in-between seeing different patients is very poor among the surgical teams. What do you do?

Rank in order the following actions in response to this situation (1= Most appropriate; 5= Least appropriate):

A.   Make a list of ways how one could improve the system.

B.   Re-audit after improvements have been made to complete the cycle.

C.   Make a grand round presentation, focusing on your views and way of improving.

D.   Start a quality improvement project to audit the handover system.

E.   Discuss your views with senior colleagues.

Question 18

You are one of the medical junior doctors on-call and your patient needs a chest drain. You feel that you have had little exposure to procedures such as chest drains as you have a junior registrar who is very keen to do all of them. You have had some training in chest drain insertion at medical school and know about the theory and indications behind the procedure.

Rank in order the following actions in response to this situation (1= Most appropriate; 5= Least appropriate):

A. Ensure the patient consents to the chest drain being performed by you.

B. Explain to the patient why the chest drain is needed.

C. Ensure that you have seen a chest drain being carried out before attempting one.

D. Speak to your registrar and ask if you can do the chest drain this time under their supervision instead of them doing it on their own.

E. Politely ask the other members of the team if they would mind if you performed the chest drain procedure this time as you have not had the chance to do this on your current rotation yet.

Question 19

You are the on-call junior doctor. In quick succession, you receive three bleeps from different wards regarding different patients. The first bleep is about a patient who is known to have COPD and is desaturating despite being on high levels of oxygen. The second bleep is about a young lady who has sickle cell disease and is complaining of unbearable chest pain. The third bleep is about a lady with known rheumatoid arthritis that is complaining of bilateral knee pain.

Rank in order the following actions in response to this situation (1= Most appropriate; 5= Least appropriate):

A. As the sickle cell patient and the gentleman with COPD both sound urgent to you, contact the other on-call junior doctor up on the ward and ask them to see the patient with sickle cell disease whilst you see the man with COPD.

B. Obtain as much basic information as possible (such as clinical observations and medications) from each nurse who is bleeping you so that you can prioritise better.

C. Inform the nurse who contacted you about the lady with rheumatoid arthritis that unfortunately due to more urgent situations you will not be there immediately, but you will see the patient as soon as possible.

D. Arrive at the patient with COPD. Read the notes to obtain a thorough history, fully examine the patient and manage appropriately.

E. Contact the registrar on-call as you feel that you cannot manage.

Question 20

Whilst writing up a patient's drug chart in the emergency department, the patient tells you that they usually take methadone for heroine replacement therapy but he does not know the dose. He says he requires this medicine and cannot cope without it and gets rather agitated that you are not writing him a dose of this immediately.

Rank in order the following actions in response to this situation (1= Most appropriate; 5– Least appropriate):

A. Contact the pharmacy for more information.

B. Do not prescribe anything and seek no further information.

C. Call the patient's GP for more information regarding the patient's regular dose.

D. Look at any previous discharge letters for more information.

E. Ask the patient to guess what dose he takes and prescribe whatever he says.

Question 21

You are the on-call junior doctor and are reviewing the drug chart of a patient with a urinary tract infection when you notice they seem to be on a different antibiotic than the trust's policy for urinary tract infections.

Rank in order the following actions in response to this situation (1= Most appropriate; 5= Least appropriate):

A. Go through the notes to try and find out why this particular antibiotic was chosen.

B. Change the antibiotic to the one you think is correct.

C. Ask the on-call microbiologist why the patient might be on this antibiotic.

D. Do nothing today and ask the person who wrote the antibiotic prescription for the patient if you happen to see them around the hospital.

E. Look up any urine culture sensitivity results for this patient to determine whether the antibiotic they are on is going to be effective.

Question 22

You are a junior doctor seeing an elderly gentleman in the emergency department who presents with weight loss, bony hip pain, haemopytsis and several neurological symptoms. A lung biopsy, CT scan and bone scan reveals a primary lung lesion with cerebral and bony hip metastasis, in keeping with a diagnosis of widespread cancer. It appears the patient has not had the news broken to him yet about his diagnosis. Your registrar has asked you to gather some information about the patient's circumstances and his feelings regarding the illness before he goes to see the patient to explain the exact situation.

Rank in order the following actions in response to this situation (1= Most appropriate; 5= Least appropriate):

A.   You only go to see how the patient is doing but will attempt to avoid speaking to him regarding the investigations and his symptoms.

B.   Tell the patient that he has a confirmed diagnosis of cancer.

C.   Take a history from the patient regarding his symptoms and circumstances but do not give the diagnosis – say that your registrar will see him shortly.

D.   Ring the patient's GP, the radiologist who did the scan and also get advice from the oncologist regarding the patient's background details and further actions for management. Report back to your registrar.

E.   Tell the registrar that it is beyond your competency to deal with such complicated cases and that the senior house officer should speak to him instead.

Question 23

Whilst doing your normal ward round you are writing up some medication for a patient as instructed by your registrar. You then notice as you do this that you had incorrectly prescribed this patient a stat dose of vitamin K the previous day when you should have actually done this for a different patient.

Rank in order the following actions in response to this situation (1= Most appropriate; 5= Least appropriate):

A.   Fill in a clinical incident form.

B.   Request that you speak to your team in private to inform them of the mistake.

C.   Apologise to the patient who you prescribed the vitamin K incorrectly to.

D.   Go and prescribe the vitamin K to the patient that you were meant to.

E.   Assess both patients for implications of receiving/not receiving the vitamin K.

Question 24

A patient is admitted with recurrent episodes of asthmatic attacks. It becomes evident to your team that she is not adhering to her asthma medications. She says she find it very difficult to take her inhalers and feels she does not know how to use them properly.

Rank in order the following actions in response to this situation (1= Most appropriate; 5= Least appropriate):

A. Instruct the patient that if she does not take her inhalers then she will eventually have a severe attack of asthma and die a horrible death. Hope that shocking your patient will get them to sit up and listen to you.

B. Explain why it is important she takes her inhalers and reiterate the risks and complications of untreated asthma.

C. Empathise with her and explore her ideas, concerns and expectations regarding her attitudes to asthma.

D. Suggest an appointment with the asthma specialist nurse as an outpatient to talk about issues regarding her asthmatic medications.

E. Demonstrate to the patient how to use their inhalers and try to get them to demonstrate this back to you so that you can correct anything they are doing wrong.

Question 25

During your on-call, one of the ward patients that was admitted today following a suicide attempt threatens to self-discharge. She is awaiting review by the psychiatry team but her clinical observations are unremarkable. Her blood results are still pending.

Rank in order the following actions in response to this situation (1= Most appropriate; 5= Least appropriate):

A. Let the patient leave without intervening as you do not want to get involved.

B. Call your senior colleague immediately.

C. Calm the patient down. Explain to her why you want to keep her in. Ask the nurse to call the psychiatrist while you are with the patient.

D. Tell the patient she needs to sign a self-discharge form.

E. Ask the nurse to urgently bleep the on-call psychiatry team to come and assess the patient.

Question 26

While carrying out the ward jobs in the afternoon you get bleeped by a ward sister who tells you that one of your patients has a potassium reading of 7.0. You are unsure of the protocol for treating hyperkalaemia in this particular hospital but are vaguely familiar with the necessary steps to take.

Rank in order the following actions in response to this situation (1= Most appropriate; 5= Least appropriate):

A.   Take a venous blood gas as a repeat sample of the potassium reading after giving treatment.

B.   Ask the nurse (on the phone) to take a complete set of observations and to perform an ECG immediately.

C.   Ensure the patient has vascular access.

D.   See the patient and perform a full review, commencing treatment with insulin and dextrose, calcium gluconate and salbutamol.

E.   Look up the protocol on the intranet and escalate the scenario up your own team if unsure.

Question 27

During a consultant ward round, it becomes evident to you that a lot of jobs are accumulating. There are a number of patients to be discharged and consequently many discharge summaries to be written. In addition, you have to bleed a few patients as the phlebotomists were unable to do so this morning. You are aware the deadline for the pharmacy to dispense discharge medications is 16:30.

Rank in order the following actions in response to this situation (1= Most appropriate; 5= Least appropriate):

A.   Have a group discussion after the ward round and split the jobs evenly between the junior members of the team.

B.   Rank the jobs in order of urgency.

C.   Send off the medication component of each discharge summary as soon as possible to the pharmacy so patients will get their medications before they are discharged.

D.   Chase up blood results taken from each patient so that appropriate actions can be taken.

E.   Request permission from a senior member of your team to peel off the ward round to action the most urgent jobs.

Question 28

During a post-take ward round, the consultant asks you to request a CT pulmonary angiogram (CTPA) for a patient that he believes may have a pulmonary embolism. You go down to speak to the radiologist who asks you multiple questions about the patient's history and states that you should be treating the patient if clinical suspicion is high. He also suggests that the patient is too young for such a high radiation dose and recommends a V/Q scan instead. However, you are certain that your team want a CTPA over a V/Q scan.

Rank in order the following actions in response to this situation (1= Most appropriate; 5= Least appropriate):

A. Go and speak to a different radiologist who might be more amenable to your plea.

B. Suggest to the radiologist that a V/Q scan would be less conclusive and reiterate that your consultant wanted a CTPA.

C. Ask your consultant whether he would like you to schedule a V/Q scan instead as the radiologist has recommended this instead.

D. Go back to your team and relay the discussion that took place with the radiologist.

E. Document in the notes the name of the radiologist, the advice and suggestions given and the time of the discussion.

Question 29

You have finished all the urgent ward jobs and are left with six discharge summaries to write for your patients who are due to be discharged within the next week. Not all your patients will be discharged home tonight, but some will need to be discharged in the next few hours. How will you go about prioritising which discharge summaries including medications need to be written up?

Rank in order the following actions in response to this situation (1= Most appropriate; 5= Least appropriate):

A. Do the discharge letters of the patients you know the best as they will take you less time. Write the more complex ones later on.

B. Confirm with your senior colleague which patients will be discharged earlier than others.

C. Do the discharge summaries for those going home tomorrow and assume that your colleague has already done the discharge summaries for those to be discharged today.

D. Do the discharge summaries in alphabetical order.

E. Do the discharge summaries first for those that will be discharged first.

Question 30

An obese young girl presents to you (the junior doctor) with pleuritic chest pain, shortness of breath and hypoxia. Your immediate concern is that she may have a pulmonary embolus. You have requested a chest X-ray which appears normal. It is during normal hours in the hospital and the patient tells you that she is not pregnant or breastfeeding at present. She denies any contra-indications to being anti-coagulated.

Rank in order the following actions in response to this situation (1= Most appropriate; 5= Least appropriate):

A.   Start prophylactic dose Fragmin and wait for imaging to confirm pulmonary embolus.

B.   Request a V/Q scan.

C.   Request a CT pulmonary angiogram.

D.   Discuss the situation with the general medical registrar on-call.

E.   Start the patient on a treatment dose Fragmin.

Question 31

You are a junior doctor on a surgical firm. Mrs Finchley's CT scan result has come back showing resolution of her volvulus and she is due to be discharged first thing tomorrow morning. However, you believe you can see a mass on her left kidney but this is not included in the radiology registrar report.

Rank in order the following actions in response to this situation (1= Most appropriate; 5= Least appropriate):

A.   Contact your consultant and explain your findings.

B.   Make a referral to the urology team.

C.   Contact the radiology consultant and ask him to report on the kidneys.

D.   Discuss it with your junior doctor colleague and see if they agree with your observations.

E.   Document it in the notes to be reviewed on the ward round in the morning.

Question 32

You are a junior doctor on surgical take and see a rather unkempt middle-aged man smelling of alcohol in the emergency department who is complaining of intense abdominal pain. All of his investigations are normal yet he is asking to be prescribed opiates for his intense pain.

Rank in order the following actions in response to this situation (1= Most appropriate; 5= Least appropriate):

A.   Prescribe the patient a very low dose of oramorph yourself and see if that alleviates his pain.

B.   Agree to prescribe the patient paracetamol and tramadol first to see if this helps.

C.   Contact your registrar explaining your concern about drug-seeking behaviour.

D.   Contact your senior house officer to ask them to sign a prescription for oramorph.

E.   Refuse to prescribe painkillers since there is no medical problem with the patient.

Question 33

It is 6pm and you are coming to the end of your shift on a vascular surgery firm. The junior doctor who is meant to take over from you for the evening is not able to come to her shift and you have two patients arriving later that evening who need to be clerked and have bloods taken before their operations the next day.

Rank in order the following actions in response to this situation (1= Most appropriate; 5= Least appropriate):

A. Inform your immediate senior about the situation and ask them whether they can see the patients, and take the bloods.

B. Discuss the situation with your consultant so a plan can be formulated in your team for dealing with these situations.

C. Prepare drug charts and clerking based on the patients' old notes and then tell the ward staff to contact your senior when the patients arrive.

D. Plan to come in early the next day to see the patients and prepare them for surgery.

E. Leave a note with the names of the two patients due to arrive for your senior colleague (who is to cover the late shift) in the doctor's office and a message asking her to see them.

Question 34

You are reviewing the notes of a patient who has overdosed on piriton and paracetamol tablets. She is now medically fit for discharge but the community mental health team feel that she should stay for another night on the acute medical ward. She has stayed in hospital for three days now and appears not to have any active psychiatric symptoms but feels 'safe' in hospital. Your consultant does not believe that keeping a 'fit' patient in an acute medical bed is appropriate and asks you to discharge the patient. How will you go about explaining the need for her to be discharged to the mental health team?

Rank in order the following actions in response to this situation (1= Most appropriate; 5= Least appropriate):

A. Tell the mental health team that they are incompetent for making such a bad decision.

B. Express your concerns that she has no acute medical problems and therefore does not need to be on an acute medical ward.

C. Explain to the mental health team that she is medically fit for discharge and ask them to clarify their reasoning for keeping her in for another night.

D. Ask the mental health team to see her again first thing in the morning to assess if the situation has changed.

E. Ask the liaison psychiatrist to review the patient, taking into account she is medically fit for discharge.

Question 35

A 38 year old male, Mr Smith, is admitted with general malaise. During admission he is diagnosed with hepatitis C. On discharge, he asks you not to mention his diagnosis to his GP as he is embarrassed by the diagnosis.

Rank in order the following actions in response to this situation (1= Most appropriate; 5= Least appropriate):

A.   Respect Mr Smith's wishes. You must respect patient confidentiality.

B.   Advise Mr Smith that it is in his best interests for his GP to be informed so that he can receive optimum care. However, if he still asks you for this information to be confidential, you must respect his wishes.

C.   Explain that it is mandatory for you to inform his GP of the diagnosis.

D.   Explain that you will have to inform his GP as there is an infection risk to the GP.

E.   Contact Mr Smith's family and ask them to inform his GP.

Question 36

You are a Foundation year representative and a fellow junior doctor approaches you. He tells you that he is concerned about one of the surgical senior house officers who is going out most nights and turning up inebriated for work.

Rank in order the following actions in response to this situation (1= Most appropriate; 5= Least appropriate):

A.   Arrange a private meeting with the surgical consultant to discuss the senior house officer's behaviour.

B.   Take a full written report from your colleague and discuss it with the postgraduate team.

C.   Talk to the senior house officer in question and get a full report from both your colleagues before discussing it with the postgraduate team.

D.   Tell your colleague not to get involved with other people's business. If the surgical senior house officer has a problem then they can come to you themselves.

E.   Monitor the senior house officer to see if he causes any harm with his behaviour.

Question 37

One of your junior doctor colleagues has been getting a lot of verbal abuse from her registrar. Recently you heard her upset in the doctor's office when she thought no one was around.

Rank in order the following actions in response to this situation (1= Most appropriate; 5= Least appropriate):

A.   Confront the registrar and politely tell him his behaviour is making your colleague upset.

B.   Explain the situation to your consultant and ask him to talk to the registrar.

C.   Start giving abuse to the registrar to see if he gets the message.

D.   Talk to your colleague in a private area and encourage her to do something about it.

E.   Tell your colleague to stop taking things so personally.

Question 38

You are the junior doctor on a surgical attachment. You are asked to clerk and examine patients in the pre-assessment clinic before they are seen by the registrar who will consent them and explain the surgery to them. One day the registrar is unavailable and you are asked to explain the procedures and consent the patients.

Rank in order the following actions in response to this situation (1= Most appropriate; 5= Least appropriate):

A.   Agree as you have watched the registrar consent patients several times (although you have not seen the operations the patients are being consented for).

B.   Discuss the matter with your registrar explaining that you feel this is not appropriate.

C.   Clerk and examine the patients as you would anyway, and find an alternative senior to consent the patients.

D.   Refuse to consent the patients.

E.   Check with your consultant if this is appropriate.

Question 39

You have had a hectic few days as you were on-call earlier in the week. As a result you have been very tired and forgetful. You are a type 1 diabetic and you realise that you have forgotten to bring your insulin with you for lunchtime and begin to feel rather faint.

Rank in order the following actions in response to this situation (1= Most appropriate; 5= Least appropriate):

A.   Go to the emergency department to obtain a prescription for insulin.

B.   Ask one of the staff nurses on the ward to administer insulin to you.

C.   Call home and see if there is anyone available that can bring your insulin in for you.

D.   Write a prescription for insulin for yourself and pick it up from an outside pharmacy whilst your colleague attends to your bleep.

E.   Contact your GP and ask him to fax a prescription to an outside pharmacy so that you can pick it up.

Question 40

You are a junior doctor and have started a busy orthopaedic job at a district general hospital. Your consultant mentions that they are understaffed at the moment and asks if you would mind seeing patients in fracture clinic on the days when the registrar or senior house officer are away. Even though you have done an orthopaedic attachment when you were a medical student, you feel out of your depth.

Rank in order the following actions in response to this situation (1= Most appropriate; 5= Least appropriate):

A.   Ask your registrar or consultant if you could sit in a few clinics with them, and ask them to supervise you seeing a few patients before you do your own clinic.

B.   Ask your registrar or consultant if you could sit in a few clinics with them before you do your own clinic.

C.   Inform your consultant of your situation and explain that you are happy to do clinics on your own provided that you can ask him for help when needed.

D.   Proceed with clinics and do not implement any management for patients you are not sure how to treat. They will be seen in six weeks for a follow-up appointment in which case the registrar or consultant can implement their management.

E.   Proceed with clinics and do not implement any management for patients you are not sure how to treat. Ask the patients to return to the fracture clinic the following day when you know a registrar will be in clinic to see them.

Question 41

You are an on-call junior doctor and are asked by the registrar to insert a catheter into a patient called Mr Smith on ward 3. The patient is quite elderly and confused but you manage to insert the catheter. Later you mention to the registrar that Mr Smith is quite confused. It then becomes apparent to you that your registrar was talking about a different patient, a young man also called Mr Smith who is on ward 3.

Rank in order the following actions in response to this situation (1= Most appropriate; 5= Least appropriate):

A.   Do nothing as you are embarrassed.

B.   Insert a catheter into the correct patient but do not tell the other patient or the ward about your mistake and leave the wrong catheter in situ.

C.   Inform the rest of your team there are two patients with the same surname on the same ward to try and stop any other mistakes.

D.   Go and tell the ward staff what happened and ask them to remove the wrong catheter, and insert one into the correct patient.

E.   Go and apologise to the patient, remove the catheter and insert one into the correct patient.

Question 42

You are the junior doctor on a surgical firm and feel you are being bullied by your registrar who consistently berates you in front of patients and continually asks you why you don't know anything, even though you are trying and working very hard on the ward to keep all the patients happy and content.

Rank in order the following actions in response to this situation (1= Most appropriate; 5= Least appropriate):

A. Inform your friends outside work about the problem but keep this information to yourself at work.

B. Do not do anything – you just need to toughen up.

C. Ask your registrar if you can speak to them in private. Explain how you are feeling and ask why he is acting in this manner towards you.

D. Inform your consultant about the situation.

E. Inform the Foundation Programme director about the situation.

Question 43

Since starting your first Foundation year job a few months ago you have been feeling very down and are not your usual self. You are withdrawn and no longer socialise with your friends. You feel overwhelmed by the work and feel that others think you are a useless doctor.

Rank in order the following actions in response to this situation (1= Most appropriate; 5= Least appropriate):

A. Take time off sick to try and recover but do not tell anyone what is really wrong.

B. Speak to your consultant about how you are feeling.

C. Speak to occupational health about how you are feeling.

D. Speak to your parents about this.

E. Do not tell anyone how you feel and continue with work despite feeling more and more depressed day by day.

Question 44

You are a junior doctor on a vascular surgical firm. Your registrar asks if you would mind seeing patients in clinic by yourself as the consultant is away as he has been called to theatre. You know very little about vascular surgery and do not feel you understand how basic conditions in vascular surgery should be managed.

Rank in order the following actions in response to this situation (1= Most appropriate; 5= Least appropriate):

A. Explain you are happy to see the patients but will require his input regarding formulating management plans and reviewing investigation results.

B. Explain you are not happy to see the patients without a senior colleague present in clinic.

C. Refuse to come to clinic stating that this is wholly inappropriate.

D. Complain to the Foundation Programme director about being asked to act outside your competency level.

E. Complain to your consultant about being asked to act outside your competency level.

Question 45

You are a junior doctor and are assisting your consultant in theatre. You start to feel faint and dizzy and can't seem to continue standing up straight. You are in a sterile gown and conscious of the fact that you do not want to desterilize anyone or anything.

Rank in order the following actions in response to this situation (1= Most appropriate; 5= Least appropriate):

A. Immediately tell your consultant that you aren't feeling very well.

B. Tell the scrub nurse that you feel faint.

C. Tell the anaesthetist that you feel faint.

D. Try and move away from the operating table so you do not compromise the sterile field.

E. Do nothing and faint onto the patient.

Question 46

You are a junior doctor working in general medicine. Whilst at work on a ward round, you notice you are developing a strange itchy rash on your arms that is spreading very quickly.

Rank in order the following actions in response to this situation (1= Most appropriate; 5= Least appropriate):

A. Inform the rota coordinator and go to occupational health.

B. Immediately inform your senior colleague and go to the emergency department to get assessed.

C. Inform your consultant and then go home.

D. Take piriton and do not tell anyone.

E. Continue with your jobs and do not tell anyone.

PART TWO – Multi-Action Questions

Question 47

You are a junior doctor working on a cardiology firm. You have volunteered to teach a group of medical students on cardiovascular examination and know several patients on the ward with good heart murmurs that would be useful to the student's learning. Unfortunately you did not ask the patients in advance whether this would be all right and several of them are now refusing to let the students examine them.

Choose the THREE most appropriate actions to take in this situation:

A.   Accept the patients' decisions not to be examined and leave them in peace if they continue to refuse despite you asking for permission and explaining the situation.

B.   Question the patients' decision not to be examined and try to bribe them with better and swifter medical care in exchange.

C.   Offer to give the students a lecture on cardiac murmurs instead.

D.   Apologise to the patients on your ward for not asking them first. Try to explain to them that it is very important for the students to learn about heart disease and they would be extremely grateful even for a few minutes of the patients' time.

E.   Cancel the student teaching and tell them that they should find someone else to teach them instead as you are not able to accommodate.

F.   Allow the students to examine yourself instead (even though you personally do not suffer with a cardiac murmur or any valve disease).

G.   Ask your registrar to tell the patients that this is a teaching hospital and it is part of the course of their stay to be examined by students and they should expect this.

H.   Ask a junior doctor colleague if they happen to have any interesting patients who you may be able to approach instead if none of the patients on your cardiac ward are keen to participate in bedside teaching.

Question 48

You are a junior doctor working on an endocrinology firm. A patient on your ward has been admitted with a urinary tract infection. She has a past medical history of schizophrenia, type 2 diabetes mellitus and chronic renal failure. Her diabetes is poorly controlled and in the past she has been reported to have said that "voices" have told her to stop taking her insulin. On this admission, however, she appears to understand her condition and its consequences, does not report any psychiatric symptoms and tells you she would like to return to her own nursing home after treatment.

Choose the THREE most appropriate actions to take in this situation:

A.   Let her go back to the nursing home after treatment as she has demonstrated she has capacity and does not appear to be suffering from psychotic episodes.

B.   Keep her in hospital as her psychiatric symptoms may relapse and you can never be too sure what will happen next.

C.   Educate the patient's family and nursing home staff on the importance of diabetic control so they can help ensure the patient is taking her diabetic medication appropriately when discharged.

D.   Refer the patient for renal dialysis as she clearly has poorly-controlled diabetes and renal problems.

E.   Get some advice from a liaison psychiatrist regarding her schizophrenia.

F.   Try to refer her to a psychiatric hospital for long-term care so that she does not end up with poor diabetic control again.

G.   Section her even if she says she wants to go home as it would be in her best interests to remain in hospital in case her diabetes becomes worse.

H.   Treat her in whatever way you feel are her best interests without much consultation with her as she probably isn't aware of what she wants.

Question 49

You are the junior doctor working on a care of the elderly rotation. One of your patients, Mrs Brice, is an 80 year old woman with known renal cell carcinoma and Alzheimer's dementia. In her medical records you see a signed consent from Mrs Brice to participate in a clinical trial investigating a new drug thought to improve prognosis in renal cell carcinoma. The study is due to begin next week; however, on conversing with Mrs Brice about this you realise that she has no recollection of the trial.

Choose the THREE most appropriate actions to take in this situation:

A.   Continue with the trial as there is signed consent from Mrs Brice in her medical notes.

B.   Contact the clinical investigator to discuss Mrs Brice's participation in the trial.

C.   Contact Mrs Brice's next of kin to obtain consent.

D.   If Mrs Brice is deemed not to have capacity, consider obtaining consent by proxy if you believe that the trial is in her best interests.

E.   Assess whether Mrs Brice is competent to give consent in this situation and check with the next of kin whether there was any discussion they can remember regarding enrolment onto the trial.

F.   Do not allow Mrs Brice to continue with the trial as she is clearly not capable of having signed up for and understand the potential risks of taking part in the research.

G.   Continue with the trial. Treat Mrs Brice under the Mental Health Act.

H.   Take no action. As a junior you are out of your depth to deal with this situation.

Question 50

You are a junior doctor working on a general practice rotation. A 58 year old female comes to see you for the administration of an intra-articular steroid injection for her knee. You feel out of your depth to administer this injection as you have never done it before.

Choose the THREE most appropriate actions to take in this situation:

A. Quickly read up about administration of intra-articular injections, and attempt the injection.

B. Ask the patient to book another appointment with the senior GP who is competent to administer these injections.

C. If you have previously observed the administration of intra-articular injections try to find a senior colleague to supervise you whilst you have an attempt.

D. Ask the patient to go to the hospital emergency department to get her injection.

E. Ask one of the senior GPs within the practice if they can come and help you administer the injection whilst you watch and learn from the experience.

F. Blindly inject the steroid injection into the joint – it can't be that difficult.

G. Prescribe her alternative medication to relieve her symptoms.

H. Explain to the patient that you have never administered these injections before but are aware of the theory behind the method of administration and are keen to have an attempt if she agrees.

Question 51

You are the junior doctor on a busy medical firm. You notice a drug error you have made on a prescription chart where you prescribed double the maximum recommended safe daily dose of Tramadol. This has been given to the patient over the last 24 hours and fortunately no ill-effects have been noted.

Choose the THREE most appropriate actions to take in this situation: (not in order)

A. Do nothing as there were no serious consequences.

B. Inform the nurse looking after the patient and the nurse in charge to ensure they will not re-administer the incorrect medication.

C. Explain what has happened to the patient.

D. Inform your senior colleagues.

E. Fill out a clinical incident form against yourself.

F. Double-check the rest of the drug chart for any further errors or interactions making sure to correct any errors that you come across.

G. Tell the nurse that it is her job to ensure that the drugs on the drug chart are correct and blame them for giving the incorrect dosage.

H. Discuss the situation with the ward pharmacist.

Question 52

You are the junior doctor on a gastroenterology attachment. You clerk a patient who has presented with abdominal pain and on examination is found to have massive ascites. Your registrar has also reviewed the patient and has made the decision that an ascetic drain should be inserted. He is extremely busy and is getting bleeped almost every 5 minutes so asks you to carry out the paracentesis alone. You feel confident explaining the procedure to the patient as you have seen them done on several occasions but you have never actually had to insert an ascetic drain yourself.

Choose the THREE most appropriate actions to take in this situation:

A.   Perform the paracentesis under aseptic technique.

B.   Find a nurse to assist you in the procedure.

C.   Inform the patient you have never carried out the procedure alone before. If he consents regardless, continue with the paracentesis.

D.   Tell your registrar that you are not comfortable performing the procedure alone and ask them if there is any way that they can help you later on in the shift.

E.   Refuse to do the procedure and complain to the registrar that they are putting you in a very difficult position.

F.   Find an alternative senior colleague who is familiar with the procedure and ask them to supervise you performing the drain.

G.   Wait until your registrar is free to supervise you performing the procedure as it is not an emergency.

H.   Google the procedure to refresh your memory then perform it to the best of your ability.

Question 53

You are a junior doctor working in a general medicine. One of your friends who is not a doctor, has been feeling very ill with a chest infection and begs you to help him by prescribing a course of antibiotics. He tells you he is very lethargic and incapable of going to work.

Choose the THREE most appropriate actions to take in this situation:

A.   Advise your friend to telephone and make an appointment with his GP immediately.

B.   Sneakily steal a box of antibiotics from the hospital ward and bring them home for your friend.

C.   Try to ask the nurse on the ward if she can give you the antibiotics for your friend from the ward drugs cabinet.

D.   Tell him that it is illegal for you to prescribe medication for him under all circumstances.

E.   Advise your colleague to try to go to work despite the infection, as sometimes these infections get better throughout the day.

F.   Ask one of your work colleagues to write the prescription for your friend without seeing him.

G.   Advise your friend that if his symptoms deteriorate and he cannot get a GP appointment then he should attend the hospital emergency department.

H.   Offer your friend reassurance and support. Give advice on keeping hydrated, eating healthily and getting enough bed rest.

Question 54

You are a junior doctor working on a busy surgical ward. On 'operating days' you find that you often have to deal with difficult problems on the ward with no supervision by any senior colleagues as they are all in theatre. Your consultant initially said that having this amount of responsibility was something to welcome and that 'it would make you a better doctor' but you disagree and feel that certain situations may be beyond your competency and jeopardise patient safety.

Choose the THREE most appropriate actions to take in this situation:

A.   Do nothing and see what happens over the next few weeks. You are sure that these things will get better and the last junior doctor seemed to cope fine.

B.   Discuss the issue with other junior doctor colleagues and see if anyone else is experiencing similar problems and if so, how they have overcome the problems or if not, whether they would like to come with you to discuss it with the consultant.

C.   Approach your consultant and tell them that you feel out of your depth and although you welcome more responsibility, you feel that many issues are too far out of your comfort zone.

D.   Ask the nurses on the ward about what you should do.

E.   Speak directly with your educational supervisor and/or Foundation Programme director regarding these issues.

F.   Approach the general surgical services manager with the issue, ask to quit and advise them to find a replacement junior doctor.

G.   Ask to change your job and be under another consultant as you feel uneasy being in this current situation.

H.   Ask your parents and your best friends what you should do.

Question 55

Due to unforeseen circumstances you find yourself to be the only doctor from your team in the hospital to do a ward round of your regular patients one morning. Although you know your patients very well, this is the first time you have been left alone to perform a full ward round. Fortunately the medical registrar from another team has kindly offered to review your patients once he has finished his ward round but would like you to first see your own patients and update him afterwards on all the important issues so it will be easier for him to come up with a management plan later.

Choose the THREE most appropriate actions to take in this situation:

A.   Start ordering investigations that you think may be appropriate as you feel you should save time before the registrar arrives.

B.   Spend as long as possible on each patient so you do not miss anything.

C.   Start with a problem list containing all the different patients' acute medical problems and diagnoses.

D.   Act on any abnormal findings by implementing management plans as the medical registrar will wonder why you didn't correct the patients' problems later on.

E.   Check that all the patients are still alive but don't speak to them and don't write in the notes. You don't want to waste paper if you are going to see the patients with the registrar later anyway.

F.   Note down all the patient observations, relevant scan results and blood tests in the notes.

G.   Start by seeing the most complicated and sickest patients first so the registrar can be informed early on if help is needed sooner.

H.   Copy what the previous doctor has written as it is unlikely the patient's condition would have changed.

Question 56

It is now 5.10pm and you have just finished a busy day shift. As you are gathering your coat and bags from your locker you receive a bleep from your ward. You are in a hurry to leave the hospital as you have made plans to go to your sister's surprise birthday party and do not want to arrive late.

Choose the THREE most appropriate actions to take in this situation:

A. Answer your bleep and explain that you are coming to the end of your shift. If the task is non-urgent, request for the on-call doctor to be bleeped.

B. Ignore the bleep. The on-call doctor should be bleeped for any matters out of hours that need to be attended to and you are not expected to answer.

C. Answer your bleep. Stay behind and deal with the task concerned, and go to your sister's birthday party late.

D. Answer your bleep and hand the task directly over to the on-call doctor, explaining that you need to leave on time today.

E. See if any of your team members are still on the ward and ask them to answer your bleep even though they all finish at 5pm as well.

F. Answer your bleep and go back to the ward to check that the matter really is not serious or urgent. If the task is non-urgent, request for the on-call doctor to be bleeped to deal with the matter.

G. Answer your bleep. Stay behind and deal with the task concerned and cancel your plans to go to your sister's birthday party.

H. Answer your bleep and tell the person bleeping that this is not your business after 5pm.

Question 57

It is already 5.30pm and you have just finished your usual day shift at the hospital, which is contracted to finish at 5.00pm. You arrive home and realise that you have forgotten to prescribe some analgesia for the last patient you reviewed on the ward round. The patient in question was extremely anxious and very distressed about their pain, although all investigations have so far not yielded any conclusive diagnosis. You worry about the patient's discomfort overnight, but also about being shouted at in front of your team at the next ward round.

Choose the THREE most appropriate actions to take in this situation:

A. Rush back to the hospital immediately to prescribe the patient's analgesia.

B. Do nothing. The patient will just have to get through the night without any analgesia. You can only hope that they are in a good mood tomorrow morning.

C. Do nothing. Hopefully the patient will call the nurses if he requires any analgesia. The nurse will be able to bleep the on-call doctor to prescribe it.

D. Call the ward and inform the senior sister about the situation and ask her to bleep the on-call doctor to prescribe analgesia.

E. Call the operator and ask them to put you directly through to the on-call doctor and ask him to prescribe analgesia.

F. Call your SHO or registrar in case they are still on the ward. If this is the case, ask them if they could prescribe analgesia for the patient.

G. Contact the pain team to review the patient and ask if the anaesthetic registrar can also review.

H. Call the ward and ask the senior sister to give the patient a few pills of paracetamol and codeine. If the patient makes a complaint the whole ward will get into trouble, so it is in their interest to help you.

Question 58

Your contracted hours as a junior doctor are from 8.30am to 5pm but for the first few weeks of your new job you have been coming into work 30 minutes early to update the patient list and are not finishing work until 8pm due to pending duties that could not be omitted. For the first few weeks you think that you are leaving late as you are not used to the job, however, after one month has passed you are still leaving at 8pm.

Choose the THREE most appropriate actions to take in this situation:

A.   Discuss these issues with other colleagues within your team and find out if other members are leaving on time. Perhaps they can help you learn to prioritise your tasks better.

B.   Talk to other junior doctors to see if they are experiencing the same problems with a view to writing a joint letter of complaint about this issue to the consultant.

C.   Leave at 5pm from now on regardless of pending duties. You are not paid to stay late anyway and if you stay late you will be too tired to carry out your duties the next day.

D.   Issue a formal request to your hospital lead and rota coordinator for diary carding to take place.

E.   Raise your concerns with your clinical and educational supervisor. Explain that you are struggling to finish on time and seek their advice on what further actions should be taken.

F.   Raise the issue anonymously at the next Foundation trust visits your hospital.

G.   Do nothing as you have a responsibility for the safe care of your patients regardless of working hours.

H.   Take it in turns with your fellow junior doctors to stay late even if it means they need to finish off jobs for other colleagues for patients that they do not know.

Question 59

You are the junior doctor on a busy medical firm. A few minutes before handover, the on-call medical registrar bleeps you to review a patient in the medical admissions unit as she is busy with medical referrals in the emergency department. You are due to go to your parent's anniversary celebrations straight after your shift and are keen to leave on time.

Choose the THREE most appropriate actions to take in this situation:

A.   Call back the on-call medical registrar and ask if she would mind handing over the matter to the junior doctor on the night shift during the handover meeting.

B.   Handover the matter directly yourself to the junior doctor on the night shift during the handover meeting provided the matter is non-urgent.

C.   Stay behind to review the patient and go late to your parent's anniversary celebrations.

D.   Stay behind to review the patient and cancel your plans to go to your parent's anniversary celebrations.

E.   Call back the on-call medical registrar and ask for more information about the patient that needs to be reviewed. If it is urgent, go to review the patient quickly and if more issues arise then hand this over to the night team.

F.   Call back the on-call medical registrar and inform her of your situation. Ask her if she would mind reviewing the patient when she has finished in the emergency department.

G.   Call back the on-call medical registrar and question whether reviewing the patient is really necessary or whether it can wait until the next day.

H.   Tell the medical registrar that this is not your problem to deal with and that they should know it is unfair to ask you to do this.

Question 60

You are one of the junior doctors working on the general medical team. You have just finished a busy ward round and are splitting jobs with your fellow junior doctor colleague. Whilst doing this you notice your colleague becoming upset and she suddenly tells you she feels this is 'all too much' and doesn't think she is coping with the pressures of the job. She mentions that the demands placed by senior colleagues on the team are unreasonable and are affecting the quality of her work. Although you work on the same team, you have never felt this way and don't know what to say.

Choose the THREE most appropriate actions to take in this situation:

A. Report the situation immediately to the Foundation School Training Programme director and tell them that you don't feel your colleague is coping.

B. Comfort and empathise with your colleague.

C. Suggest to her that she should schedule an appointment with her clinical supervisor/ consultant to discuss the situation.

D. Explain the circumstances are likely to change and that most Foundation doctors feel like this in the first few months.

E. Suggest that she discuss these issues with the consultant in charge of the team.

F. Offer to increase your own workload to lighten hers.

G. Tell all your other junior doctor colleagues about what has happened and tell them to avoid putting too much pressure on this particular doctor.

H. Suggest that she just needs to learn to prioritise and manage her time better. Take no other further action.

Question 61

You have just started your first week on a gastroenterology rotation as a junior doctor. There is a 50 year old male with ascites on the ward who requires an ascitic tap. Your registrar states that he is happy to watch you do the ascitic tap and complete an assessment for you on your ePortfolio. You have seen this procedure being done several times, but you have never actually performed this procedure yourself. You have prepared your equipment and your registrar asks you to start the procedure without him as he just needs to quickly attend to his bleep.

Choose the THREE most appropriate actions to take in this situation:

A. Contact the senior house officer on your team to supervise you whilst you perform the procedure.

B. Explain to the patient that you will return with your registrar to perform the procedure once he has answered his bleep.

C. Leave the job undone and contact the registrar if he hasn't tried to chase you up on putting the drain in later on in the afternoon.

D. Wait for your registrar to return and explain to him that you have not done the procedure before but will attempt it provided that he can supervise you.

E. Attempt the procedure as much as you can and accept that some mistakes may be made but that the registrar can sort them out when they return.

F. Contact the senior house officer on your team to ask him to perform the procedure.

G. Whilst waiting for the registrar, explain to the patient what the procedure involves and any potential complications or side effects.

H. Return to your other ward jobs and inform the patient that you are not happy to perform the procedure as you have not done it before.

Question 62

You are the junior doctor on a general surgical firm and you have just finished a ward round with your consultant. You have a lot of new patients on the ward who have recently been admitted, some of whom are very complicated and ill. On top of this, it appears both your registrar and senior house officer are off and no extra cover has been arranged. You were already feeling quite overwhelmed by the amount of work generated from the ward and knowing that you will be the only doctor available to complete these jobs has made you feel very anxious.

Choose the THREE most appropriate actions to take in this situation:

A.   Carry out the jobs you have listed to the best of your ability without telling anyone how you feel about this.

B.   Try and manage as many of the jobs as possible yourself and discuss any complex patients or queries that arise with the consultant or get some advice from a registrar from another medical team.

C.   Refuse to do any of the jobs as it is unsafe working on your own.

D.   Only do the most important jobs – there isn't any need to do routine jobs.

E.   Make sure you do all the urgent jobs first and then do all the routine jobs.

F.   Discuss the jobs with the consultant, clarifying which jobs are the most important ones to complete and make him aware of the predicament you find yourself in.

G.   Refuse to do any of the jobs unless medical staffing can provide you with another doctor to help you.

H.   Demand that the senior house officer from a different medical team should help you even though they are not aware of any of your patients.

Question 63

You are a junior doctor working in general medicine and have been very involved in the care of a famous minor celebrity on your ward who was admitted following mild central chest pains. The wife of the patient is impressed by the attention you have given to her husband and privately offers you a £100 cheque for your efforts. Even though you politely decline, she insists on giving you the cheque and forces it into your pocket before you can give it back.

Choose the THREE most appropriate actions to take in this situation:

A.   Take the money and thank her for the kind gesture.

B.   Offer the money to your consultant who diagnosed the VIP.

C.   Take the money and tell her to inform nobody of this.

D.   Suggest that she buys something for the head nurse and consultant instead.

E.   Suggest that she donates the money to the hospital/ward as many people were involved in caring for her husband.

F.   Thank her for the gesture but again state that you cannot accept this from her.

G.   Inform your team about her gratitude for her husband's care.

H.   Take the money and spend it on a night out with your team.

Question 64

Whilst passing through the care of the elderly ward on your routine ward round you notice a senior nurse scold a patient for spilling his drink. The patient is visibly frail and is hard of hearing. After continued shouting from the nurse the patient begins to cry and gestures that he cannot understand her. He looks visibly upset and confused.

Choose the THREE most appropriate actions to take in this situation:

A. Confront the nurse and in the same manner she used for the way she treated the patient. She shouldn't treat patients badly and deserves to know how it feels the other way around.

B. Offer to help the patient and explain to the nurse the patient is frail and has a multitude of medical problems so is not able to feed himself properly.

C. Express your concerns with the nurse later on and ask why she treated the patient in such a harsh way.

D. Don't take any notice of it assuming that the patient is just being difficult.

E. Refer the nurse to hospital protocol regarding the appropriate treatment of elderly patients who are hard of hearing.

F. Assume that the nurse knows what she is doing and don't get involved in the situation.

G. Tell the nurse that the patient is hard of hearing and that she needs to scold him in a louder tone or write down what she is saying for him to understand.

H. Have a look through the notes to review if the patient's deafness has been picked up and how it may be affecting his overall care.

Question 65

You are on-call for general surgery and have just been informed by the emergency department nurse that there is a pending trauma call due to attend the hospital in the next 10 minutes. The patient was riding a motorcycle and has been in a head-on collision with a large van. He is haemodynamically unstable with multiple suspected fractures. Unfortunately, both the orthopaedic and general surgical registrars are busy in theatre operating and will not be able to attend the emergency department in the next 10 minutes. Your senior house officer is tied up on the wards with a very sick patient who is about to be transferred to the intensive care unit. You are the only surgical doctor available to attend the trauma call.

Choose the THREE most appropriate actions to take in this situation:

A.   Tell the referring nurse to speak to one of the senior emergency department doctors who will just need to cope until your seniors are freer.

B.   Try and find one of your other junior doctor colleagues to deal with the situation and try to not have anything to do with the trauma call if you can possibly help it.

C.   Go to theatre to find the general and orthopaedic surgeons. Inform them verbally of the trauma call and patient details as they will not be able to answer their bleep or speak on the phone whilst operating.

D.   Tell the emergency department nurse that it is not your responsibility to attend trauma calls as a junior doctor so you are not obliged to act on the information she is telling you.

E.   Inform one of the emergency department consultants of the current situation and tell them that if a general or orthopaedic surgeon is urgently required, they can escalate the situation by contacting the orthopaedic or general surgical consultants directly.

F.   Try to organise and manage the trauma call on your own to the best of your abilities.

G.   Do nothing with this information and carry on as normal.

H.   Tell the radiologists that an emergency trauma case is pending and ask that they prioritise the request when it arrives so the patient's injuries can be quickly defined.

Question 66

You are part of the general medical gastroenterology team in a busy district general hospital. Your consultant is on-call today and all admitted patients will be under the care of your team tomorrow. Although you personally are not on-call you notice the on-call team is struggling to keep up with the numbers of patients that are coming in via referrals from the local GP surgeries. Your current inpatient list is very light and you have very little to do.

Choose the THREE most appropriate actions to take in this situation:

A. Go to the hospital mess/cafe once you finish your routine ward jobs so that you will not be easily found if someone wants to give you extra tasks.

B. Continue your day as normal completing current outstanding jobs. It is not your business to get involved with the on-call team issues.

C. Do nothing unless you are specifically bleeped to help out. It is the on-call team's responsibility to deal with the admissions and you know you will have your work cut out for you tomorrow anyway!

D. Arrange between yourself and the senior house officer to distribute any jobs generated by the on-call team when you have finished dealing with your own ward patients.

E. Offer to help the on-call team to clerk in the new patients.

F. Contact your rota coordinator and ask them to urgently organise a locum doctor to help the on-call team.

G. Contact the on-call registrar after you have finished your ward jobs. Ask if there is anything you can do.

H. Contact the bed manager and tell her that there are currently too many medical admissions. Ask her to divert any non-urgent admissions to another hospital within the same trust.

Question 67

You are a junior doctor working in urology on a night shift. One of the elderly male patients on your ward has become acutely confused and has pulled out his catheter. You have been asked by the nursing staff to re-insert it. The patient is incontinent and quite difficult to catheterise due to their confusion and not being able to stay still. Your senior house officer and registrar are both busy with other jobs and will not be available until much later. The nurses insist you get on with it now so that the patient can be put to bed early and will not continue to disrupt the ward.

Choose the THREE most appropriate actions to take in this situation:

A. Obtain full written consent from the patient for re-catheterisation.

B. Refuse to re-catheterise the patient as you feel he will just pull the catheter out again.

C. As the patient's urine output is not being measured, reassess whether a conveen may be a more appropriate solution to the patient's incontinence in the short-term.

D. Tell the nurses to prevent the patient from having too much fluid intake so that his incontinence will not cause as much distress.

E. Re-catheterise the patient with the help of several nursing staff (who will be restraining him) so he will not move too much during the procedure.

F. When your seniors finish in theatre, discuss the matter with them and ask for any further advice on the management of this patient.

G. Prescribe the patient something to calm him down overnight such as diazepam. This will allow him to sleep better and reduce the risks of pulling another catheter out.

H. Try to obtain a urine sample from the patient and check if he may be suffering from an acute urinary tract infection. This may explain his increasing confusion.

Question 68

You are a junior doctor on a general medical ward and are called to see a young patient who has just fainted. The nurses have placed her back in bed and called you to review the patient. You try to take her blood pressure but find that both the automated and manual blood pressure machines in the ward bay are not working. The patient is alert and a little dizzy but tells you she is feeling OK and is not in pain.

Choose the THREE most appropriate actions to take in this situation:

A.   Assess the patient but do not take the patient's blood pressure.

B.   Send a nurse to bring you a working manual blood pressure machine whilst you begin to examine the patient.

C.   Contact the bed manager and ask for the patient to be transferred to a different ward bay with working blood pressure machines.

D.   Document the lack of a working blood pressure machine in the medical notes next to your assessment findings.

E.   Go to another ward and take one of their blood pressure machines.

F.   Report the faulty equipment to hospital management.

G.   Report the faulty equipment to the ward matron and ask that she replaces the faulty machine in the patient's bay.

H.   Take sitting and standing pulses from the patient instead of sitting and standing blood pressures.

Question 69

You see a mother and her 4 year old daughter in the GP surgery. The mother tells you that her child has been feeling generally unwell for the past few days with a fever and a bit of a cold. You deal with the presenting complaint but before you conclude your consultation you cannot help but notice how grossly overweight the child is.

Choose the THREE most appropriate actions to take in this situation:

A.   Tell the parent that you think their child is fat and needs to lose weight.

B.   Contact social services. You believe the fact the child is obese is akin to child abuse by neglect and the parent is not making their child's health a priority.

C.   Perform a full examination of the patient including taking the their weight, height, BMI measurements.

D.   Enquire about the child's eating habits (at home and at school). Ask whether the parent has noticed the child gaining much weight recently or if they have always been rather large for their age.

E.   Take blood tests to screen for diabetes and hypothyroidism.

F.   Simply treat the current medical problems as you have a full waiting room and this is not the actual presenting complaint the parent has brought the child into clinic for.

G.   Take a full family history and determine if other members of the family are also obese.

H.   Educate the parent regarding a typical healthy diet for a child and the average amount a normal child should be eating. Refer for a dietician review if the parent is amenable to the suggestion.

Question 70

You are a junior doctor on a care of the elderly ward. It is a Tuesday afternoon and you are due to attend to the weekly multidisciplinary social team meeting. As you approach the ward to attend the meeting, you get bleeped by the nurses stating that one of your patients on the ward has had an episode of chest pain and dizziness. You are already running 15 minutes late to your ward meeting and your senior house officer is in the emergency department clerking in a patient.

Choose the THREE most appropriate actions to take in this situation:

A.   Go to the meeting first as you are already very late and are the only member who will be representing your team. You can visit the patient after the meeting has finished.

B.   Tell the ward nurse to put out a cardiac arrest call. This way there will be an immediate response from several medical staff and they can deal with the patient problems first.

C.   Ask the ward nurse to administer oxygen to the patient and perform a repeat set of observations and an ECG straightaway.

D.   Explain to the ward nurse that you cannot attend to the patient as you have to attend the multidisciplinary social meeting. Ask them to stabilise the patient until you are finished with the meeting.

E.   Contact your senior house officer about what has happened. Ask if they can go to the meeting in your place or alternatively if they can go and see the acutely unwell patient so you can attend the meeting instead.

F.   Ask the ward nurse to contact the on-call senior house officer to attend to the patient in the meantime if they are really worried as you will not be able to review the patient until after the meeting.

G.   Inform the senior sister that you will not be able to attend the multidisciplinary social meeting as one of your patients is acutely unwell. Explain you will ask another member of the team if they are available to go in your place.

H.   Apologise to the senior sister in the meeting but explain that none of the medical doctors are available to attend the meeting as there are too many ill patients to attend to.

Answers to Examination 5

PART ONE – Answers to the Ranking Questions

Answer Question 1

ACEBD

The best answer would be option A as you can explain why the test was done, what it shows and the implications it has on his driving. The next best option would then be to explore the nature of the patient's job and find out about his family and social support network. However, it is not your role as a junior doctor to discuss treatment options as this will probably evoke more questions from the patient that are beyond your competency to answer. Thus referring him to an ophthalmologist and reassuring him that all the questions will be addressed is the next best course of action. Although it is true that the patient should stop driving, he may not need to stop working altogether and alternative roles may be found for the patient.

Answer Question 2

ACDEB

The best option is to arrange to attend a formal teaching session and this should hopefully be enough to give you confidence in reading ECGs. The next best thing would be to resolve the issue with the students themselves so that you both can present. If this cannot happen then telling the team is also good as some arrangement can be made with the medical students. Students are there to learn and giving them no opportunity to present will do them no good. Clearly, doing nothing is the worst option as the basic competence of ECG reading is not being fulfilled.

Answer Question 3

ACEBD

This patient is undergoing an urgent surgical procedure which requires a few pre-operative investigations. However, his new shortness of breath if serious may cause his surgery to be cancelled as he will need to be optimised first. Out of all the investigations an urgent ECHO needs to be done first. Considering this patient will need increased support post-operatively an ITU bed will have to be booked in advance. Not doing so will definitely cancel the surgery. Following this, other important but less urgent investigations can be arranged like group and save, liaising with the endocrine registrar etc.. Concerning the latter, this can be done later on as they usually can see the patient once they are on the ward and it only really needs organising post-operatively.

Answer Question 4

ADECB

The majority of the answers here are all correct except for B, which is dangerous and should not be done without senior advice. In this scenario, it is not apparent whether the consultant has taken into consideration the oncologist's opinion and then decided on the dose. Hence, to save any embarrassment the first thing is to do is check the dose as stated in the BNF. Then, if there is any discrepancy you should contact your consultant straightaway and deal with it immediately, especially if the patient is suffering harmful effects. Waiting until tomorrow is fine, but the issue might be forgotten or not highlighted properly.

Answer Question 5

CBDEA

In this case, a critical incident form should be filled out clearly outlining what happened. This should be discussed with your consultant who ultimately has responsibility for the patient. Informing the team is also valuable as they can learn from this experience and be more aware of how such issues arise. As the patient's family is present and are distressed it is also paramount for someone senior to go through what had happened. In such a sensitive situation (considering the possible implications i.e. suing the hospital) it is probably best if a consultant speaks to them. There is no need at this time to find the person responsible for misplacing the form. The critical incident form will ensure that this will be investigated.

Answer Question 6

CEADB

Given that this is an emergency situation the consent form needs to be found. The first thing is to at least contact the doctor who consented the patient. He can try and remember whether amputation was mentioned. If this is not possible, statements concerning the surgery and its risks may be written and signed in the notes. If no statement about consent can be found then the medico-legal advisor needs to be contacted. Ultimately, if the consent cannot be found the team will still have to make the decision in the best interests of the patient – and given the patient's age it is always wise to get a second opinion although the final decision lies with the patient's consultant.

Answer Question 7

BCDAE

Option B would be the best option although it may appear confrontational if done wrongly. You can report the incident to the nurse in charge and discuss the issue directly with your colleagues. By doing this you take decisive action and at least then someone senior can deal with the situation through the correct channels. Option A does not take any immediate action and option E is worse as no action at all is taken.

Answer Question 8

DEBCA

Given your lack of knowledge and the urgency of the request, the best option is to find out the information as soon as possible. Even though the swallow may be delayed at least the radiologist will have all the necessary information to perform the correct type of scan. It is obviously better for you to find this out but alternatively, the radiologist can contact your seniors and ask them for the information directly. Usually, the radiologist will have a good idea of what type of scan needs to be done and might be able to deduce this by reading the operative notes. Options C and A are inappropriate, but option A is worse as you are giving out information which you know you are unsure of.

Answer Question 9

ACBDE

In this case it is important that you obtain an accurate history from the patient, and ascertain what she wants rather than what her parents want. It is best not to use a family member as an interpreter as you cannot necessarily rely on them interpreting reliably for her. It would be most appropriate to obtain an interpreter and ask the parents to leave the consultation room to ensure that she does not feel threatened and can be open with you about her wishes and concerns.

Answer Question 10

BCDEA

This patient is clearly very anxious and therefore it is most appropriate in such a situation to explore the patient's concerns and reassure him that he does not have epilepsy. The GMC states that patients do have a right to seek a second opinion, and so in this case it is wise to advise the patient to speak to your registrar or his GP. Calling the on-call psychiatrist is not appropriate as it is not a psychiatric emergency and it may be better to explain to the patient that you think his episodes are non-organic in origin before you contact a psychiatrist, as it may cause the patient more distress. Alternatively it may be suitable to ask his GP to refer him to a psychiatrist as an outpatient.

Answer Question 11

CDEBA

It is important to get some history if possible, so asking anyone who is able to translate is the best option. Speaking to the neighbour and GP is also a good idea. Initially treating the patient based on test results and then obtaining the history is the next best option. Not trying to obtain any history is wholly inappropriate and is a danger to patient care.

Answer Question 12

BCEAD

The patient should be calmed down in a quiet environment, and the dangers of pulmonary embolism should be explained. He should be told that the CT scan will be able to show if he has an embolus or not. If he still decides to leave, then a self-discharge form needs to be signed and his GP should be made aware of the events that have occurred.

Answer Question 13

ACEBD

The best way to teach the student is to carry out the ABG yourself and explain in real time what you are doing. As they already understand the theory they should be able to do one after watching you. Such a procedure can only be learnt from practical exposure so if the first option cannot be done then they should learn it on mannequin arms. This way they can practise as much as they want. Even though it is not ideal, explaining how you would carry out the procedure may help with improving their technique. Students should in no circumstances undertake procedures without having seen it first, and should be supervised at all times.

Answer Question 14

BCEAD

Certain teaching sessions are mandatory and you must attend to these as there might be issues with successfully completing your training as a junior doctor. Considering you have already missed a few sessions, it is vital that you raise the issue with your consultant. Alternatively if you continue to have a high workload, getting a senior colleague to cover for you whilst in teaching should be arranged. Some doctors may feel that normal duties take priority over mandatory teaching, but considering it happens only once a week, you can prepare and make arrangements for this short period of time in advance. Attending teaching without organising any cover is irresponsible.

Answer Question 15

ADCEB

Being proactive and trying to do as many DOPS (directly observed procedures) during your current rotation is the best option when compared with waiting to start your new rotation. Asking team members to alert you of any potential DOPS procedures will give you more opportunities to do these DOPS. Carrying out other assessments is better than simply not doing any.

Answer Question 16

ABDCE

If you come across an interesting case that you would like to discuss, ensure that you find an appropriate time to go over the details of the case with a senior colleague, preferably one who is familiar with the case as well. You should ensure that the discussion is conducted in a timely manner when there are no urgent/emergency tasks on the ward to complete. To make the most of the discussion you can either do some background reading before the case or after the discussion to consolidate your knowledge.

Answer Question 17

AEDCB

Making a list of problems you have noticed will enable you to address each one individually. Discussions with senior colleagues will help gain their opinions on flaws and possible improvements. You could then start a quality improvement audit, initiate change and finally re-audit to complete the cycle.

Answer Question 18

CDEBA

You should not attempt a procedure that you have not previously observed or had specific training in. However, if you have had training and find yourself in a situation where you are performing a procedure but you still need some practice, you should be honest and ensure your patient and your seniors know so appropriate supervision is arranged. It is always a good idea to try to observe such a procedure first to familiarize yourself with the steps and equipment used as in option C. Ensure your registrar is happy to supervise you (option D), and none of your other team members object (option E). You should then discuss all the information, risks and potential complications with your patient prior to starting the drain insertion.

Answer Question 19

BADCE

Whilst you have the nurses on the phone, get as much information as you can from them. Ask them to perform basic observations whilst you are on your way. The sickle cell patient could be having a sickle cell chest crisis and the man with COPD could be suffering from an exacerbation of his respiratory disease. Both are emergencies and should be attended to. It would be helpful if you could get your colleague to see the other gentleman. A thorough examination is now essential so that you can manage the patient appropriately. One should always contact senior colleagues if you feel out of your depth at any point.

Answer Question 20

CDABE

It is important to try and get more information about the medication and the dosage the patient is normally on. This can be found either by contacting the patient's GP or rehabilitation drug clinic (if he is being treated at one). It is not good practice to simply do nothing (i.e. not prescribe the medicine but also not seek further information). It is worse to guess the dosage of a medication without seeking professional expert opinion from your senior colleague or a pharmacist.

Answer Question 21

AECDB

Trying to discover more information about why the patient has been placed on an unusual antibiotic regime is the best course of action before jumping to any conclusions and changing the medication. Nevertheless, doing nothing is better than changing the antibiotic without finding out why the patient is on it as this could compromise patient care.

Answer Question 22

CDAEB

This is a difficult scenario for any junior doctor. The registrar will see the patient afterwards, so take a history first and do not explain the diagnosis until your registrar has had a chance to see the patient. If you personally give the diagnosis, then questions concerning life expectancy and treatment may ensue which you are in no position to answer. Hence, it is best to avoid this situation altogether. It is also advised to contact radiology and oncology to give some details of the scan and nature of the cancer. This will be useful information for the registrar when speaking to the patient. Ringing the GP is valuable in knowing what the patient already understands about the possible cause of his symptoms. Any relevant social history can also be obtained then as well. Despite being a complicated case it is unprofessional to avoid the patient completely or to just say it is beyond your competency. Taking a basic history and examining the patient is well within the scope of a junior doctor's role.

Answer Question 23

BCEDA

All five choices are valid and should be carried out. Your team must be informed so that your senior colleagues can advise you about appropriate further actions that need to be taken. The decisions concerning giving/not giving vitamin K should not be made by you alone. Both patients should be informed about the mistake and assessed for effects. It is imperative that an incident form is completed so that a record of the incident is in place for legal and medical reasons. Thorough documentation is also strongly recommended.

Answer Question 24

CEDBA

This patient needs adequate medical and emotional counselling and support from a multidisciplinary team. Offering to show the patient how to use the inhaler is good practice. Specialist nurses are excellent at providing supervision and education, and may recommend that the patient use a spacer if she cannot learn how use to her inhalers correctly.

Answer Question 25

CEBDA

It is your duty to try and stop the patient from leaving, while asking the nurse to urgently call the psychiatrist. The patient may not be deemed currently mentally competent and hence might need to be sectioned. However, you require the input of the psychiatrist to know what further steps need to be taken. Calling your senior is the next best option. Asking the patient to sign a self-discharge is not appropriate and doing nothing is even worse.

Answer Question 26

BCEDA

Hyperkalaemia can cause cardiac arrhythmias. It is important that an ECG is performed to see if there are any changes consistent with hyperkalaemia. If there are, a coronary care unit bed may be needed for telemetry. Rapid assessment and treatment are vital to prevent arrhythmias from ensuing. If there is any doubt at any point, senior advice should be sought. A repeat sample usually four hours after treatment should be taken. This can be done on the spot with a venous blood gas and through normal phlebotomy for a more accurate reading.

Answer Question 27

EABCD

If there are too many jobs to finish in a short amount of time, it may well be prudent for one member of the team to peel away from the ward round to carry out urgent tasks. It would be important to ensure that there are enough people on the ward round to provide documentation and keep a record of what jobs need to be done later on. A group discussion regarding the current situation of each patient will ensure members of the team is kept abreast of each patient and also enable a jobs list to be created. Any blood that has been taken must be chased up so that the appropriate measures can be taken.

Answer Question 28

BDCEA

A V/Q scan is less conclusive than a CTPA but can give less radiation dosage to the patient. Different clinicians will have different opinions as to which type of scan will be better, but it would be wise to explore the radiologist's reasoning before returning to your consultant. If there is a disagreement, ask your seniors to discuss the matter between themselves. Thorough documentation is again vital so that other members of the multidisciplinary team can follow a sequence of events.

Answer Question 29

BEADC

Despite discharge summaries seeming quite routine, they need to be done efficiently as they will be sent to the patient and GP. Sometimes patients need to be discharged quicker than others as they have additional appointments to get to the same day or specific transport arrangements. The next best option is to ask your senior about any urgent discharges as they will usually have a good idea of follow-ups needed. After doing the urgent letters, those being discharged tomorrow do not need to be done the same day. Some will definitely take longer than others so those can probably be done last.

Answer Question 30

EDBCA

If clinical suspicion regarding a pulmonary embolism is high, one should prescribe the patient a therapeutic dose of Fragmin immediately and not wait for imaging to confirm this. As your patient is young with a normal looking chest X-ray and is attending during normal working hours, it would be better to perform a V/Q scan rather than a CTPA initially as this has a lower radiation dose. (If the patient had an abnormal chest X-ray the accuracy of a V/Q scan in detecting a pulmonary embolism would be decreased. Outside of normal working hours V/Q scans are not performed.) Discussion with a senior colleague would be prudent.

Answer Question 31

ACBDE

When an unexpected result is found you should always inform a senior colleague. They will have more experience in the matter and may be able to provide more insight into the CT findings in this scenario. Referrals should always be appropriate and this often involves consultation with a senior colleague before continuing. Documentation is important but in this scenario the findings of the CT should be acted on promptly, especially as the patient is due to be discharged early tomorrow morning. Although it is not ideal to discuss the matter with another junior doctor who is also inexperienced in this situation, this is better to do this than not mentioning it to anyone and just writing something in the notes.

Answer Question 32

BCDAE

Regardless of your impression of a patient, you cannot refuse them pain relief. If you do suspect drug-seeking behaviour and weaker pain relief does not have the expected effect then you should ask for senior advice. As a junior doctor prescribing opiates and other controlled drugs, you should always ensure a fully registered doctor countersigns the prescription.

Answer Question 33

AECBD

In extreme situations such as this it is important to ensure patient care is not jeopardised. Adequate communication and handover with senior colleagues is vital, which would preferably be in person. Discussing the situation with your consultant will not help in this acute scenario but may prevent a similar situation occurring again. You should not leave without informing anyone despite plans to come in the next day.

Answer Question 34

CBEDA

Working in partnership with the mental health team is important to ensure the best outcome for the patient. Asking them to clarify their concerns regarding patient care is important and can also help your team to understand better how to treat the patient. You should explain to the team that the patient is medically fit for discharge and negotiate a management plan acceptable to both teams.

Answer Question 35

BADCE

The GMC states that "you must respect the wishes of any patient who objects to particular information being shared with others providing care, except where this would put others at risk of death or serious harm." In this case, there is no immediate risk to the health of the GP, and thus patient confidentiality must be respected. However, if this case was concerning a health professional who may participate in exposure-prone procedures, then it would be acceptable to break patient confidentiality and disclose the patient's diagnosis.

Answer Question 36

CBAED

If you are in a position of management or leadership, even as an junior doctor, you should ensure people can approach you with any concerns about patient safety. You should never discourage people from raising concerns and not wait until harm has been done to act.

Answer Question 37

DBAEC

Respect for colleagues is essential in maintaining a healthy, productive working environment. If feasible you should always talk to your upset colleague before confronting anyone else. If they really cannot be persuaded to talk to someone and it is affecting work in the team then the team leader (i.e. the consultant) should be informed.

Answer Question 38

BCEDA

As a junior doctor, you should not be consenting patients for procedures you have never witnessed or fully understood the complications of yourself. Your registrar will be aware of this, so discussing with them (option B) is the most suitable option. Finding an alternative senior (option C) would also be appropriate. If these options are not available, you should discuss the situation with your consultant (option E) before refusing to consent the patients (option D) – although you are well within your rights to do this. You should not consent them anyway even if you do know all of the complications etc. as you are still unable to carry out the surgery yourself.

Answer Question 39

ACEDB

The GMC clearly states that "you should not treat yourself" and "you should be registered with a general practitioner outside your family to ensure that you have access to independent and objective medical care". Nevertheless, you still have a duty to protect our own health and there is also a patient safety issue if you do become unwell and have to leave your patients unattended. Therefore the most appropriate options are to either have someone bring in your insulin for you or go to the emergency department to get a prescription. That way you remain on the hospital premises and can answer your bleep in case there is an emergency and still have treatment yourself.

Answer Question 40

ABCED

It is most appropriate to observe a few clinics so that you can learn the basics, and if possible consult a few patients under supervision so that you can receive feedback on how to improve your skills before you start seeing patients on your own. It is unacceptable to refuse managing patients who may require timely treatment. You cannot rely on them seeing a GP, the registrar or a consultant in a few weeks about a fracture which may need immediate management to prevent any further complications.

Answer Question 41

EDCBA

Apologising to the patient and correcting your mistake yourself is the most important thing to do. Informing the nurses and asking them to correct your mistake is the next best option. It is good to let other team members know about the patients to avoid further mishaps. Options B and A are clearly wrong and would be unprofessional approaches.

Answer Question 42

CDEAB

It is most appropriate to tell someone if you feel you are being bullied. Speaking to the person directly is the best option. Not telling anyone is bad for your emotional well-being and self-esteem. If this issue continues it may start to affect your work, which will put patients at risk.

Answer Question 43

BCDAE

Beginning to tackle the stress and workload of clinical work can be quite a culture shock to many junior doctors and it can be normal to feel a little overwhelmed at the beginning. It is most appropriate tell a senior colleague if you feel this way at work. Taking time off sick, after discussion with your GP or occupational health, is better than doing nothing and continuing to work while falling into a deeper and deeper depression.

Answer Question 44

ABCED

It is most appropriate to help your firm out by seeing the patients with input from the registrar so long as he can be reached easily and his advice sought in a timely manner. Explaining you are not happy to see the patients due to your lack of experience is the next best option. Complaining to anyone should only be done if the situation cannot be resolved without it and your seniors are bullying you or pressurizing you, putting patient safety at risk.

Answer Question 45

ABCDE

You must tell someone – ideally your consultant – so that your safety and the patient's safety can be assured. If you feel very dizzy you should ask someone who is not scrubbed to bring you a chair and you should remove yourself from the sterile field and descrub until you are feeling better. Sometimes drinking a cup of cold water or sitting down for a few minutes can ease the fainting feeling.

Answer Question 46

BACDE

If you suddenly become ill or notice that your health is suffering at work for whatever reason you should make this clear to your senior colleagues and seek medical help, if appropriate. In this situation it is unclear what this rash is but it appears to be spreading fast and causing itchy symptoms. It is most appropriate to go to the emergency department. Taking piriton and not telling anyone is marginally better than not doing anything and continuing with your work.

PART TWO – Answers to the Multi-Action Questions

Answer Question 47

ADH

This vignette highlights issues regarding teaching and patient autonomy. In the scenario, the patients may not be aware of how much they can help by allowing the students to examine them and there may also be a reason why patients are not happy to be examined, in which case you should investigate further (option D).

It is wrong to bribe your patients with better medical care and this answer (option B) should not be encouraged. Although some patients may expect to participate in bedside teaching when admitted to a teaching hospital, you should not force this onto any unwilling patients (option G) and respect a patient's autonomy at all times (as suggested by option A).

Learning is an essential part of continued patient care and all doctors are expected to engage in teaching activities with their juniors as well as peers. It would be unfair on the students to cancel their teaching at the last minute (option E) and although offering them a lecture (option C) or practicing on a normal subject (option F) are alternatives to cancelling teaching, they are no substitute for actual clinical experience. Hence the next best option in this scenario would be to find a colleague who might recommend a patient that does not mind being examined by students (option H).

Answer Question 48

ACE

This scenario is based around the issues of patient capacity and clinical problem solving. Despite the issues faced with the patient on their previous admissions, it is clear that this time the patient has capacity to negotiate a management plan for herself. She is therefore perfectly entitled to leave should she wish (option A) and should not be sectioned (option G) or have her views ignored (option H).

However, given the patient's multiple medical problems, it is good practice to ensure that future re-admissions to hospital are minimized and management of her co-morbidities optimised. Advice concerning her mental health problems (option E) and further education on the management of her diabetes (option C) can aid in this respect. Referral for dialysis requires specialist renal medical input and is usually reserved for patients with end stage renal failure. There is not enough information in this scenario for you to consider this management option (option D).

Answer Question 49

BDE

This scenario is centred on patient capacity. There is some doubt as to whether Mrs Brice had the capacity to make a decision regarding participation in the clinical trial as she is known to suffer from long-term dementia and therefore this issue should be investigated.

If she does not have capacity, it is important to weigh-up the benefits and risks of this new drug and consider obtaining proxy consent if you believe treatment would be in her best interests (option D) or discussing the matter with the next of kin (option E) bearing in mind that they may not be in the situation to consent for the patient (option C). The clinical investigator must be informed that the signed consent in Mrs Brice's notes may not be valid and that her participation in the trial will need to be reviewed (option B).

It would be negligent to completely ignore the situation (option H) or refuse to look into the matter further (options A and G) and by completely refusing the patient any option of being involved in the trial, you may be preventing them from beneficial treatment (option F).

Answer Question 50

BCE

This scenario is based upon determining your awareness of your limitations. It is never appropriate for you to attempt a procedure unsupervised if you are not competent to perform it, therefore trying to read up on a procedure (option A) or blindly 'having a go' (option F) are considered negligent behaviour. It is in the best interests for you and the patient to contact a senior clinician who is familiar with the procedure to administer the injection (option B) or to ask for supervision and assistance whilst you have an attempt (options C and E). This is a good learning opportunity, and if you have already seen this procedure being done before, would be a suitable option.

The patient has made a specific clinical appointment at your practice to have her steroid injections so sending her away to the hospital (option D) or trying to avoid providing the patient with different treatment which may have failed to control their symptoms previously (option G) are not suitable alternatives.

Answer Question 51

BEF

This vignette is concerned with patient safety. Although there were no serious consequences as a result of your actions, it is important to firstly ensure the situation will not arise again by informing the relevant medical staff (option B) and double-checking for other similar mistakes (option F). Filling in a clinical incident form (option E) is an important way of ensuring errors are documented.

You may wish to apologise to the patient (option C). However, this might be best left until after discussion with your seniors (option D) and although important, would not necessarily be the most appropriate immediate action. Blaming your colleagues for an error that is partly your own fault would not create good relations within the medical team and is best avoided (option G). A discussion with the ward pharmacist would be useful for your own future learning and they may be able to provide some information on other drug interactions that you were previously unaware of (option H), but in the acute setting this is not the best option. Doing nothing (option A) is tempting, however, selecting this option does not portray you as a safe and moral doctor.

Answer Question 52

DFG

This scenario is regarding patient safety and the importance of personal limitations for procedures you have not performed before, even if you feel confident. It is therefore not ideal for you to be starting the procedure without supervision (options A and C) or in the presence of a nurse (option B) who is unable to perform the procedure themselves should your run into difficulty. 'Googling' information on a procedure over the internet is not ideal as several websites may not be trustworthy or might demonstrate how to perform an ascetic drain using equipment not available in your hospital or unfamiliar to you (option H).

When performing a drain for the first time, ensure you make this fact clear to your seniors and ask whether you can perform it under supervision (options D and G) or whether another doctor who is familiar may be able to help (option F). Refusing to do the procedure entirely would mean missing out on a good learning opportunity (option E).

Answer Question 53

AGH

The GMC *Duties of a Doctor* guidelines state that, "Wherever possible, you should avoid providing medical care to anyone with whom you have a close personal relationship."

Although it is not strictly illegal for you to prescribe medication for your friend (option D), unless it is an absolute emergency situation where your friend cannot get urgent medical attention elsewhere, this is not recommended.

It would be most appropriate for you to advise your friend to speak to their GP (option A) or go to a hospital/walk-in clinic if he cannot get an appointment (option G). Offering your friend good medical advice on keeping well hydrated (option H) would also be appropriate. It is unwise to ask your friend to ignore their infection as there is the danger they may spread the infection to colleagues at work or the infection may get much worse without medical attention.

To steal medication from the hospital (option B) is illegal and to ask a colleague to prescribe medication for a patient they have not personally examined (options C or F) is bad medical practice.

Answer Question 54

CEB

This question tests your ability to cope with pressure and in recognising your clinical limitations. Foundation doctors should always have prompt access to senior cover and if you find that your team is not supportive of this, the first port of call would be to discuss the matter with your consultant (option C). If he/she is not willing to listen to your issues, then the next appropriate person you should speak to is your education supervisor (option E). This person is usually another consultant working in the hospital who has been specifically allocated to you at the start of your Foundation Programme with the purpose of dealing with any training/job issues. Avoiding the situation altogether by leaving your job or doing nothing will only prolong the poor circumstances you are finding on the ward and further compromise patient safety (options F and G).

It may be comforting and helpful to hear what your relatives and friends as well as the nurses feel on the topic but in this scenario it is not the most appropriate immediate action to take.

Answer Question 55

CFG

This scenario is centred on recognizing your own clinical limitations as well as coping under pressure. All patients on the ward round need to be assessed for emergency issues and dealing with the most sick patients first will ensure any urgent treatment is not delayed and your seniors are aware of their situation (option G).

Spending a long time with each patient is counterproductive and does not display efficient management of your time (option B). What would be helpful to your seniors when they review your patients is a summary of the most recent blood tests and up-to-date clinical history for each person as well as outstanding problems that require medical decisions for (options C and F).

Although it may be tempting to request complicated investigations and tests to impress your seniors, it is better to run these decisions past them first to avoid any complications later on (options A and D). Doing a ward round without reviewing or properly assessing any of your patients (options E and H) is bad medical practice.

Answer Question 56

ADF

Although you have technically completed your shift in the hospital, this does not mean that you are no longer required to put patient care as your main priority as a doctor. If you are in a position to answer your bleep, then you should not ignore it (unlike in option B).

Nevertheless, if the task is non-urgent and patient safety is not compromised, then you are well within your rights to delegate the task to a colleague who is contracted to work on-call and can handle the issue at hand (options A and D). You should find out what the issue is first to confirm it is non-urgent, but if the message is unclear then it is worth checking on the patient to be sure their safety is not compromised (option F).

It is important for all doctors to remember to also maintain a good work-life balance and spending longer than is necessary at the hospital can compromise a healthy life outside of work.

Answer Question 57

DEF

This case demonstrates the importance of time management by delegating tasks to other colleagues where appropriate. Although the fault of not prescribing the analgesia lies with yourself, you should ensure that the highest standard of patient care is achieved and take steps to rectify this problem rather than wait for someone else to notice (unlike in options B and C).

As you have already reached your home and are not within the close vicinity of the hospital, it is not necessary for you to return (option A), but you should delegate the task to a responsible professional who can help prescribe the medication. The GMC *Good Medical Practice* guidelines state that when delegating "you must be satisfied that the person to whom you delegate has the qualifications, experience, knowledge and skills to provide the care or treatment involved." It is therefore important you find some way of alerting another doctor as the medication will need to be prescribed (options D, E and F). Asking the ward nurse to dispense medications without a prescription (option H) is not deemed appropriate delegation of a task.

Answer Question 58

ADE

This task assesses your ability as a doctor to prioritise tasks and ask for help when required. In the first instance discussing your concerns with colleagues can serve to highlight what your peers are doing that you are not (option A) and thereby helping to cope better with the workload. If, however, you find that you are working at your most efficient state and still struggling to cope, the next port of call would be to raise concerns with your consultant or educational supervisor (option E). They may be able to suggest advice on the next appropriate steps to take.

Writing a letter of complaint (option B) or raising the issues in a public forum (option F) without first having mentioned the matter to your consultant may be viewed as discourteous and can stir up more questions and trouble than first trying to solve the problems in-house. Leaving patients with outstanding medical tasks unfinished (option C) is bad medical practice.

Asking to be diary card monitored is your right as an employee of the trust and is a good way for the medical staffing department to discover which jobs are understaffing and overworked. If there are simply too many jobs to complete within the allocated working hours, then this can lead the staffing department to hiring extra staff to help with the work (option D). Asking your colleagues to stay late on your behalf (option H) is not a viable solution as the doctors will be required to stay later than their contracted hours and they will not solve the issue you have been faced with in the long-term.

Answer Question 59

ABE

In this scenario, you are still officially on duty as your shift has not yet ended. Although the task will most probably mean you will not finish on time, you should still act upon the information rather than ignore instructions (option H) or question your senior on their medical judgment (option G).

If the matter is non-urgent, it can be handed over to the night team (options A and B) and this can be communicated to the night team by either yourself or your registrar. If, however, it is an urgent matter then patient safety must be prioritized and you should attend to the sick patient (option E). It would be unfair to ask the medical registrar to stay even later to review a patient when you are available to do so and they are seen to be very busy (option F), especially if they may have plans of their own after work as well.

Nevertheless, you do have a right to a life outside of work and cancelling or putting off plans to attend your parent's anniversary celebrations need not be necessary (options C and D).

Answer Question 60

BCE

According to the *New Doctor* publication issued by the GMC, "Trainees must be supported to acquire the necessary skills and experience through induction, effective educational supervision, an appropriate workload, personal support and time to learn." The person responsible for this includes the clinical and educational supervisors, the deaneries as well as the hospital.

In this scenario you should offer your support to your colleague (option B). However, if they are finding their job and workload excessive you should advise them to approach their trainers for advice (option E and C). It is not your position to report your colleague in this first instance to the Foundation School Programme director (option A) or to make your colleague feel they are inadequate (option H). The matter disclosed to you by your colleague may be personal and it is insensitive to spread the word amongst the other junior doctors in the hospital (option G).

Although you may want to help your colleague by taking on more work yourself (option F) or reassure them that things will get better (option D), these are only short-term solutions and if other junior doctors appear to be coping well in their job with the same amount of workload, then it is likely your colleague should seek advice from her seniors sooner rather than later.

Answer Question 61

BDG

According to the *New Doctor* publication issued by the GMC, "Support, training and effective supervision must be provided for Foundation doctors." If you have never performed a procedure unsupervised before, then you are not deemed competent to carry this out and should not attempt it (unlike in option E).

If you know about the risks and complications of the procedure then it is reasonable to explain these to the patient first whilst waiting for your registrar (option G). Maintain honesty with the patient by explaining the cause for the delay (option B) and why you are not supposed to start without a senior doctor. When your registrar returns, you should explain your previous experience of the procedure to them so they are aware of the level of support you require (option D).

It may be reasonable to ask another doctor who is competent to perform the task if your senior registrar has been delayed and the matter is urgent (options A and F), however, this may mean that you miss a good training opportunity or that the other doctor you ask is unwilling to teach you if they are themselves not confident about the task to be performed.

Answer Question 62

BEF

This scenario is concerned with time management, communication and prioritization. Although junior doctors should all be supported in their workload, sometimes shortages of staffing or sickness can mean more tasks are allocated to one individual doctor.

In order to prioritise tasks it is necessary to first perform all urgent jobs (option E) and then perform routine jobs later. If you are unsure what is urgent and what is not urgent, then clarifying this with a senior is a good idea (option F). Seeking timely and appropriate advice regarding any clinical situations you do not feel capable of dealing with (option B) is also a reasonable action to take.

It would be unprofessional and unsafe for patients if you refused to carry out any tasks and walked out of the hospital (option C). Although you may wish to seek extra help from colleagues on different teams it is not your place to demand that these requirements be met. It would be more appropriate for a senior doctor to decide upon this action (options G and H).

Answer Question 63

FEG

According to the GMC's *Conflicts of Interest* guidelines (published September 2008), "You must not encourage patients to give, lend or bequeath money or gifts that will directly or indirectly benefit you, nor must you put pressure on patients or their families to make donations to other people or organizations."

By thanking the relative, you are acknowledging their gratitude for your help and care (options F and G) but you should not accept the money or suggest other members of staff accept the money (options A, B, C, D and H). If the relative is still insistent on donating the money to healthcare professionals, you may suggest that the money be put towards the ward fund (option E), but you must not place any pressure on her to do this if she does not wish to.

Answer Question 64

BCH

You have a responsibility to put patient care above all other matters as a doctor. This includes ensuring that patients are not harmed or mistreated by other colleagues. Although the situation outlined above may simply be an issue regarding miscommunication between the nurse and the patient, you should still intervene (unlike in options D or F), especially if the patient is looking distressed.

The most professional manner in dealing with this situation is to explain the situation to the nurse (option B) and when in private, question the nurse further about her conduct with the patient (option C). It would not be appropriate to start an argument with the nurse in public on an open ward (options A or E).

In general, nursing staff are well aware of patient needs and disabilities. If the nurse in question was genuinely unaware of the patient's deafness and frailty, a review through the notes to determine whether this is a new finding and how it may impact on the patient's life (option H) can be extremely useful, especially when other healthcare professionals assess the patient's needs at home and level of carer input.

Answer Question 65

CEH

This is a rather unusual clinical situation to find yourself in, but it is worth thinking about how to prioritise your tasks whilst maintaining high levels of patient care and safety. As a junior doctor you are too out of your depth to be running a trauma call on your own (option F) and neither should you try to implicate another colleague who is equally as inexperienced as yourself (option B). As the only surgical doctor available to attend to the patient, you cannot pretend that this situation has nothing to do with you (option G) or ignore the referral from the emergency department nurse (option D).

The most appropriate actions would be to alert your direct seniors regarding a pending trauma call (option C) and if they are unable to help you straightaway the next best option would be to seek help from a senior member of another team such as the emergency department (option E). There may be things you can do to help make the trauma call run more smoothly such as ensuring the radiology department are aware of a pending urgent scan (option H).

Answer Question 66

DEG

This clinical scenario is trying to assess your initiative and teamworking skills as a junior doctor. Although you are not obliged to help the on-call team if you are not on-call, the GMC *Good Medical Practice* guidelines state that "when working in a team you should act as a positive role model and try to motivate and inspire your colleagues." Letting your colleagues struggle when you are in a position to help is clearly not a way of presenting yourself as a positive role model.

You should first ensure all your ward patients have been cared for and you have no outstanding jobs before offering to take extra tasks on (option G) and liaise with the doctor managing the on-call team (senior registrar/consultant) to determine whether there are specific tasks they feel would be appropriate for you to help with. Offering to help with specific tasks that you would like to do (option E) may also be appropriate if there are certain skills you would like to improve upon. If you find that the inflow of patients is very high, then trying to get some help from your own team to help the on-call team (option D) is another good idea.

It is not appropriate for you to ask the medical staffing department to hire a locum doctor (option F) and certainly not for yourself to ask the bed manager to divert emergency patients to another hospital (option H).

Answer Question 67

CFH

This scenario is regarding clinical management and decision-making. The patient is acutely confused and has pulled out their catheter. It is difficult to know whether the patient will do this again if they are re-catheterised and unless it is absolutely necessary to catheterize the patient, restraining the patient in order to perform an unnecessary procedure is inappropriate (option E). If, however, you do need to cathetarize the patient, written consent would not be needed, only implied consent (option A).

In any case, if you are unsure of what you should do in a clinical situation and patient management is an issue, help should be sought from senior members of the team (option F). A urinary tract infection can exacerbate symptoms of confusion and testing for this is a good idea (option H). Catheterisation in the presence of an urinary tract infection or advising the patient not to have adequate fluid intake (option D) can make the infection worse, not better. If urine output is not being measured and the staff are worried about the patient's incontinence, a conveen instead of a catheter can be a good alternative in male patients (option C).

Prescribing the patient a sedative (option G) is not in the patient's best interest and will not help to understand why the patient has become acutely confused. It only helps to serve the nursing staff to manage the patient more easily.

Answer Question 68

BFG

If you have concerns that patient safety may be compromised by inadequate or faulty equipment then you should document your concerns and the steps you have taken to try and correct them. It is important to report the faulty equipment to the management (option F), the ward matron (option G) and not forget to complete the initial task you set out when reviewing your patient, namely to assess their blood pressure (option B). If you do not fully examine your patient including your clinical observations, you may be missing important clinical information (option A).

It is important that you do not steal equipment from another ward (option E) as this may be the only machine on the other ward. Always ensure that if you need to borrow equipment, a member of the team on the ward is aware of the whereabouts of their equipment should they also require it in an emergency setting.

Answer Question 69

CDH

This scenario is about communication and clinical skills with patients. It is important to remember the reason for the clinic appointment and ensure that the patient is satisfied regarding treatment of the presenting compliant. Antibiotics are not required for all flu-like illnesses in children as they are commonly viral, however, a full clinical examination is needed.

One of the duties of a good doctor is to promote 'the health of patients and the public' meaning that patients do not need to be acutely unwell for doctors to ensure good advice regarding general well-being is given. As childhood obesity is a major problem facing children in the UK it would be prudent not to ignore the child's large size. Discussing the child's diet (option D) and giving advice to the mother (option H) are simple initial measures that can be taken. A family history (option G) may be useful but not necessary in the initial assessment. Blood tests are unnecessary during this initial consultation (option E), and referral to a dietician may be something to consider if there is no improvement after initial measures. The parent may not be aware of the dangers of obesity and contacting social services because you believe the parent to be abusive may not be appropriate (option B).

Answer Question 70

CEG

This case demonstrates the importance of coping with pressure by prioritising jobs and delegating less urgent tasks to other team members. As a good doctor your primary concern should always lie with patient care. In this scenario, a patient has become acutely unwell and must be seen immediately. Therefore, delaying a review of the patient is not appropriate (options A, D and H). Asking the nurse to put out a cardiac arrest call for a patient who is not experiencing a cardiac arrest is not only inappropriate, but may prevent the cardiac arrest team from dealing with a true emergency and is consequently not an option (option B).

As you are available to immediately review the patient it is better for you to go to the ward first and ask your senior house officer who is currently indisposed to attend the meeting when they are finished. Asking your senior house officer to attend to the acutely unwell patient when they are already attending another sick patient will delay any immediate management (option F).

It is polite to contact the senior sister running the multidisciplinary team meeting to apologise for your absence (option G), ensure immediate investigations are performed on your sick patient (option C) and alert your senior house officer about the situation and arrange cover (option E).